Ivey and Ivey take your students "back to the basics" with:

W9-DEK-111

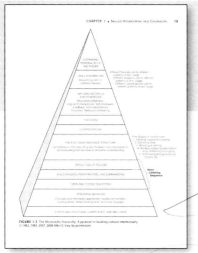

◀ Concepts presented through the popular and time-tested **Microskills model**, which allows students to develop beginning competence in four approaches to the interview: decisional counseling, person-centered, cognitive behavioral assertiveness training, and brief counseling.

▶ An **active voice** and **modular style** that quickly engages students with the material regardless of the order you choose to present the material.

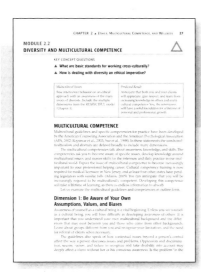

◀ A strong **multicultural focus** that gives students the insight they need not only to draw out client stories, but also to identify and understand the importance of the thoughts, feelings, and behaviors in those stories.

▶ **Exercises** that encourage students to define their natural style of helping and assess their integration of helping skills in their own interviewing behaviors.

Also available with the text:

ESSENTIALS OF
INTENTIONAL INTERVIEWING

ESSENTIALS OF INTENTIONAL INTERVIEWING

Counseling in a Multicultural World

Allen E. Ivey
*University of Massachusetts at Amherst
and University of South Florida at Tampa*

Mary Bradford Ivey
*University of South Florida at Tampa
and Microtraining Associates, Inc.*

THOMSON
★
BROOKS/COLE

Australia · Brazil · Canada · Mexico · Singapore · Spain · United Kingdom · United States

THOMSON

BROOKS/COLE

Senior Acquisitions Editor: *Marquita Flemming*
Assistant Editor: *Samantha Shook*
Editorial Assistant: *Meaghan Banks*
Technology Project Manager: *Julie Aguilar*
Marketing Manager: *Meghan McCullough*
Marketing Communications Manager: *Shemika Britt*
Project Manager, Editorial Production: *Rita Jaramillo*
Creative Director: *Rob Hugel*
Art Director: *Vernon Boes*
Print Buyer: *Nora Massuda*

Permissions Editor: *Roberta Broyer*
Production Service: *Anne Draus, Scratchgravel Publishing Services*
Text Designer: *Lisa Henry*
Copy Editor: *Patterson Lamb*
Cover Designer: *Lisa Henry*
Cover Image: © *Lee Hocker/Lisa Henry*
Compositor: *ITC*
Text and Cover Printer: *West*

Printed in the United States of America
1 2 3 4 5 6 7 11 10 09 08 07

Thomson Higher Education
10 Davis Drive
Belmont, CA 94002-3098
USA

For more information about our products, contact us at:

**Thomson Learning Academic Resource Center
1-800-423-0563**

For permission to use material from this text or product, submit a request online at
http://www.thomsonrights.com.

Any additional questions about permissions can be submitted by e-mail to
thomsonrights@thomson.com.

Library of Congress Control Number: 2006938497

ISBN-13: 978-0-495-09724-2
ISBN-10: 0-495-09724-1

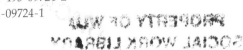

Love is listening.
PAUL TILLICH

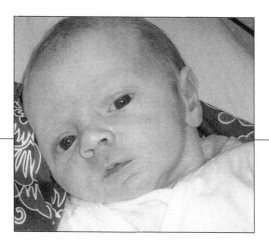

Dedicated to our latest grandson,
Charlie Quirk.
He was incubated simultaneously
with this book.

ALLEN E. IVEY is Distinguished University Professor (Emeritus), University of Massachusetts, Amherst, and Courtesy Professor, Counseling, University of South Florida, Tampa. He is president of Microtraining Associates, an educational publishing firm. He received his undergraduate degree (Phi Beta Kappa) from Stanford University in psychology with a minor in social work. After a Fulbright year studying social work at the University of Copenhagen, Denmark, he earned his counseling doctorate at Harvard University.

Allen is the author or coauthor of more than 40 books and 200 articles and chapters, translated into 18 languages. A past president and Fellow of the Society of Counseling Psychology of the American Psychological Association, he is a Diplomate of the American Board of Professional Psychology. He is also a Fellow of APA's Society for the Study of Ethnic and Minority Psychology and the Asian American Psychological Association. He received the International Award from the Division of Counseling and Psychotherapy of the Portuguese Psychological Association for his new writings on developmental counseling and therapy. Allen's contributions led him to the top recognition of the American Counseling Association, the Professional Development Award. He was named "Distinguished Elder" for lifetime contributions to multicultural psychology at the National Multicultural Summit and Conference. His recent work focused applying Developmental Counseling and Therapy to the analysis and treatment of severe psychological distress. With Mary, he is writing and conducting workshops on counseling and spirituality.

Allen enjoys skiing with his grandchildren and is currently trying to recondition himself for more running. He enjoys the cultural and beach life of Sarasota, Florida, and is on the Steering Committee of Sarasota's Coalition for Inclusion & Diversity.

MARY BRADFORD IVEY is Vice President of Microtraining Associates and Courtesy Professor of Counseling, University of South Florida, Tampa. She is a former school counselor in the Amherst, Massachusetts, schools and has served as visiting professor at the University of Massachusetts, Amherst; University of Hawai'i, Manoa; and Flinders University, South Australia. Mary's undergraduate degree in social work and education is from Gustavus Adolphus College, and she has a master's degree in counseling from the University of Wisconsin. She earned her doctorate in organizational development at the University of Massachusetts, Amherst.

Mary is the author or coauthor of 14 books, translated into multiple languages, and several articles and chapters. She is a Nationally Certified Counselor (NCC) and a licensed mental health counselor (LMHC), and she has held a certificate in school counseling. She has presented workshops and keynote lectures with Allen throughout the world, including Australia, New Zealand, Japan, China, Israel, Greece, Sweden, Canada, Great Britain, Portugal, and Germany. She is also known for her work in promoting and explaining developmental guidance and counseling in the United States and abroad. Mary received national recognition when her elementary counseling program at the Fort River School was named one of the 10 best in the nation at the Christa McAuliffe Conference. She is one of the first 15 honored Fellows of the American Counseling Association and is also a recipient of the American Counseling Association's O'Hana Award for her work in multicultural counseling in the schools.

Mary also skis, but swimming and tennis are her real loves in sports. She enjoys all the activities of Sarasota and works actively in her church and community, but Lake Sunapee, New Hampshire, in the summer brings her home to the grandchildren for fun and relaxation.

SECTION I INTRODUCTION

Essentials of Intentional Interviewing: Counseling in a Multicultural World is a helping skills text with the most complete interactive web-based learning system available today. There are also extensive ancillaries to support student learning and teaching.

We wrote this book because we envisioned the clearest possible presentation of the most essential interviewing and counseling skills. Important in our vision is ensuring that students learn concepts that they can immediately take into direct practice in role-plays—and later into real interviewing work in the field. Through the step-by-step procedures of microcounseling, students will learn to predict the impact of diverse skills on client thinking, feeling, and behavior and will be able to intentionally flex and use another skill when the prediction does not hold. This is a results-oriented approach, thoroughly tested and researched in thousands of settings and in over 450 data-based research articles.

Microcounseling introduced diversity and multicultural issues to our field as important issues in 1974 and we have constantly expanded that awareness over the years. The chapters here thoroughly infuse a broad definition of diversity. You will find boxes in each chapter on "National and International Perspectives" where authorities around the world present their viewpoints on skills and strategies. We believe that multicultural factors enrich our understanding of individual uniqueness and that all interviewing involves multicultural issues. *All of us are cultural beings, full of diversity that is essential to our unique individual differences and humanity.*

Who is this book for? The book is also designed to meet the needs of both beginners and more advanced students. It will clarify interviewing and counseling skills for community college students, undergraduates, and graduate students in courses oriented toward the helping professions such as human services and all types of mental health work, counseling, nursing, psychology, and social work. In addition, the microskills approach has been proven effective in training in many other groups including nutritional counselors, AIDS counselors and refugees in Africa, and those in management and leadership training. All of us can profit from more skill in communication.

ThomsonNOW™　　The web-based learning system ThomsonNOW increases student learning by providing a complete package of diagnostic quizzes, a personalized study plan, and learning modules. These include pre- and posttests, cases for discussion and analysis,

xiii

video clips depicting key ethical issues and interview examples, links to websites, and recommended Internet sites. ThomsonNOW also provides the specifics for a student *Portfolio of Competence. Practice in interviewing skills* is the most important and often the most enjoyable part of microskill study. You will find chapter group practice instructions, feedback forms, and PowerPoint® slides in the web-based *Instructor Resource Guide* at www.thomsonedu.com/counseling/Ivey. These instructions provide specifics for important classroom exercises to help students master the skills under your supervision. They also provide the opportunity for students to practice "micro-supervision" in which they give feedback and guidance to each other. This helps set the stage for a lifetime of growth through self-awareness, sharing one's interviewing work with others, and future work in supervision. The feedback forms can be down-loaded, printed, and made available to your students. The PowerPoint® slides accompanying each chapter include summaries of the group practice instructions and the appropriate feedback sheets.

The group instructions and feedback forms are available on the student website: www.thomsonedu.com/counseling/Ivey. You may prefer to ask students to download this material themselves.

The Organization of *Essentials of Intentional Interviewing*

This book is a shorter, more incisive version of our *Intentional Interviewing and Coun-seling.* Every sentence and concept has been thoroughly reviewed for its relevance and clarity for beginning helpers. Discussions of research and more complex therapeutic applications are reduced in scope. This book focuses on the most essential ideas for a successful introduction to the key microskills of helping.

The first three chapters (Section I) introduce foundational concepts that will facili-tate later understanding and competence in interviewing skills and strategies. Chapter 1 introduces the book and defines the distinctions among interviewing, counseling, and (more briefly) psychotherapy, and ends by asking students to make an audio- or videotape of their natural interviewing style before going further. We find that encour-aging students to tape their practice sessions is critical to their learning and enjoyment of the course as well as their eventual success as interviewers. Making a transcript and evaluating one's interviews is a time-consuming task, but students often comment that this effort yields the most benefit for their current and continuing development.

Chapter 2 emphasizes key ethical issues for beginning helpers, defines diversity and multiculturalism (including "political correctness"), and concludes with a discus-sion of the importance of a wellness and positive psychology approach to helping. Chapter 3 presents attending and observation skills as fundamental to all interview-ing and counseling.

Section II presents the listening skills of questioning, encouraging, paraphrasing, summarization, and reflecting feelings. Learning and mastery of these skills leads to Chapter 7 in which students are asked to complete a full interview with a role-played client *using only listening skills.*

Section III moves to the influencing skills and strategies. Central here is Chapter 8 on "supporting while challenging," which introduces confrontation and the Client Change Scale (CCS). The CCS is included throughout all the influencing skills and shows how to assess client change in the *here and now* of the interview and over a series of interviews. Students will also discover how effective listening produces client change. This is followed by Chapter 9, which demonstrates how to balance individual concerns with contextual issues and *en*course clients to take multiple perspectives. Chapter 10 presents basics of reflection of meaning and interpretation/reframing, which help clients find news ways of thinking about their issues. The closely related *here-and-now* skills of feedback and self-disclosure are discussed in Chapter 11. Chapter 12 speaks to the more directive skills including logical consequences, information/advice, and giving directions to the client.

Section IV focuses on integration of interviewing and counseling skills. Chapter 13 show how all the skills, strategies, and concepts of the book can be integrated in a smoothly flowing decisional counseling interview. Armed with this background, students will learn the basics of person-centered counseling, cognitive-behavioral assertiveness training, and brief solution-focused counseling in Chapter 14. The conclusion, Chapter 15, focuses on student self-examination and evaluation of their progress during the term.

What, Specifically, Can You Find in This Book for You and Your Students?

This results-oriented book will enable students to do the following:
- ▲ Draw out client stories and understand the importance of thoughts, feelings, behaviors, and meanings in those stories.
- ▲ Predict how clients will respond to the use of microskills; and, if this prediction does not hold true, students will be able to flex intentionally and meet client needs by selecting another approach.
- ▲ Complete a full interview using only listening skills by the time they are halfway though this book.
- ▲ Understand and apply three foundations of effective helping: ethics, multicultural competence, and a positive psychology wellness approach.
- ▲ Develop beginning competence in four approaches to the interview: decisional counseling, person-centered counseling, cognitive-behavioral assertiveness training, and brief solution-focused counseling.
- ▲ Define their natural style of helping and their own integration of helping skills. They will be able to analyze their own interviewing behavior and its effectiveness with clients.
- ▲ Through the web-based program, allow students to present a *Portfolio of Competencies* bringing together their learning and individual orientations to the helping fields. The web programs bring the cognitive concepts to action with many practical exercises and videos.

What Does the Interactive Website Offer?

Students are almost always enthusiastic about our work in interactive learning and comment that they enjoy the involvement with cases; they find that they often do better in exams if they have worked through the exercises. We are excited to find ourselves learning new things through the specificity and lucidity required by interactive learning. ThomsonNOW, an interactive web-based program, is something that students and we enjoy while learning material that stays with us. Among the many activities available in the program are the following:
- ▲ Over 30 interactive case studies. Students are presented with transcripts of interviews and are then asked to respond to client statements by selecting specific interviewer responses. They receive immediate feedback on their choices. In addition, presentations are provided by professionals from around the world.

Students can compare their responses to case questions to what the professionals actually did in the United States, Romania, Japan, and other countries.

▲ Video clips of interviews demonstrating key issues in ethics, multiculturalism, and skills. Students will view an interview by Mary Bradford Ivey demonstrating that reflection of feeling can be used solely for a considerable period of time.

▲ Pre- and posttests of cognitive material for student self-evaluation. Incorrect answers from the pretest immediately refer the student to specific pages in the text for elaboration of why their early responses may need changing. Flashcards are available for learning and self-testing.

▲ Practice exercises for each chapter module that will help students master and generalize interviewing skills to their home environments.

▲ Recommended supportive website connections.

▲ Exercises and forms that can be downloaded. By the end of the term, students can use this information to assemble a detailed *Portfolio of Competencies*. We have had many students take these portfolios with them to present to potential field supervisors and future employers.

Additional Teaching Aids

The *Online Instructor's Resource Guide* (ISBN 0-495-38165-9) provides chapter summaries, suggested class procedures, discussion of web-based exercises, two example syllabi, and the *Portfolio of Competencies* as well as multiple-choice and essay questions. A partial IRG without the test bank items is available for download at the password-protected Instructor Resource Site. To request the complete online IRG, or to obtain the password for the instructor site, contact your Thomson sales representative or the Academic Resource Center at 1-800-423-0563. Or you can contact the authors at info@emicrotraining.com for the Resource Guide.

A comprehensive set of PowerPoint® slides by Esther Dyer is now available on the Instructor's Book Companion site at http://thomsonedu.com/counseling/Ivey. You may download these slides to make overhead transparencies or to show them on your computer. Important in these are specifics for using the microskills in classroom practice sessions.

Videotapes illustrating the microskills are available from Microtraining Associates, 25 Burdette Avenue, Framingham, MA 01702, phone/fax 888-505-5576, and on their website, www.emicrotraining.com. A new *Basic Attending Skills* videotape is now available featuring Deryl Bailey and Azara Santiago-Rivera as well as Mary and Allen Ivey and Norma Packard. The *Basic Influencing Skills* video is available for the last half of this book. A new video on microcounseling supervision is now available with a supplementary CD-ROM. This should be helpful to students in classifying and working with skills. Microtraining, a privately owned company independent of Thomson Brooks/Cole, is known for its wide array of multicultural training videos and now has supplementary materials on most areas of multicultural concern as well as many videos on counseling and therapy skills and strategies.

Teaching microskills and social skills to individual clients, peer helpers, and others has become a central part of practice for many professionals. Health maintenance organizations, social work agencies, community helpers, AIDS and cancer volunteers, and many others benefit from the skills training approach. Thus, the *Instructor's Resource Guide* presents specifics of teaching skills.

Alternative Instructional Sequences

Some instructors will want to reorder chapters to meet their own instructional goals. We have tried to organize the chapters in such a way as to make alternative sequencing easy.

Specifically, some prefer to teach questioning *after* the listening skills of encouraging, paraphrasing, and reflection of feeling. They point out that some students have difficulty "going beyond" questions and really listening to clients. This more person-centered approach is certainly effective and a good way to emphasize the importance of active listening.

Another major sequencing issue concerns the placement of confrontation. In our book with Paul Pedersen, *Intentional Group Counseling: A Microskills Approach* (Brooks/Cole, 2001), we place confrontation skills as the last set of microskills to be learned. We do this because confrontation in groups is particularly complex. We are aware that it can be equally complex with individuals. Despite this, we have placed confrontation as Chapter 8. We find that the attending, observing, and basic listening skill emphasis of the first half of the book allows effective and early teaching of basic confrontation. The Client Change Scale of Chapter 8, while introduced with confrontation, is useful in work with all microskills and strategies—both listening and influencing.

Chapter 14 presents three methods of counseling and therapy. Not all students will be able to master these in one semester. We suggest that you select one or two for central emphasis. Students can later master the other theories on their own as needed. Advanced students will be able to engage in all by the end of the course.

Another approach to Chapter 14 would be to pair material on person-centered interview with the first seven chapters. Behavioral assertiveness training may appropriately be paired with Chapter 12. Brief solution-oriented approaches could be paired with the chapter on questions, particularly if you teach questions after the other listening skills.

Each of us needs to shape and adapt textbooks to meet our students' needs and our own approach to teaching. Other sequences of skills can be arranged, and we welcome your feedback on this important and challenging instructional issue.

Acknowledgments

Lisa Gebo inspired the ideas that led to this book and we recognize her major contributions to our personal and professional growth over the years. Special thanks and appreciation to Esther Dyer for her advice and suggestions on clarity of writing and definitions of concepts. Esther has been a wonderful "critical artist" as we reviewed the many details of this new text together. Thomas Daniels, Memorial University, Cornerbrook, has been central to the development of the microskills approach for many years. His summary of research on over 450 data-based studies is available by request. We appreciate and thank Penny John, one of our favorite students, for permission to use her interview as an example in Chapter 14.

Weijun Zhang's writing and commentaries are central to this book. We also thank James Lanier, Courtland Lee, Robert Manthei, Mark Pope, Kathryn Quirk, Azara Santiago-Rivera, Sandra Rigazio-DiGilio, and Derald Wing Sue for their written contributions. Robert Marx and Joseph Litterer were important in the early development of this book. Discussions with Otto Payton and Viktor Frankl helped clarify the presentation of reflection of meaning. William Matthews was especially helpful in formulating the five-stage model of the interview. Lia and Zig Kapelis of Flinders University and Adelaide University are thanked for their support and participation while we served as visiting professors in South Australia.

David Rathman, Chief Executive Officer of Aboriginal Affairs, South Australia, has constantly supported and challenged this book, and his influence shows in many ways. Matthew Rigney, also of Aboriginal Affairs, was instrumental in introducing us to new ways of thinking. These two people first showed us that traditional, individualistic ways of thinking are incomplete, and therefore they were critical in the development of the focusing skill with its emphasis on the cultural/environmental context.

The skills and concepts of this book rely on the work of many different individuals over the past 40 years, most notably Eugene Oetting, Dean Miller, Cheryl Normington, Richard Haase, Max Uhlemann, and Weston Morrill at Colorado State University, who were there at the inception of the microtraining framework. The following people have been especially important personally and professionally in the growth of microcounseling and microtraining over the years: Lori Russell-Chapin, Bertil Bratt, Norma Gluckstern Packard, Jeanne Phillips, John Moreland, Jerry Authier, David Evans, Margaret Hearn, Lynn Simek-Morgan, Dwight Allen, Paul and Anne Pedersen, Lanette Shizuru, Steve Rollin, Bruce Oldershaw, Oscar Gonçalves, Koji Tamase, and Elizabeth and Thad Robey.

Many of our students at the University of South Florida, Tampa, University of Massachusetts, Amherst, the University of Hawai'i, Manoa, and Flinders University, South Australia, also contributed in important ways through their reactions, questions, and suggestions.

Machiko Fukuhara, Professor Emeritus, Tokiwa University, and president of the Japanese Association of Microcounseling, has been our friend, colleague, and co-author for many years. Her understanding and guidance have contributed in many direct ways to the clarity of our concepts and to our understanding of multicultural issues. We give special thanks and recognition to this wise partner.

Finally, it is always a pleasure to work with the group at Brooks/Cole. Marquita Flemming, Julie Martinez, and Julie Aguilar, have gone beyond the "call of duty" and have constantly provided new and innovative ideas to improve both the book and the ThomsonNOW website. We also appreciate the expertise and support of Vernon Boes, Rita Jaramillo, Caroline Concilla, Meghan McCullough, Sheila Walsh, Samantha Shook, and Meaghan Banks. Our manuscript editor, Patterson Lamb, has become an important advisor to us. Anne and Greg Draus of Scratchgravel Publishing Services always do a terrific job. We thank all of the above.

We are grateful to the following reviewers for their valuable suggestions and comments: Kerri Augusto, Becker College; LuAnnette Butler, Austin Peay State University; Sherilyn Cormier, West Virginia University; Christopher Faiver, John Carroll University; Lorri Petties Glass, Valparaiso University; Alvin Lewis, Pima Community College; Cheryl McGill, Darlington Technical College; Paul Pedersen, University of Hawai'i at Manoa; Phyllis Robertson, Western Carolina University; Mark Van Lent, Ferris State University; and Carlos Zalaquett, University of South Florida.

We would be happy to hear from readers with suggestions and ideas. Please use the form at the back of this book to send us your comments. Feel free to contact us also via email. We appreciate the time that you as a reader are willing to spend with us.

Allen E. Ivey
Mary Bradford Ivey
Email: info@emicrotraining.com

ESSENTIALS OF
INTENTIONAL INTERVIEWING

INTRODUCTION

Listening is the necessary condition and the foundation of counseling and interviewing. We want to help clients tell their stories and explore their issues, concerns, and problems. Through this narrative exploration, we can help clients rewrite their stories and find solutions. Our task is to discover clients' potential and empower them to think, feel, and behave in new and more satisfying ways. *But listening always comes first.*

You can make a difference in the lives of others—for the better or for the worse. Through the interview, you can enrich your clients or hinder their growth. This first section of the book is oriented to joining clients through attending to their stories and clarifying issues. Often empathic listening is sufficient to help clients resolve their concerns. Later sections of this text supplement the listening foundation with influencing skills such as confrontation and reframing/interpretation.

Chapter 1, *Skilled Interviewing and Counseling,* provides an overview and a road map of theory and practice. Most important, we ask you to identify the natural skills you bring to the interview. You are not taking this course by chance; something has already led you to this work. We urge you to conduct an interview with a volunteer client as soon as possible. By audio- or videotaping an interview, you will have a base-line from which you can develop and improve your *natural style* of helping. After the interview, ask your client for feedback and discuss the session with him or her. Pay special attention to what you have done right and also listen to what the volunteer feels that you might have missed. Search for your own personal strengths to use as a foundation for further development as a skilled interviewer or counselor.

Chapter 2, *Ethics, Multicultural Competence, and Wellness,* presents three crucial aspects of all interviewing and counseling. Presented first are ethical standards of the helping professions—counseling, family therapy, human services, psychology, and social work. Here you will find key issues that will guide you as you develop as an interviewer or counselor.

We are all multicultural beings as each of us comes from a unique array of cultural and environmental contexts. These multicultural contexts embrace many dimensions of diversity including age, ethnicity/race, gender, geographical location or community, language, sexual orientation, spiritual/religious beliefs, socioeconomic situation, physical ability, and experience with traumatic situations. In this sense, all interviewing and counseling is cross-cultural as no two individuals have the same life experiences. The terms *diversity, cross-cultural,* and *multicultural* will be used interchangeably to refer to the richness that is within us all. Multicultural awareness enhances our sensitivity to individual uniqueness and helps us to avoid stereotyping.

Wellness and the positive psychology are the final topics in this chapter. Helping clients identify their strengths and resources is vital to growth in the interview. We solve our problems with what we *can do* rather than with what we can't do. Yes, we need to listen carefully to client stories and understand their difficulties, but an important part of the counseling process is helping clients search out and understand what is right with them and their world. Interviewing and counseling are optimistic professions that believe people can change and that they have the resources needed to resolve issues and lead more satisfying lives.

Chapter 3, *Attending and Observation Skills: Basic to Communication,* presents the verbal and nonverbal foundations of interviewing and counseling. We must *attend* or listen to the client if we are to help. Many beginning helpers inappropriately strive to solve client problems in the first 5 minutes of the interview by giving premature advice and suggestions. Set one early goal for yourself as you start learning interviewing skills: *Allow your clients to talk.* It often takes your clients several years to develop their problems. It makes sense that you will need to take time to listen to their stories carefully before you undertake problem solving. *Observation skills* will enhance your awareness of yourself and your clients.

Virtually all who work in interviewing, counseling, and psychotherapy believe that the ability to listen, to enter the client's world, is the most important component of effective helping.

SKILLED INTERVIEWING AND COUNSELING

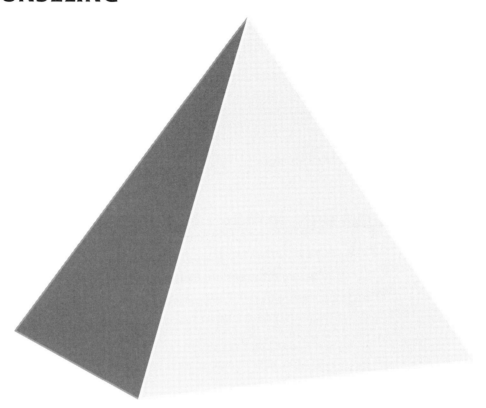

How can the microskills of the interview facilitate your growth and that of your clients?

CHAPTER GOALS

This chapter describes the microskills approach and shows how the step-by-step model of the microskills hierarchy relates to broad concepts of interviewing and counseling. Intentional interviewing facilitates drawing out client stories, enabling clients to find new ways of thinking about these stories and discover new ways of acting. It is important that the interviewer have multiple ways of responding to clients in a culturally sensitive fashion. But, *you* are the person who will implement these ideas—you are asked to record an interview as soon as possible and identify your own natural talents and skills as you start systematic study of interviewing and counseling.

Awareness, knowledge, and skills developed through the concepts of this chapter will enable you to

- ▲ Define and discuss differences and similarities among interviewing, counseling, and psychotherapy.
- ▲ Examine yourself as a holistic and unique multicultural being, one who avoids stereotyping and recognizes that all interviewing involves a wide array of multicultural issues.
- ▲ Understand the importance of wellness and a positive approach to interviewing.
- ▲ Define cultural intentionality and intentional competence.
- ▲ Gain knowledge of the microskills hierarchy and its step-by-step developmental approach that encourages you to define your personal style and theory of counseling.
- ▲ Recognize that microskills are used in all theories of counseling and psychotherapy, but that each theory has different patterns of skill usage.
- ▲ Record and document your own natural helping style for comparison with your subsequent skill development as you work through the microskills hierarchy.

MODULE 1.1
COUNSELING AND INTERVIEWING

KEY CONCEPT QUESTION

▲ How do we differentiate counseling and interviewing?

The terms *counseling* and *interviewing* are used interchangeably in this text. Though the overlap is considerable (see Figure 1-1), interviewing is the more basic process used for gathering data, solving problems, and providing information and advice to clients. Interviewers may be found in many settings including schools, hospitals, businesses, law offices, and a wide variety of helping professions. Counseling is a more intensive and personal process than interviewing. It is generally concerned with helping people cope with normal life challenges and develop opportunities for further growth. Though many people who interview may also counsel, counseling is most often associated with the professional fields of counseling, human relations, psychology, pastoral counseling, social work, and, to a limited extent, psychiatry.

For example, a personnel manager may interview a candidate for a job but in the next hour may counsel an employee who is deciding whether to accept a promotion that requires a move to another city. A school guidance counselor may interview a student to check on course selection but may counsel the next student about college choice or a conflict with a friend. A psychologist may interview one person to obtain research data and in the next hour counsel another concerned with an impending divorce. In the course of a single contact, a social worker may interview a client to obtain financial data and then move on to counsel the same client about personal relationships.

Clinical counseling is new terminology that is entering the field and is expected to become more important in the next few years. A clinical counselor covers the same areas as counseling does on the three bell curves in Figure 1-1, but the counselor also

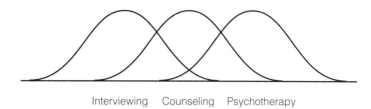

Interviewing   Counseling   Psychotherapy

FIGURE 1-1 The interrelationship of interviewing, counseling, and psychology

may be expected to engage in a fair amount of therapeutic practice. This means that the expertise of clinical counselors will demand competence in interviewing and counseling skills plus training in diagnosis and treatment with more severely stressed clients. Important in our developing field is whether or not clinical counseling will focus on positive human development or perhaps revert to a more traditional (and less effective, in our opinion) remedial model.

Many people who interview find themselves counseling, and most counselors find themselves interviewing. Both interviewing and counseling may be distinguished from psychotherapy, a more intense process, focused on deep-seated personality or behavioral difficulties. But most therapists find themselves also functioning as both interviewer and counselor. The skills and concepts of intentional interviewing are equally important for the successful conduct of psychotherapy.

▲ **MODULE 1.1**

SUMMARY

- ▲ Interviewing is a basic process designed for gathering data, solving problems, and providing information and advice.
- ▲ Counseling is more comprehensive and generally concerned with helping people cope with life challenges and developing new opportunities for further growth, whereas psychotherapy is focused on more deep-seated personality or behavioral difficulties.
- ▲ All use the microskills presented in this text, but with varying emphasis and objectives.

MODULE 1.2
OUR MULTICULTURAL WORLD

KEY CONCEPT QUESTION

▲ How is all interviewing and counseling multicultural?

Cultural and social influences are not the only influences on mental health service and delivery, but they have been historically underestimated—and they do count. Cultural differences must be accounted for to ensure that minorities, like all Americans, receive mental health care tailored to their needs.

This quotation is from the U.S. Surgeon General's Report entitled "Mental Health, Culture, Race and Ethnicity." We encourage you to visit the website for the full report: www.mentalhealth.org/cre/toc.asp.

Professional associations in counseling and psychology have developed guidelines for multicultural awareness and proficiency. Several of these diversity guidelines that relate specifically to interviewing practice are presented in Chapter 2, pages 27–29. Part of cultural intentionality and multicultural competence is your awareness of yourself as a cultural being and your ability to work empathetically with people different from you.

OPEN YOURSELF TO DISCUSSION OF MULTICULTURAL DIFFERENCE

As all behaviors are learned and displayed in a cultural context,
all interviewing and counseling are multicultural.
Paul Pedersen (2006)

It is often helpful to discuss obvious multicultural differences early in the session. The issue is trust; many who are culturally different from a White European American counselor may start with a lack of trust based on their history of encountering racism, sexism, heterosexism, or other forms of discrimination. Many People of Color become more comfortable entering counseling with a White helper who openly discusses difference. Similarly, a White client may be uncomfortable with a Person of Color. Many women and gays/lesbians will feel more comfortable with a helper who understands and discusses issues of gender or sexual orientation.

For example, you may say, "Our skin color (our gender, our sexual orientation, etc.) is different. Sometimes this might lead you to wonder if you can trust me as the right person to help you. As we start, do you have any questions that you'd like to ask me about myself or my background? Later, if you see me missing something important, please let me know." If your age is markedly different from that of your client, trust and confidence may be more difficult to establish. Frank discussion of age differences could facilitate better communication.

However, do not overuse this type of discussion. It may be inappropriate if the client comes in for a one-session interview on choosing courses, planning a school activity, or other relatively neutral topic. Each client and situation is different, and you must use common sense and skilled judgment when bringing up topics of multicultural difference.

RESPECTFUL INTERVIEWING AND COUNSELING

The RESPECTFUL model points out that all of us are multicultural beings (D'Andrea & Daniels, 2001). Multiculturalism refers to far more than race and ethnicity. As you review the list below, first identify your own multicultural dimensions. Then, examine your beliefs and attitudes toward those who are similar to and multiculturally different from you on each issue below.

R Religion/spirituality. What is your religious and spiritual orientation? How does this affect you as an interviewer or counselor?

E Economic/class background. How will you work with those whose financial and social background differs from yours?

S Sexual identity. How effective will you be with those whose gender or sexual orientation differs from yours?

P Personal style and education. How will your personal style and educational level affect your interviewing practice?

E Ethnic/racial identity. The color of our skin is one of the first things we notice. What is your reaction to different races and ethnicities?

C Chronological/life span challenges. Children, adolescents, young adults, mature adults, and older persons all face different issues and problems. Where are you in the developmental lifespan?

T Trauma. It is estimated that 90% or more of the population experience serious trauma(s) in their lives. Trauma underlies the issues faced by many of your clients. War, flood, rape, and assault are powerful examples, but also divorce, loss of a parent, or being raised in an alcoholic family are more common sources of trauma. The constant repetition of racist, sexist, heterosexist acts and comments can also be traumatic. What is your experience with life trauma?

F Family background. We learn culture in our families. The old model of two parents with two children is challenged by the reality of single parents, gay families, and varying family structures. How has your life experience been influenced by your family history (both your immediate family and your intergenerational history)?

U Unique physical characteristics. Become aware of disabilities, special challenges, and false cultural standards of beauty. Help clients think about themselves as physical beings and the importance of nutrition and exercise. How well do you understand the importance of the body in the interview, and how will you work with others different from you?

L Location of residence and language differences. Whether in the United States, Great Britain, Canada, or Australia, there are marked differences between the south and north, the east and west, urban and rural. Remember that a person who is bilingual is advantaged and more skilled, not disadvantaged. What languages do you know, and what is your attitude toward those who use a different language from you?

As you review this list, perhaps you can see more clearly that all interviewing and counseling is multicultural. Broaden your definition of diversity beyond race and ethnicity to include gender, lifespan, and the other factors in the RESPECTFUL model. All your sessions will involve these dimensions (and more). You will spend a lifetime increasing your multicultural competence.

▲ **MODULE 1.2**
SUMMARY

▲ Culture counts! Discussion of multicultural differences early in the session is often important, but common sense also dictates that such discussion is not appropriate for all situations.

▲ Race and ethnicity are especially important multicultural issues, and we need to be aware that White skin color, being male, and being economically advantaged often puts the person in a privileged group.

▲ The RESPECTFUL model lists ten key multicultural dimensions, thus showing that cultural issues inevitably will be part of the interviewing and client relationship.

▲ Developing multicultural awareness, knowledge, and skills is a lifelong process of continuing learning.

MODULE 1.3
LISTENING TO CLIENT STORIES FROM A BASE OF WELLNESS

KEY CONCEPT QUESTION

▲ Why is a positive orientation so important?

Hurricane Katrina, which hit New Orleans in 2005, provides a particularly powerful example of the need to focus on strengths and wellness in the face of trauma. "You can't build a city on problems—we've got to look to the future and what we CAN do to make things better." Similarly, those who lose a family member, experience divorce, or face any of life's many challenges need assistance in finding strengths so that they can develop resilience for the future.

Our first wellness goal is to understand the client's world as fully as we can, using empathic listening to draw out the client's story. Listen for strengths and assets— empowerment, wellness, and positive psychology are a vital part of both interviewing and counseling (cf. Peterson & Seligman, 2004; Sweeney & Myers, 2005). With an understanding of clients' issues and their internal and external resources, you have a foundation for positive change. Include a focus on what clients *can do* as part of your standard interviewing plan. Too many helpers focus on clients' inadequacies.

The story—positive asset—restory—action model summarizes a basic strength-based framework for human change.

STORY

The listening skills detailed in Section I of this text are fundamental in learning how clients make sense of their world. Through effective listening, we learn the stories of their lives, their problems, challenges, and issues. Help them tell their stories in their own way. See Box 1-1 for ideas that will help in bringing out stories in a way that may enable clients to become more optimistic about change.

POSITIVE ASSETS AND WELLNESS STRENGTHS

In addition, search for clients' positive strengths, assets, and resources. Listen for stories in which clients describe times they have succeeded in overcoming obstacles. Listen for and be "curious about their competencies—the heroic stories that reflect their part in surmounting obstacles, initiating action, and maintaining positive change" (Duncan, Miller, & Sparks, 2004, p. 53). Counseling and interviewing can degenerate into a depressing repetition of negative stories, whining, and complaining. You will find that a positive base of strengths and assets can help clients deal with more challenging and complex issues.

RESTORY

If you understand clients' stories and strengths, you can help them restory—generate new ways to talk, think, and feel about themselves. One important strategy for restory-ing is using only listening skills to conduct a full interview (see specifics in Chapter 7). Many times, effective listening is sufficient to provide clients with the strength and power to develop their own new narratives. However, focusing, confrontation, and the influencing skills are important parts of helping clients generate new stories and meanings (see Section III).

BOX 1-1   National and International Perspectives on Counseling Skills

Problems, Concerns, Issues, and Challenges—How Shall We Talk About the Story?
JAMES LANIER, UNIVERSITY OF ILLINOIS, SPRINGFIELD

Counseling and therapy historically have tended to focus on client problems. The word *problem* implies difficulty and the necessity of eliminating or solving the problem. Problem may imply deficit. Traditional diagnosis such as that found in the *Diagnostic and Statistical Manual of Mental Disorders-TR* (American Psychiatric Association, 2000) carries the idea of problem a bit further, using the word *disorder* with such terms as *panic disorder, conduct disorder, obsessive-compulsive disorder,* and many other highly specific *disorders.* The way we use these words often defines how clients see themselves.

I'm not fond of problem-oriented language, particularly that word "disorder." I often work with African American youth. If I asked them, "What's your problem?" they likely would reply, "I don't have a problem, but I do have a concern." The word *concern* suggests something we all have all the time. The word also suggests that we can deal with it—often from a more

positive standpoint. Defining *concerns* as *problems* or *disorders* leads to placing the blame and responsibility for resolution almost solely on the individual.

Finding a more positive way to discuss client concerns is relevant to all your clients, regardless of their background. *Issue* is another term that can be used instead of *problem.* This further removes the pathology from the person and tends to put the person in a situational context. It may be a more empowering word for some clients. Carrying this idea further, *challenge* may be defined as a call to our strengths. Some might even talk about *an opening for change.*

Beyond that, the concepts of the wellness and positive asset search make good sense for the youth with whom I have worked. Change is most easily made from a position of strength—criticism and problem-oriented language can weaken. However, don't be afraid to challenge people to grow. Confrontation can help your clients develop in positive ways.

ACTION

The influencing skills help clients shift from thinking into action. Through the use of action-oriented directives, the skilled use of the interpretation/reframe, or assertiveness training, you may enable clients to take their new ideas and stories into concrete action. Something must change in terms of thoughts, feelings, and behaviors outside the interview for interviewing and counseling to be effective.

If your work with this text is successful, you will develop a solid understanding of foundation skills and strategies, an ability to conduct interviews from several perspectives, and—perhaps most important—you will begin the process of writing your own narrative, your own personal theory of interviewing and counseling. We hope your personal construction of theory and practice will remain open to constant challenge and growth from your clients and from your professional colleagues.

▲ **MODULE 1.3**

SUMMARY

- ▲ Wellness and positive psychology provide a foundation for client change. With an understanding of client strengths and personal power, you have a base for facilitating change.
- ▲ Story: Draw out clients' stories through effective listening.
- ▲ Positive Asset: Search for client strengths and resources in their stories.
- ▲ Restory: Help clients write new more positive stories using the identified strengths.
- ▲ Action: Encourage clients to take their new stories into their daily lives and take positive action to resolve their issues and meet their challenges.

MODULE 1.4
CULTURAL INTENTIONALITY: Developing Multiple Responses

KEY CONCEPT QUESTIONS

▲ **Why are many potential responses critical to effective cultural intentionality?**

▲ **What are we to expect when we intentionally use a specific skill or strategy in the session?**

One of the goals of this text is to help you look at yourself and your typical response style. Your present communication style and social skills are valuable natural tools on which you can build your unique approach to helping others. Imagine that you are interviewing a client. What would you say in response to the following?

MALE CLIENT: (talking about a conflict on the job): I just don't know what to do about my new boss. It seems he's always on me, blaming me even when I do a good job. He's new on the job, I know. Perhaps he doesn't have much experience as a supervisor. But he's got me all jumpy. I'm so nervous I can't sleep at night, and yesterday I even lost my lunch. My family isn't doing well, either. I've been arguing with Farah and she doesn't seem to understand what's going on and is upset. Even the kids aren't doing well in school. What do you suggest I do?

How would you respond? How would you respond if the client were a woman going through the same issues?

Men and women going through exactly the same problems may have very different experiences. What you say and how you formulate the central issues of the presented problem may say as much about you and your style as they say about your client. Compare your responses with others. What do you learn from their ideas? What is the "correct" response in this case?

Of course, there are many potentially useful responses in any interviewing situation. The absolutely "correct" response likely does not exist. Asking an open question ("Could you tell me more?") may be particularly useful so that you can understand issues more fully. Or reflecting feelings may be helpful ("Looks like you are upset over the situation with the new boss"). Self-disclosure and direct advice may be what is needed for some clients ("My experience with such situations is . . . and I suggest you try . . .").

Beginning interviewers can be eager to find the "right" answer for the client. In fact, some often give quick, inappropriate, patch-up advice. How ideal it would be to find the perfect empathic response to unlock the door and free the client for more creative living. The tendency to move too quickly and search for a single "right" response can be damaging.

Cultural intentionality is a core goal of effective interviewing. Culturally intentional interviewing is concerned with how many potential responses may be helpful. We can define it as follows:

Cultural intentionality is acting with a sense of capability and deciding from among a range of alternative actions. The intentional individual can generate alternatives in a given situation and approach a problem from different vantage points, using a variety of skills and personal qualities, adapting styles to suit different individuals and cultures.

The culturally intentional interviewer remembers a basic rule of helping: *If a helping lead or skill doesn't work—try another approach!* A critical issue in interviewing is that the same comment may have different effects on individuals who have unique personal life experiences and multicultural backgrounds. Intentional interviewing requires awareness that cultural groups each have different patterns of communication. For example, in European and North American cultures, middle-class patterns call for rather direct eye contact, but in some cultural groups direct eye contact is considered rude and intrusive. Some groups find the rapid-fire questioning techniques of many North Americans offensive. Many Spanish-speaking groups have more varied vocal tones and a more rapid speech rate than do English-speaking people.

INTENTIONAL PREDICTION

This text is action- and results-oriented; it is founded on research revealing that you may expect specific results when you use a specific microskill or strategy in the interview. If you work intentionally in the interview, you can anticipate predictable client responses. And even if the expected does not happen, you can intentionally flex and come up with a helpful alternative comment.

Let us briefly define two important skills discussed in later chapters. You are likely very familiar with questions, but intentionally using the specific microskill of questioning will enable you to be more effective in obtaining client information economically and respectfully. Another critical skill is reflection of feeling, which is central to clarifying client emotions. If used skillfully, reflection of feeling facilitates more meaningful resolution of client's issues, concerns, and problems.

If you use questioning skills, you can *predict* how clients respond. If you reflect feelings, you can *predict* clients will focus on their emotions. Note below the brief definitions of these two skill areas and the predictions that you can make when you use these skills intentionally. But be ready to intentionally flex and be prepared with a new skill when your first choice does not produce the expected result.

Open and Closed Questions	*Predicted Result*
Open questions often begin with *who, what, when, where,* and *why.* Closed questions may start with *do, is,* or *are. Could, can,* or *would* questions are considered open but have the additional advantage of being somewhat closed, thus giving more power to clients, who can more easily say that they don't want to respond.	Clients will give more detail and talk more in response to open questions. Closed questions provide specific information but may close off client talk. Effective questions encourage more focused client conversations with more pertinent detail and less wandering. *Could, would,* and *can* questions are often the most open of all.
Reflection of Feeling	*Predicted Result*
The interviewer identifies the key emotions of a client and feeds them back to clarify affective experience. With some clients, the brief acknowledgment of feeling may be more appropriate.	Clients will be able to experience their emotional states more clearly. They also may correct the interviewer's reflection with a more accurate descriptor.

A summary of all brief definitions and predicted results may be found in Appendix I. It is important to stress that predictability and ability to anticipate results of your interventions will never reach 100%. Please recall that if the first skill does not produce the expected result, be ready with another skill or concept to help clients grow in their own way. Eventually, you will have a large array of competencies for effective interviewing, thus strengthening your flexibility and cultural intentionality.

▲ **MODULE 1.4**
SUMMARY

- ▲ Cultural intentionality is defined as acting with a sense of capability and deciding from among a range of alternative actions.
- ▲ When you use a specific microskill skill or strategy, you may predict how the client will respond. Be flexible and if one skill isn't working, try another.
- ▲ The use of microskills will increase your cultural intentionality and flexibility by showing you many ways to respond to a single client statement or concern.

MODULE 1.5
THE MICROSKILLS APPROACH

KEY CONCEPT QUESTION

▲ What microskills lead to intentional interviewing and counseling?

Microskills are communication skill units that help you to interact more intentionally with a client. The microskills model was developed through years of study and analysis of hundreds of interviews. Specific skills of effective interviewing, counseling, and therapy are identified and taught one at a time.

Your natural talent and style will be enhanced by careful study of the interview and its critical components. As you master each skill, you are prepared for learning the next, more challenging microskill. This approach is similar to that employed by world-famous golf pros and tennis stars, as well as accomplished musicians and dancers. You begin with natural talent, but talent needs to be amplified by careful study and practice of specific skills. Extensive feedback from experienced experts and trainers also facilitates enhanced performance and true mastery. The microskills of the interview are critical dimensions of effective interviewing, counseling, and psychotherapy just as the specifics of the golf swing are to Tiger Woods, rounding a corner for a NASCAR driver, or harmony and style for an *American Idol* winner.

The microskills hierarchy (see Figure 1-2) summarizes the successive skill steps and provides an overview of this text. Interview skills rest on a base of *ethics, multicultural competence, and wellness* (Chapter 2). On this foundation lies the first microskill, *attending behavior,* culturally and individually appropriate listening skills, including patterns of eye contact, body language, vocal qualities, and verbal tracking (Chapter 3).

Once you have mastered attending behavior, you will move up the microskills pyramid to *questioning, paraphrasing, and other listening skills* (Chapters 4, 5, and 6). It is important to remember that the foundation for effective interviewing and eventual skill integration is the ability to listen to and understand the client.

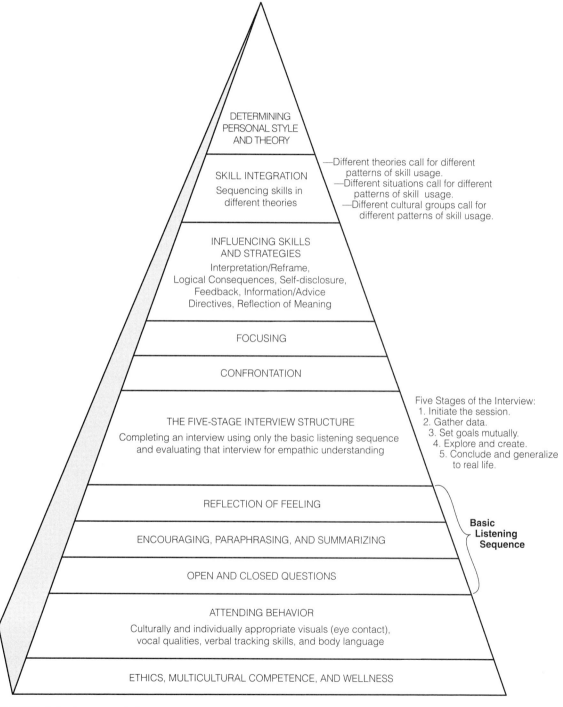

FIGURE 1-2 The Microskills Hierarchy: A pyramid for building cultural intentionality
© 1982, 1985, 2007, 2008 Allen E. Ivey, by permission.

With a solid background in these most important skills, you will learn how to *structure a "well-formed interview"* (Chapter 7). In addition to being able to conduct a complete interview using only listening skills, you will learn that the structure of the interview can be adapted and shaped to help you master several alternative methods and theories of counseling. Here you will engage in a modified person-centered interview, thus starting early theoretical integration.

The first direct action skill of interviewing and counseling is *confrontation,* which is considered basic to the developmental change process (Chapter 8).

The microskill of *focusing* shows you how to engage the *person* in the interview while maintaining awareness of the affect of family and environmental/contextual factors (Chapter 9). The *influencing skills (reflection of meaning, interpretation/reframe, directives, feedback,* and others) help clients restory their thoughts and feelings and learn to behave in new ways (Chapters 10, 11, 12).

With a mastery of listening, the ability to conduct an interview using only listening skills, and a command of the advanced skills, you are prepared to encounter alternative theories and modes of helping. You will find that microskills can be organized into different patterns used by different theories. For example, if you have mastered the listening skills and the structure of the interview, you already have an important beginning in learning person-centered theory.

Chapter 13, *Decisional Counseling, Skill Integration, and Developing Treatment Plans,* includes treatment planning for future sessions and presents decisional counseling, an important and widely used theoretical interviewing orientation. You are also asked to develop your own transcript and analyze your own style after reviewing a transcript of a full decisional interview, along with key aspects of treatment planning.

But as you can see from a glance at the apex of the microskills hierarchy, *determining personal style and theory,* it isn't enough just to gain mastery. You will eventually have to determine your own theory and practice of counseling and interviewing. Interviewers, counselors, and therapists are an independent lot; the vast majority of helpers prefer to develop their own style, and through eclecticism move toward their own blend of skills and theories. Chapter 14 shows you how microskills are used with three key theories of helping: person-centered, cognitive-behavioral assertiveness training, and brief interviewing and counseling. Chapter 15 provides a chance to reflect on where you are and where you wish to go in the future.

Different theories have varying patterns of microskill usage, although all give emphasis to the listening skills. As one route toward your own skill integration, examine Table 1-1, which presents samples of microskill usage among different theoretical orientations to the interview. Once you have mastered the microskills, you are well prepared to learn and decide from specific theories of helping.

▲ MODULE 1.5
SUMMARY

- ▲ Microskills are communication skill units that help you develop the ability to interact more intentionally with a client.
- ▲ The microskills hierarchy provides a visual picture of the skills and strategies.
- ▲ Natural talent in golf, tennis, ballet, and many other activities is enhanced by the study and practice of single skills.
- ▲ Note that important theories of counseling and interviewing have distinctive differences in how they use the microskills (Table 1-1).

▲ **TABLE 1-1**   Microskills Patterns of Differing Approaches to the Interview

MICROSKILL LEAD	Decisional counseling	Person centered	Behavioral (assertiveness training)	Solution oriented	Motivational interviewing	Psychodynamic	Gestalt	Rational-emotive behavioral therapy	Feminist therapy	Business problem solving	Medical diagnostic interview	Eclectic/metatheoretical
BASIC LISTENING SKILLS												
Open question	●	○	◐	●	●	◐	●	◐	◐	◐	◐	◐
Closed question	◐	○	●	◐	◐	○	◐	◐	◐	◐	●	◐
Encourager	●	◐	◐	◐	●	◐	◐	◐	◐	◐	◐	◐
Paraphrase	●	●	◐	●	●	◐	○	◐	◐	◐	◐	◐
Reflection of feeling	●	●	◐	◐	●	◐	◐	◐	◐	○	○	◐
Summarization	◐	◐	◐	●	●	◐	○	◐	◐	◐	◐	◐
INFLUENCING SKILLS												
Reflection of meaning	◐	●	○	○	○	◐	◐	◐	●	○	○	◐
Interpretation/reframe	◐	○	○	○	●	●	●	●	◐	◐	◐	◐
Logical consequences	◐	○	◐	○	●	○	○	●	◐	●	◐	◐
Self-disclosure	◐	◐	○	○	◐	○	○	○	●	◐	◐	◐
Feedback	◐	◐	◐	◐	●	○	◐	●	◐	◐	○	◐
Advice/information/ and others	◐	○	◐	○	◐	○	◐	●	◐	●	◐	◐
Directive	◐	○	●	○	◐	○	●	●	◐	●	◐	◐
CONFRONTATION (Combined Skill)	◐	◐	◐	◐	●	◐	●	●	●	●	◐	◐
FOCUS												
Client	●	●	●	●	●	●	●	●	○	◐	◐	◐
Concern, main theme	●	○	◐	●	◐	◐	○	◐	◐	●	●	◐
Significant others	◐	○	◐	◐	◐	◐	○	○	◐	◐	○	◐
Mutuality	○	◐	○	◐	◐	○	○	○	◐	○	○	◐
Counselor/interviewer	○	◐	○	○	◐	○	○	◐	◐	○	○	◐
Cultural/ environmental context	◐	○	◐	◐	○	○	○	○	●	◐	○	◐
ISSUE OF MEANING (Topics, key words likely to be attended to and reinforced)	Decisions	Relationship	Changing behavior	Change	Change	Unconscious motivation	Here-and-now behavior	Irrational ideas/logic	Women's issues	Problem solving	Diagnosis of illness	Varies
AMOUNT OF INTERVIEWER TALK-TIME	Medium	Low	High	Medium	Medium	Low	High	High	Medium	High	High	Varies

LEGEND

● Frequent use of skill
◐ Common use of skill
○ Occasional use of skill

MODULE 1.6
THE MICROSKILLS LEARNING MODEL AND RESEARCH VALIDATION

KEY CONCEPT QUESTIONS

▲ How do you learn the microskills of the interview?

▲ What does research say that may facilitate your own practice?

Each of us has a unique learning style. It is vital to develop cognitive understanding of each microskill if you are to develop competence in interviewing. This can be accomplished through reading or a lecture. Observing the skill in operation in the interview provides a context and illustrates clearly how the skill affects clients. This can be accomplished through reading a transcript of an interview, viewing a videotape of the skill in action, or observing live action demonstrations. But most important is real-life practice and experience in using the microskill. Research has shown that a five-step model that encompasses several learning styles is most effective in developing mastery in the microskills and practical competence in the interview.

1. *Define the skill, its central features, and its purpose.* Skills are learned one at a time, then later integrated into practice and real interviews.
2. *Observe the skill in action.* This may be through reading a transcript of an interview or listening to an audiotape. Viewing interview videos or seeing a live demonstration is more powerful and immediate.
3. *Learn the skill and its implications.* Further reading or attending lectures builds deeper understanding and is vital for skill maintenance.
4. *Practice the skill in role-play.* Ideally, you will see yourself on video, but role-played practice with observers and feedback sheets is also effective.
5. *Plan for generalization.* How can you put this skill into action in your interviewing practice?

This five-step model will be used throughout this text. The microskills are basic dimensions of emotional intelligence and social competence. Teaching clients these skills can be an effective counseling and therapeutic strategy. These skills are used widely in teaching peer counselors and community volunteers. It is very possible that you will include using and teaching communication skills as part of your daily work, whether it is in interviewing, counseling, social work, nursing, management, or many other professions.

More than 450 microskills research studies have been conducted (Daniels, 2007; Daniels & Ivey, 2006). The model has been tested nationally and internationally in over 1,000 clinical and teaching programs. Microcounseling was the first systematic video-based counseling model to identify specific observable interviewing skills. It was also the first skills training program that emphasized multicultural issues (Ivey, Gluckstern, & Ivey, 2006). Some of the most important research findings include these:

> *You can expect results from microskills training.* Several critical reviews have found microtraining an effective framework for teaching skills to a wide variety of people ranging from beginning interviewers to experienced professionals who need to relate to patients and clients more effectively. Consistent data attest to the effectiveness of teaching microskills to clients and patients. Teaching your clients many of the microskills will facilitate their personal growth and ability to communicate with their families or coworkers.

Practice is essential. Practice the skills to mastery if the skills are to be maintained and used after training. *Use it or lose it!* Complete practice exercises and generalize what you learn to real life.

Multicultural differences are real. People from different multicultural groups (e.g., ethnicity/race, gender) have different patterns of skill usage. Learn about people different from you and use skills in a culturally appropriate manner.

Different counseling theories have varying patterns of skill usage. Expect person-centered counselors to focus almost exclusively on listening skills whereas cognitive behaviorists use more influencing skills (see Table 1-1). Microskills expertise will help you define your own theory and integrate it with your natural style.

If you use a specific microskill, then you can expect a client to respond in predictable ways. You can predict how the client will respond to your use of each microskill, but each client is unique and predictability is not perfect. Cultural intentionality prepares you for the unexpected and teaches you to flex with another microskill.

The microskills approach was originally used for counselor and interview training in English-speaking countries; it is now available in 18 languages throughout the world. The model has proven useful in training workers for AIDS prevention in Africa, refugees in Sri Lanka, Aboriginal social workers in Australia, alcohol counselors with Dene and Inuits in Canada, elementary peer mediators, governmental officials, nurses, and physicians throughout the world. Business managers in the United States, the United Kingdom, Sweden, Israel, and Japan have participated in microskills training.

All professions need effective communication skills. The microskills program is continually growing in influence and applications. We look forward to your reactions to this book and your ideas for future improvement.

▲ MODULE 1.6
SUMMARY

- ▲ The five-step learning model of microskills is as follows: (1) Define the skill, (2) observe the skill in action, (3) learn more through reading or lectures, (4) practice the skill in role-play, and (5) take what you learn to the "real world."
- ▲ Over 450 data-based studies have tested the microskill model, used in over 1,000 settings throughout the world.
- ▲ Key research findings include validation of the teaching model, the reality of cultural differences in the ways skills are used, and importance of practice if the skills are to be learned and maintained.
- ▲ Key research findings include validation of the teaching model, the reality of cultural differences in skill usage, and the vital importance of practice if the skills are to be generalized to the real world.

MODULE 1.7
YOUR NATURAL STYLE: An Important Audio or Video Exercise

KEY CONCEPT QUESTION

▲ **How will you document your natural personal style and current skill level before you begin systematic microskills training?**

On page 10 you were asked to give your response to a client who came to you to discuss multiple issues. The microskills learned through this text will provide you with additional alternatives for intentional responses to the client. However, these responses must be genuinely your own. If you adopt a response simply because it is recommended, it is likely to be ineffective for both you and your client. Not all parts of the microskills framework are appropriate for everyone. You have a natural style of communicating, and these concepts must enhance your natural style, not detract from it.

You will need varying patterns of helping skills with the clients with whom you work. Couple your natural style with awareness and knowledge of multicultural differences. How will clients respond to your natural style? You may need to "flex" or be flexible as you encounter diversity among clients. You may work more effectively with some clients than others. Because of past experiences, a woman may feel uncomfortable with a male counselor or vice versa. Many clients lack trust with interviewers who come from a different race or ethnicity than their own. You may be less comfortable with teenagers than you are with children or adults. In all these cases, you will want to expand your competence and add new knowledge and methods to your natural style.

You are about to engage in a systematic study of the interviewing process. By the end of the book you will have experienced many ideas for analyzing your interviewing style and skill usage. Along the way, it will be helpful to have a record of where you are before you begin this training. It is invaluable to identify your personal style and current skill level before you begin systematic training.

Eventually, it is YOU who will integrate these ideas into your own practice, let's start with your own work. Please read Box 1-2 below and make plans to record your natural style *before* continuing much farther in this text.

BOX 1-2   Exercise: Discovering Your Natural Style of Interviewing

Instructions

It is important to conduct this exercise as soon as possible. Your choice of audio or videotape will document an accurate baseline of your natural style and skill level. As you progress through this text, compare this session with your later work.

Guidelines for Audio- or Videorecording

1. *Find a volunteer client* willing to role-play a concern, problem, opportunity, or issue.
2. *Interview the volunteer client* for at least 15 minutes. Seek to avoid sensitive topics.
3. *Use your own natural communication style.*
4. *Ask the volunteer client,* "May I record this interview?"
5. *Inform the client* that the tape recorder may be turned off at any time, as requested by the client.

6. *Select a topic.* You and the client may choose interpersonal conflict, a specific issue selected by the client, or one of the elements from the RESPECT-FUL model.
7. *Follow the ethical guidelines* from pp. 21–26. Common sense demands ethical practice and respect for the client.
8. *Obtain feedback.* You will find it very helpful to get immediate feedback from your client. As you practice the microskills, use the Client Feedback Form (Box 1-3). You may even find it helpful to continue the use of this form, or some adaptation of it, in your work as an interviewing professional.
9. *Compare this baseline* with subsequent recordings of your work throughout this text.

▲ **MODULE 1.7**
SUMMARY

▲ The microskills are meant to add to and enhance, not detract from, your natural style of communicating.
▲ Your ability to vary use of microskill patterns allows you to flex as you encounter client diversity.
▲ It is critical to document a baseline of your natural style and skill level before you begin the systematic study of the microskills.

BOX 1-3   Client Feedback Form

(Note: You and your instructor may wish to change and adapt this form to meet the needs of varying clients, agencies, and situations. You may copy this form.)

1. What one thing stood out for you from this session? What might you remember and take home with you?

2. Did the interviewer listen to you? Did you feel heard? Rate this on a seven-point scale with "1" representing that you felt very much listened to and "7" that you were not heard.

High   Medium   Low
1   2   3   4   5   6   7

3. What, if anything, did the interviewer miss that you would have liked to explore today or in another session? What else might you have liked to share?

4. What did you find helpful? What did the interviewer do that was right? Be specific. For example, not "You did great," but rather, "You listened to me carefully when I talked about _____."

5. Overall: Rate the quality of this session in terms of its helpfulness.

High   Medium   Low
1   2   3   4   5   6   7

6. Other comments and suggestions are welcomed.

ETHICS, MULTICULTURAL COMPETENCE, AND WELLNESS

CHAPTER

2

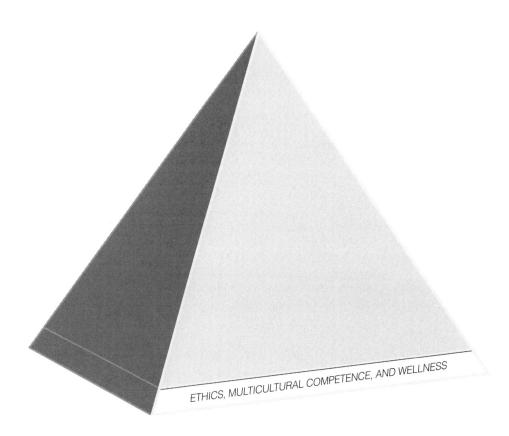

ETHICS, MULTICULTURAL COMPETENCE, AND WELLNESS

How can this chapter help you and your clients?

CHAPTER GOALS

Effective interviews build on professional ethics, multicultural sensitivity, and a positive wellness approach. Specifics are stressed that apply to use in the interview.

Awareness, knowledge, and skills developed through the concepts of this chapter will enable you to

▲ Apply key ethical principles in interviewing and counseling.
▲ Develop your own informed consent form.
▲ Define multicultural competence, including key aspects of awareness, knowledge, and skills.
▲ Apply wellness and positive psychology in an assessment interview.

MODULE 2.1
ETHICS IN INTERVIEWING AND COUNSELING

KEY CONCEPT QUESTIONS

▲ **How competent are you to work with various issues presented by clients, and when should you refer?**

▲ **How do you inform clients about key issues as they begin interviewing and counseling?**

▲ **What are major guidelines for confidentiality?**

▲ **How is power defined in relation to interviewing practice?**

▲ **What is your responsibility to work with issues of social justice?**

Ethics	*Predicted Result*
Observe and practice ethically and follow professional standards. Particularly important issues for beginning interviewers are *competence, informed consent, confidentiality, power,* and *social justice.*	Client trust and understanding of the interviewing process will increase. The client will feel empowered in a more egalitarian session. When you work toward social justice, you contribute to problem prevention in addition to healing work in the interview.

All major helping professions throughout the world have codes for ethical practice. "The codes promote professional empowerment by assisting professionals and professionals-in-training to: (a) keep good practice, (b) protect their clients, (c) safeguard their autonomy, and (d) enhance the profession" (Pack-Brown & Williams, 2003). Ethical codes can be summarized with the following statement: "Do no harm to your clients; treat them responsibly with full awareness of the social context of helping." As interviewers and counselors we are responsible for our clients and for society as well. At times these responsibilities conflict, and you may need to seek detailed guidance from documented ethical codes, your supervisor, or other professionals.

Box 2-1 presents websites of some key ethical codes in English-speaking areas of the globe. You will find guidelines on *competence, informed consent, confidentiality,* and *diversity* in all codes. Issues of *power* and *social justice* are explicit in social work and human services and implicit in all other codes. Review the complete text of your intended profession and any others you think pertinent.

BOX 2-1   Professional Ethical Codes With Websites

Listed below are some important ethical codes. Website addresses are correct at the time of printing but can change. For a keyword web search, use the name of the professional association and the words *ethics* or *ethical code*.

American Association of Marriage and Family Therapy (AAMFT) Code of Ethics	www.aamft.org
American Counseling Association (ACA) Code of Ethics and Standards of Practice	www.counseling.org
American Psychological Association (APA) Ethical Principles of Psychologists and Code of Conduct	www.apa.org
Australian Psychological Society (APS) Code of Ethics	www.psychology.org.au
British Association for Counselling (BAC) Code of Ethics and Practice for Counsellors	www.bacp.co.uk
Canadian Counselling Association (CCA) Codes of Ethics	www.ccacc.ca
National Association of Human Service Education (NAHSE) Ethical Standards of Human Service Professionals	www.nohse.com
National Association of Social Workers (NASW) Code of Ethics	www.naswdc.org
New Zealand Association of Counsellors Inc. (NZAC) Code of Ethics	www.nzac.org.nz
Ethics Updates provides updates on current literature, both popular and professional, that relate to ethics.	www.ethics.acusd.edu/index.asp

COMPETENCE

The American Counseling Association's (2005) statement on professional competence includes diversity. Note the emphasis on continued learning and expanding one's qualifications over time.

> *C.2.a. Boundaries of Competence.* Counselors practice only within the boundaries of their competence, based on their education, training, supervised experience, state and national professional credentials, and appropriate professional experience. Counselors will gain knowledge, personal awareness, sensitivity, and skills pertinent to working with a diverse client population.

Regardless of the human services profession with which you identify, competence is key. Part of personal expertise is recognizing when you may need to seek appropriate supervision and consultation. Very few of us can work with all clients; be ready to refer clients when you are unable to help them effectively.

In working with a client you need to constantly monitor whether you are competent to counsel the individual on each issue presented. For example, you may be able to help the client work out difficulties with the supervisor on the job, but you discover a more complex problem that requires family counseling. You may need to refer the client to another counselor for family counseling while continuing to work with the job issues. If a client demonstrates severe distress or presents an issue with which you are uncomfortable, seek supervision. If you are still uncomfortable, referral is essential.

INFORMED CONSENT

Counseling is an international profession. The Canadian Counselling Association (1999) approach to informed consent is particularly clear.

> *B4. Client Rights and Informed Consent.* When counselling is initiated, and throughout the counselling process as necessary, counsellors inform clients of the purposes, goals, techniques, procedures, limitations, potential risks and benefits of services to be performed, and other such pertinent information. Counsellors make sure that clients understand the implications of diagnosis, fees and fee collection arrangements, record keeping, and limits to confidentiality. Clients have the right to participate in the ongoing counselling plans, to refuse any recommended services, and to be advised of the consequences of such refusal.

The American Psychological Association (2002) stresses that psychologists should inform clients if the interview is to be supervised and provides additional specifics:

> *Standard 10.01* When the therapist is a trainee and the legal responsibility for the treatment provided resides with the supervisor, the client/patient, as part of the informed consent procedure, is informed that the therapist is in training and is being supervised and is given the name of the supervisor.

> *Standard 4.03* Before recording the voices or images of individuals to whom they provide services, psychologists obtain permission from all such persons or their legal representatives.

When you enter into role-plays and practice sessions, it is important that you inform your volunteer "clients" about their rights, your own competence, and what clients can expect from the session. For example, you might say,

> I'm taking an interviewing course, and I appreciate your being willing to help me. I am a beginner, so only talk about things that you want to talk about. I would like to audiotape (or videotape) the interview, but I'll turn it off immediately if you become uncomfortable and erase it as soon as possible. I may share the tape in a practicum class or I may develop a written transcript of this session, removing anything that may identify you personally. I'll share any written material with you before passing it in to the instructor. Remember, we will stop any time you wish. Do you have any questions?

You may use the statement above as an ethical starting point and eventually develop your own approach to this critical issue. The sample practice contract in Box 2-2 may be helpful as you begin.

BOX 2-2 Sample Practice Contract

The following is a sample contract for you to adapt for practice sessions with volunteer clients.

Dear Friend,

I am a student in interviewing skills at (insert name of class and college/university). I am required to practice counseling skills with volunteers. I appreciate your willingness to work with me on my class assignments.

You may choose to talk about topics of real concern to you, or you may prefer to role-play an issue that does not necessarily relate to you. Please let me know before we start whether you are talking about yourself or role-playing.

Here are some important dimensions of our work together:

Confidentiality. As a student, I cannot offer any form of legal confidentiality. However, anything you say to me in the practice session will remain confidential except for the important exceptions that must be reported as required by state law. Even as a student, I must report (1) a serious issue of harm to yourself; (2) indications of child abuse or neglect; (3) other special conditions as required by our state (insert as appropriate).

Audio- and/or Videotaping. I will be recording our sessions for my personal listening and learning. If you become uncomfortable at any time, we can turn off the recorder. The tape(s) may be shared with my supervisor (insert name and phone number of professor or supervisor) and/or students in my class. You'll find that recording does not affect our practice session so long as you and I are comfortable. Without additional permission, recordings or written transcripts are destroyed at the end of the course.

Boundaries of Competence. I am an inexperienced interviewer; I cannot do formal counseling. This practice session helps me learn interview skills. I need feedback from you about my performance and what you find helpful. I may give you a form that asks you to evaluate how helpful I was.

_____   _____

Volunteer Client   Interviewer

Date _____

CONFIDENTIALITY

The American Counseling Association's (2005) Ethical Code states:

> *Section B: Introduction.* Counselors recognize that trust is the cornerstone of the counseling relationship. Counselors aspire to earn the trust of clients by creating an ongoing partnership, establishing and upholding appropriate boundaries, and maintaining confidentiality. Counselors communicate the parameters of confidentiality in a culturally competent manner.

As a student taking this course, you are a beginning professional; you usually do not have legal confidentiality. Nonetheless, you need to keep to yourself what you hear in class role-plays or practice sessions. Trust is built on your ability to keep confidences. Be aware that each state has varying laws on confidentiality.

Professionals encounter *many* challenges to this issue. Some states require you to inform parents before counseling a child, and information from interviews must be shared with them if they ask. If issues of abuse should appear, you must report this to the authorities. If the client is a danger to self or others, then rules of confidentiality change and the issue of reporting such information needs to be discussed with your supervisor. As a beginning interviewer, you will likely have limited, if any, legal protection, so limits to confidentiality must be included in your approach to informed consent.

POWER

The National Organization of Human Service Professionals (2000) comments on power, an important ethical issue that often receives insufficient attention:

> *Statement 6.* Human service professionals are aware that in their relationships with clients power and status are unequal. Therefore, they recognize that dual or multiple relationships may increase the risk of harm to, or exploitation of clients, and may impair professional judgment. . . .

Power differentials occur in society. The very act of helping has power implications. The client may begin counseling with perceived lesser power than the interviewer. Awareness of and openness to talking about these issues is one way to work toward a more egalitarian relationship with the client. If your gender is opposite that of your client, it can be helpful to bring up the gender difference. For example, "How comfortable are you discussing this issue with a man? Do you have any questions that you want to ask me?" If your client is uncomfortable, it is wise to discuss this issue further. Referral may be necessary.

You will encounter many situations in which institutional or cultural oppression becomes part of the counseling relationship, even though you personally may not have been involved in that oppression. For example, a woman may have had bad experiences with men. A Person of Color being counseled by a White person may perceive the interviewer as potentially prejudiced, and a gay person may not feel safe with a heterosexual counselor. Those who have a disability may expect to be treated with a lack of real understanding by those more physically able. In each of these cases, discussion of differences in background and culture can be helpful early in the session.

Dual relationships occur when you have more than one relationship with a client. If your client is a classmate or friend, you are engaged in a dual relationship. These situations may also occur when you counsel a member of your church or school community. They can become complex issues; examine this situation in more detail in the ethical codes. The basic ethical ideal is to avoid all dual relationships. In practice, however, this is difficult and even perhaps impossible when you are learning interviewing skills. As a practicing professional in a group, you can refer people you know, or have dual relationships with, to someone else in your agency or company. If you are the only counselor in a small town, you may find yourself necessarily having to counsel someone you know from the community. Nonetheless, avoid dual relationships as far as possible.

SOCIAL JUSTICE

The National Association of Social Workers (1999) suggests that action beyond the interview may be needed to address social justice issues. The code includes a major statement on social justice.

Ethical Principle: Social workers challenge social injustice.

Social workers pursue social change, particularly with and on behalf of vulnerable and oppressed individuals and groups of people. Social workers' social change efforts are focused primarily on issues of poverty, unemployment, discrimination, and other forms of social injustice. These activities seek to promote sensitivity to and knowledge about oppression and cultural and ethnic diversity. Social workers strive to ensure access to needed information, services, and resources; equality of opportunity; and meaningful participation in decision making for all people.

When a female client discusses mistreatment and harassment by her supervisor, the issue of oppression of women should be named as such. The social justice perspective requires you to help her understand that the problem is not caused by her behavior or how she dressed. By naming the problem as sexism and harassment, you often free the client from self-blame and empower her for action. You can also support her in efforts to effect change in the workplace. On a broader scale you may work in the larger community outside the interview to promote fairer treatment for women in the workplace. Helping clients work through issues in the interview may not be enough. You also have a responsibility to promote community change through social action.

These same points hold true for any form of oppression that you encounter in the session, whether it is racism, ableism, heterosexism, classism, or other forms of prejudice. We need to remember that our clients live in relationship to the world. The microskill of focusing discussed later in this book provides specifics for bringing the cultural/environmental/social context into the interview (Chapter 9).

▲ **MODULE 2.1**

SUMMARY

- ▲ Ethical codes can be summarized as follows: "Do no harm to your clients; treat them responsibly with full awareness of the social context of helping."
- ▲ Counselors must practice within boundaries of their competence, based on education, training, supervised experience, state and national professional credentials, and appropriate professional experience.
- ▲ Informed consent requires us to tell clients of their rights. When taping sessions, we need permission from the client.
- ▲ Beginning interviewers have no legal confidentiality but must maintain confidences and follow general professional standards.
- ▲ Interviewers and counselors have more perceived power than clients and efforts need to be made to equalize power in the relationship.
- ▲ Dual relationships in interviewing should be avoided as far as possible.
- ▲ Helping professionals are asked to work outside the interview to improve society and are called upon to act on social justice issues.

MODULE 2.2
DIVERSITY AND MULTICULTURAL COMPETENCE

KEY CONCEPT QUESTIONS

▲ **What are basic standards for working cross-culturally?**

▲ **How is dealing with diversity an ethical imperative?**

Multicultural Issues	*Predicted Result*
Base interviewer behavior on an ethical approach with an awareness of the many issues of diversity. Include the multiple dimensions from the RESPECTFUL model (Chapter 1).	Anticipate that both you and your clients will appreciate, gain respect, and learn from increasing knowledge in ethics and multicultural competence. You, the interviewer, will have a solid foundation for a lifetime of personal and professional growth.

MULTICULTURAL COMPETENCE

Multicultural guidelines and specific competencies for practice have been developed by the American Counseling Association and the American Psychological Association (APA, 2002; Roysircar et al., 2003; Sue et al., 1998). In these statements the words *multiculturalism* and *diversity* are defined broadly to include many dimensions.

The multicultural competencies talk about awareness, knowledge, and skills. The competencies ask you to become aware of specific issues, develop knowledge around multicultural issues, and master skills for the interview and daily practice in our multicultural world. Expect the issue of multicultural competence to become increasingly important to your professional helping career. Cultural competency training is now required for medical licensure in New Jersey, and at least four other states have pending legislation with similar bills (Adams, 2005). You can anticipate that you will be increasingly required to be multiculturally competent. Developing this competence will take a lifetime of learning, as there is endless information to absorb.

Let us examine the multicultural guidelines and competencies in outline form.

Dimension 1: Be Aware of Your Own Assumptions, Values, and Biases

Awareness of yourself as a cultural being is a vital beginning. Unless you see yourself as a cultural being, you will have difficulty in developing awareness of others. It is important that you understand your own multicultural background and the differences that may exist between you and those who come from other backgrounds. Learn about groups different from you and recognize your limitations and the need for referral of clients when necessary.

The guidelines also speak of how contextual issues beyond a person's control affect the way a person discusses issues and problems. Oppression and discrimination, sexism, racism, and failure to recognize and take disability into account may deeply affect a client without her or his conscious awareness. Is the problem "in the individual" or "in the environment"? For example, you may need to help clients become aware that issues such as tension, headaches, and high blood pressure result from the stress caused by harassment and oppression. Many issues are not just client problems but rather problems of a larger society.

Privilege is power given to people through cultural assumptions and stereotypes. McIntosh (1988) comments on the "invisibility of Whiteness." White European Americans tend to be unaware of the advantages they have because of white skin. The idea of special privilege has been extended to include men, those of middle- or upper-class economic status, and others in our society who have power and privilege.

Whites, males, heterosexuals, middle-class people, and others enjoy the convenience of not being aware of their privileged state. The physically able see themselves as "normal" with little awareness that they are only "temporarily able" until old age or a trauma occurs. When dominant religions or sects exist within a given geographic region, they seem to be unaware of the privilege that comes as a result of their dominance. Out of privilege comes stereotyping of the less dominant group, thus further reinforcing the privileged status.

You, the interviewer, face challenges. For example, if you are a middle-class, White European, heterosexual male and the client is a working-class female of a different race, she is less likely to trust you and rapport may be more difficult to establish. You must improve your awareness, knowledge, and skills to work with clients culturally different from you.

In summary you first need to learn about yourself and whether you have a privileged status. Then your lifetime task is to avoid stereotyping any group or individual and to constantly learn about various cultural groups. Individual differences within a cultural grouping often have greater impact than the cultural "label." Your client is a unique human being. Although diversity factors influence development, always recognize the person before you as special and different from all others. Awareness of multicultural issues and diversity actually enhances individual differences and the ways each client is unique.

Dimension 2: Understand the Worldview of the Culturally Different Client

Worldview is formally defined as the way you and your client interpret humanity and the world. Because of varying multicultural backgrounds, we all view people and the larger world differently. Professional multicultural competence stresses the importance of being aware of our negative emotional reactions and biases toward those who are different from us. If you learned to view certain groups from inaccurate stereotypes, you especially need to listen and learn respect toward the worldview of the client; be careful not to impose your own ideas.

All of us need to develop knowledge about various multicultural groups, their history, and their present concerns. If you work with Spanish-speaking groups, it is critical to learn the varying history and issues faced by those from Mexico, Puerto Rico, the Caribbean, and Central and South America. What is the role of immigration? What are the distinctions and experiences among those Latinas/Latinos who have been in Colorado for several centuries as contrasted with newly arrived immigrants? Note that diversity is endemic to the broad group we often term "Hispanic."

The same holds true for White Americans and all other races and ethnicities. Old-time New England Yankees in Hadley, Massachusetts, once chained Polish immigrants in barns. The tables are now turned and it is the Poles who control the town, but tensions between the two groups still remain. Older gay males who once hid their identity are very different from young activists. Whether it is race or religion, ability or disability, we will constantly be required to learn more about our widely diverse populations.

Traditional approaches to counseling theory and skills may be inappropriate and/or ineffective with some groups. We also need to give special attention to how socioeconomic factors, racism, sexism, heterosexism, and other oppressive forces may influence a client's worldview.

Understanding various worldviews often comes first through academic study and reading. Another important approach is to become actively involved in the client's community, attending community events, social and political functions, celebrations and festivals, and—most important—getting to know on a personal basis those who are culturally different from you.

A final critical element in multicultural competence is to seek supervision and increase awareness, knowledge, and skills when you recognize that you are uncomfortable and perhaps even deficient in knowledge and skills.

Dimension 3: Develop Appropriate Intervention Strategies and Techniques

A classic study found that 50% of minority clients did not return to counseling after the first session (cited in Sue & Sue, 2003). *Essentials of Intential Interviewing* seeks to address cultural intentionality through providing you with ideas for multiple responses to your clients. *If your first response doesn't work, be ready with another.* Attend and use listening skills to understand and learn the worldview of others as they tell you their stories (Chapters 3–7). Focusing (Chapter 9) can help clients, who may be blaming themselves for a problem with a classmate or instructor, determine whether their issues are actually related to discrimination.

Traditional counseling strategies are being adapted for use in a more culturally respectful manner (Ivey, D'Andrea, Ivey, & Simek-Morgan, 2007). It is particularly important to be mindful of the history of cultural bias in assessment and testing instruments and the impact of discrimination on clients. Over time, you will expand your knowledge and skills with traditional strategies and newer methods, designed to be more sensitive to diversity as well. Box 2-3 provides a view of the ongoing process of becoming multiculturally aware.

DIVERSITY AND ETHICS

The American Counseling Association (2005) focuses the Preamble to their Code of Ethics on diversity as a central ethical issue.

> The American Counseling Association is an educational, scientific, and professional organization whose members work in a variety of settings and serve in multiple capacities. ACA members are dedicated to the enhancement of human development throughout the life-span. Association members recognize diversity and embrace a cross-cultural approach in support of the worth, dignity, potential, and uniqueness of each individual within their social and cultural contexts.

BOX 2-3 National and International Perspectives on Counseling Skills

 Multiculturalism Belongs to All of Us

MARK POPE, CHEROKEE NATION AND PAST PRESIDENT OF THE AMERICAN COUNSELING ASSOCIATION

Multiculturalism is a movement that has changed the soul of our profession. It represents a re-integration of our social work roots with our interests and work in individual psychology.

Now, I know that there are some of you out there who are tired of culture and discussions about culture. You are the more conservative elements of us, and you have just had it with multicultural this and multicultural that. And, further, you don't want to hear about the "truth" one more time.

There is another group of you that can't get enough of all this talk about culture, context, and environmental influences. You are part of the more progressive and liberal elements of the profession. You may be a member of a "minority group" or you have become a committed ally. You may see the world in terms of oppressor and oppressed.

Perhaps now you are saying, "good analysis" or alternatively, "he's pathetic" (especially if you disagree with me). I'll admit it is more complex than these brief paragraphs allow, but I think you get my point.

Here are some things that perhaps can join us together for the future:

1. We are all committed to the helping professions and the dignity and value of each individual.
2. The more we understand that we are part of *multiple cultures*, the more we can understand the multicultural frame of reference and enhance individuality.
3. *Multicultural* means just that—many cultures. Racial and ethnic issues have tended to predominate, but

diversity also includes gender, sexual orientation, age, geographic location, physical ability, religion/spirituality, socioeconomic status, and other factors.

4. Each of us is a multicultural being and thus all interviewing and counseling involve multicultural issues. It is not a competition as to which multicultural dimension is the most important. It is time to think of a "win/win" approach.
5. We need to address our own issues of prejudice—racism, sexism, ageism, heterosexism, ableism, classism, and others. Without looking at yourself, you cannot see and appreciate the multicultural differences you will encounter.
6. That said, we must always remember that the race issue in Western society is central. Yes, I know that we have made "great progress," but each progressive step we make reminds me how very far we have to go.

All of us have a legacy of prejudice that we need to work against for the liberation of all, including ourselves. This requires constantly examining yourself, honestly and painfully. You are going to make mistakes as you grow multiculturally; but see these errors as an opportunity to grow further.

Avoid saying, "Oh, I'm not prejudiced." We need a little discomfort to move on. If we realize that we have a joint goal in facilitating client development and continue to grow, our lifetime work will make a significant difference in the world.

The Ethical Standards of Human Service Professionals (NOHSP, 2000) include the following three assertions:

Statement 17 Human service professionals provide services without discrimination or preference based on age, ethnicity, culture, race, disability, gender, religion, sexual orientation, or socioeconomic status.

Statement 18 Human service professionals are knowledgeable about the cultures and communities within which they practice. They are aware of multiculturalism in society and its impact on the community as well as individuals within the community. They respect individuals and groups, their cultures and beliefs.

Statement 19 Human service professionals are aware of their own cultural backgrounds, beliefs, and values, recognizing the potential for impact and their relationships with others.

Diversity and multiculturalism have become central to the helping professions throughout the world. For example, if a client's needs are rooted in a multicultural issue with which you are not competent, you may need to refer the client. However, over the long term, referral is inadequate. You also have the responsibility to build your multicultural competence through constant study and supervision and minimize your need for referral.

POLITICAL CORRECTNESS

Political correctness (also **politically correct, P.C.,** or **PC**) is a term used to describe language that is calculated to provide a minimum of offense, particularly to the racial, cultural, or other identity groups being described. . . . The existence of PC has been alleged and denounced by conservative, liberal, and other commentators. The term itself and its usage are hotly contested. (http://en.wikipedia.org/wiki/Political_correctness)

Given this controversy, what is the appropriate way to name and discuss cultural diversity? We argue that interviewers and counselors should use language empathically and urge that you use terms that the client prefers. *Let the client define the name that is to be used.* Respect is the issue here. The client's point of view is what counts in the issue of *naming.* A woman is unlikely to enjoy being called a girl or lady, but you will find some who may use these terms. Some people in their 70s resent being called elderly or old, whereas others embrace and prefer this language. At the same time, you may find that the client is using language in a way that is self-deprecating. A woman struggling for her identify may use the word "girl" in a way that indicates a lack of self-confidence. The older person may benefit from a more positive view of the language of aging. A person struggling with sexual identity may find the words "gay" or "lesbian" difficult to deal with at first. You can help clients by exploring names and social identifiers in a more positive fashion.

Race and ethnicity present particularly important issues. African American is considered the preferred term, but some clients prefer Afro-Canadian or Black. Other Blacks may feel more comfortable being called Haitian, Puerto Rican, or Nigerian. You may talk to a person from a Hispanic background, but he or she may well prefer Chicano, Mexican, Mexican American, Cuban, Puerto Rican, Chilean, or Salvadorean. Some American Indians prefer Native American, but most prefer to be called by the name of their tribe or nation—Lakota, Navajo, Swinomish. Some Caucasians would rather be called British Australians, Irish Americans, Ukrainian Canadians, or Pakistani English. These people are racially White but also have an ethnic background.

The language of nationalism and region is important. American, Irish, Brazilian, New Zealander, or the nickname "Kiwi" may be the most salient self-identification. Yankee is a word of pride to those from New England and a word of derision from many Southerners. Midwesterners, those in Outback Australia, the Scots, Cornish, and Welsh in Great Britain often identify more with their region than with their nationality. Many in Great Britain resent the more powerful region called the Home Counties. And you must recognize that the Canadian culture of Alberta is very different from the cultures of Ontario, Quebec, and the Maritime provinces.

Capitalization is an important issue. The *New York Times* style manual does not capitalize Black and several other multicultural terms, but the capital has become a standard in counseling and psychology. White is also not capitalized by the *Times,* but it is helpful for White people to discover that they, too, have a general racial cultural identity. Capitalization of the major cultural groupings of Black and White is becoming more and more the standardized usage in counseling, human relations, psychology, and social work.

▲ **MODULE 2.2**
SUMMARY

▲ It is an ethical imperative that interviewers and counselors be multiculturally competent and continually increase their awareness, knowledge, and skills in multicultural areas.

▲ The first, vital dimension of multicultural competence is awareness of yourself as a cultural being, your assumptions, values, biases, and your potential impact on your clients.

▲ The second dimension includes understanding the worldview of clients who are culturally different from you.

▲ The third dimension focuses on developing interviewing and counseling skills and strategies to meet the needs of clients whose life experience is different from yours.

▲ The interviewer needs to be client centered rather than directed by "politically correct" terminology. This is an issue of respect, and clients need to say what is comfortable and appropriate for them.

MODULE 2.3
WELLNESS AND POSITIVE PSYCHOLOGY

KEY CONCEPT QUESTIONS

▲ **What is the history and importance of a wellness approach and positive psychology?**

▲ **How do we identify wellness and client strengths?**

▲ **How can we plan for our own wellness and that of our clients?**

Wellness	*Predicted Result*
Help clients discover and rediscover their strengths through wellness assessment. Find strengths and positive assets in the client and in the support system. Identify multiple dimensions of wellness.	Clients who are aware of their strengths and resources can face their difficulties and discuss problem resolution from a positive foundation.

The wellness approach does not deny human problems and difficulties. Rather it provides a positive foundation from which issues can be addressed more effectively. When clients discuss their concerns in a positive atmosphere of strength and wellness, this enhances their chances of working through complex issues successfully. If you start by listening only to client stories of problems and failures, client positive assets and strengths can be overlooked.

POSITIVE PSYCHOLOGY: THE SEARCH FOR STRENGTHS

Recently, the field of counseling has developed an extensive body of knowledge and research supporting the importance of positive psychology, a strength-based approach. Psychology has overemphasized the disease model. Seligman (2004, p. 1) states, "We've become too preoccupied with repairing damage when our focus should be on building strength and resilience." Positive psychology brings together a long tradition of emphasis on positives within counseling, human services, psychology, and social work.

Clients come to us to discuss their problems, their issues, and their concerns. They are talking with us about what is *wrong* with their lives and may even want us to *fix* things for them. There is no question that our role is to enable clients to live their lives more effectively and meaningfully. An important part of this problem-solving process is helping clients discover their strengths.

Leona Tyler (1961), one of the first women presidents of the American Psychological Association, developed a system of counseling based on human strengths:

> The initial stages . . . include a process that might be called exploration of resources. The counselor pays little attention to personality weaknesses . . . (and) is most persistent in trying to locate . . . ways of coping with anxiety and stress, already existing resources that may be enlarged and strengthened once their existence is recognized.

Tyler's positive ideas have been central to the microskills framework since its inception (Ivey & Gluckstern, 1974; Ivey, Gluckstern, & Ivey, 2006). The strength and resource-oriented *story—positive asset—restory—action* model is an elaboration of Tyler's original ideas. Chapters 13 and 14 discuss four concrete theoretical approaches that all focus on human strengths—person-centered theory, decisional counseling, cognitive-behavioral assertiveness training, and brief counseling.

Clinical counseling, a new conceptual frame for our field, will operate most effectively if it incorporates wellness concepts as a foundation for therapy. For a positive multiculturally sensitive approach to clinical and therapeutic work, we suggest that you visit *Theories of Counseling and Psychotherapy* (Ivey, D'Andrea, Ivey, & Simek-Morgan, 2007). There you will find many specifics of skill-oriented strategies for therapy with a positive wellness orientation.

WELLNESS ASSESSMENT DEFINITIONS AND QUESTIONS

The wellness orientation to interviewing and counseling has been most clearly defined and thoroughly researched by Jane Myers and Thomas Sweeney (2004, 2005). They speak of the "Indivisible Self" in which 17 dimensions of wellness have been found to group in five areas, discussed in detail below. Each dimension has practical implications for assessing clients and facilitating their growth and development.

The Individual Self holistic model stresses the importance of context. As appropriate to the individual client before you, it may be helpful to explore the multiple contexts of human development. For example, what is going on locally (family, neighborhood, community)? Problems here obviously affect the individual, and even more important, strengths and wellness assets may be found here as well.

The Indivisible Self model points out that change in any part of the wellness system can be beneficial through the whole person—or it may damage many of the 17 dimensions of wellness. A problem or a positive change in one part of the total system affects all others. For example, a person may have all dimensions of wellness operating effectively but then encounter a difficult contextual issue such as parents divorcing, a major flood or hurricane, or a major personal trauma. On the other hand, the individual may use wellness assets to surmount these challenges and come out of them stronger.

Other contextual issues that may be important with your client's wellness include the institutions that define so much of their experience such as education, religion, government, and business/industry. At an even broader level, political, culture, environmental events, global events, and the media can deeply affect clients. A change in governmental social services, global warming, and a call-up for military service are three examples of contextual issues that affect the individual.

A final contextual issue is lifespan development. Issues for a child entering the teenage years are very different from those for a teen entering the military, work, or college. Marriage or selection of a life partner, raising a family, and older maturity all present different contextual issues that need to be considered.

Again, the Indivisible Self concept reminds us that the individual is totally connected with social context and all parts of developing personhood all the time.

Below are brief definitions of the 17 personal dimensions and some beginning wellness questions for exploration with your clients. For a more detailed presentation of wellness research and the actual listing of factor analytic structures, we recommend consulting Myers and Sweeney (2004, 2005).

WELLNESS ASSESSMENT INSTRUCTIONS

Draw out examples and concrete specifics available to you or your clients in each area. Write down your own wellness strengths and personal assessment first so that you are familiar with the process. Later, when you work with a volunteer or real clients, we suggest that you provide them a copy of the questions that you will ask them. Work toward an egalitarian relationship. As part of this assessment you will note weaknesses that can be addressed in counseling and through a wellness plan. But the focus of this session is to find strengths and positive assets for problem solving in the future.

Dimension 1: The Essential Self

Four aspects of the core self have been identified by factor analysis and serve as a foundation for personal exploration of wellness. Each of these areas can provide important resources and strengths for positive client growth.

Spirituality. There is considerable evidence that those who have a spiritual or religious orientation have more positive attitudes and better mental health than those lacking such supports. Define spirituality and religion broadly, as a thoughtful agnostic or atheist often has many of the characteristics of a highly religious person. At times, the words *values* or *meaning* should be substituted for *spirituality* and *religion*.

- ▲ What strengths and supports do you gain from your spiritual/religious orientation? Be as specific as possible.
- ▲ How could you draw on this resource when faced with life challenges?
- ▲ Could you give a specific example of how spirituality has helped you in the past?

Gender Identity. This area has two dimensions—gender and sexual orientation. Identifying positive men and women as role models and finding other positives about their own gender may help clients develop unique strengths. Sexual orientation relates to one's identity as a heterosexual, gay, lesbian, bisexual, or transsexual individual.

You will find some clients who are unaware that heterosexuality is a sexual orientation. This lack of knowledge can lead to heterosexism. Again, seeking positive models and personal strengths can be a helpful route to wellness.

▲ What strengths can you draw on as a female or male?
▲ Who are some positive gender role models you have looked to during your life?
▲ What strengths do you draw from your sexual orientation—as a gay person, a heterosexual, a lesbian, a bisexual, or a transgendered person?
▲ Who in your community supports your sexual orientation?
▲ Could you provide concrete examples of how your gender and sexual orientation have been important to you and your development?

Cultural Identity—Race and Ethnicity. Research reveals that a positive attitude toward race and ethnicity is part of mental health and wellness. For example, being aware of the strengths of your race/ethnicity can be helpful in establishing who you are and your cultural history. For example, getting in touch with positive aspects of ancestry such as Aboriginal, African American, Italian, Korean, Maori, Navajo, or Swedish can help us all build strengths from our traditions and our families.

▲ What strengths do you draw from your race?
▲ Your ethnicity? Do you have family or role models that suggest ways of living effectively?
▲ Could you provide concrete examples of how your race and ethnicity have been important to you and your development?

Self-Care. Part of wellness is how well people take care of themselves—cleanliness, avoidance of drugs, health maintenance, and safety habits (such as wearing seatbelts) are all examples that lead to a longer life. Those clients who do not engage in self-care may be depressed or have other issues. How well versed are you in substance abuse issues and other health dimensions?

▲ How well do you care for yourself? Do you avoid drugs and alcohol?
▲ Do you attend to your health and personal hygiene?
▲ How careful or safety conscious are you in work and play situations?
▲ Do you take normal precautions and avoid risky or harmful behavior?
▲ Could you provide concrete examples of how you take care of yourself?

Dimension 2: The Social Self

Connection with others is essential for wellness, and two major components are identified here. We are selves-in-relation, and closeness to others is a central aspect of wellness.

Friendship. We are people in connection, not meant to be alone. It takes time to nurture relationships. This focuses on your ability to be a friend and have friends in healthy long-term relationships.

▲ Tell me about your friends and what strengths they provide for you.
▲ Could you tell me about a special friend, one with whom you have had a long-term relationship? What does that mean to you?
▲ Could you tell me something specific about yourself as a friend, and what you have done to be a good friend to others?

Love. Caring for special people, such as family members or a loved one results in intimacy, trust, and mutual sharing. Sexual intimacy and sharing with a close partner are key areas of wellness.

▲ Please share some positive family stories. What are some positive memories about grandparents, parents, siblings, or your extended family?
▲ How does your family value you? As a grandparent/parent? Brother/sister? Child?
▲ If your immediate family relationships are not close, please share your experiences with your equivalent of family. (Examples: church/mosque/synagogue, community, cultural group, friendship groups)
▲ Could you share an example of a positive love relationship and what this means to you?

Dimension 3: The Coping Self

To live effectively, we need to be able to cope with the situations around us, and four basic elements to help us have been identified. Each of these is related to different issues in interviewing and counseling, and often different theoretical approaches will be useful with the varying elements.

Leisure. People who take time to enjoy themselves daily are better equipped to return to work or school the next day with more energy and less stress. This area is all too often forgotten in counseling's problem-solving approach. When you have time for fun, often it is much easier to solve problems.

▲ What leisure time activities do you enjoy?
▲ Equally important—*do you take time to do them?*
▲ When was the last time you did something fun, and how did it feel?
▲ Could you tell me about a specific time when having fun and taking leisure time really benefited you?

Stress Management. Our approach to life, coupled with multiple commitments to family, career, church, and community, and even leisure activities provide us with endless opportunities to be "stressed out." Data are accumulating that stress is perhaps the central issue in producing mental ill-health and that stress due to either short- or long-term trauma produces bodily changes and affects brain development. Can you help your client build stress management resources?

▲ What do you do when you encounter stress?
▲ What are specific skills and strategies you use to cope with stress, and do you remember to use these strategies?
▲ Give at least one example when you managed stress well.
▲ Exercise alleviates stress. Can you tell me of a time when you exercised or did something else to help you calm down and relax?

Self-Worth. Self-esteem and feeling good about oneself are required for personal comfort and effective living. We need to accept our imperfections as well as acknowledge our strengths. This part of wellness is obviously especially important; unless we feel positive about ourselves, the aspects of wellness will be weak at best.

It also illustrates the holistic and relatedness qualities found in the Indivisible Self model.

- ▲ What gives you a sense of self-worth and self-esteem?
- ▲ Could you tell me about some specific times that you did something kind or helpful for others that you feel especially good about?
- ▲ How do you value your life contribution?
- ▲ What would you like to contribute to others and the world in the future?

Realistic Beliefs. Life is obviously not all positives. We also need a clear grasp of reality, the ability to examine our beliefs and those of others. We can get stuck with negative beliefs about ourselves and the world that impact effective problem solving. You will find that cognitive-behavioral theory and some of the strategies presented in the influencing skills section of this book are especially helpful here.

- ▲ How able are you to face up to difficult situations and see things as they really are?
- ▲ Do you have realistic beliefs and expectations about yourself and your abilities?
- ▲ Do you have realistic beliefs and expectations about others and their abilities?
- ▲ What has gone well for you in the past? The present? What positive anticipations do you have for the future?
- ▲ Is there a specific time you participated in a realistic assessment of yourself or others?

Dimension 4: The Creative Self

Research reveals five elements of creating ways to positively impact the world. Each one of these can serve as a springboard for a wellness approach.

Thinking. This refers to thoughts and thinking patterns that guide your life. For example, effective problem solving can lead to better personal adjustment. Important in this process is avoiding negative thoughts about oneself and others. An optimistic view is clearly helpful.

- ▲ What is the nature of your "inner speech"—particularly, words and ideas "inside your head" that you say to yourself? Are you encouraging to yourself? To others?
- ▲ How are you at problem solving? Tell me about a time when you effectively solved a difficult issue.
- ▲ Could you give an example or two when positive thinking and optimism worked for you?

Emotions. Coupled with our thoughts are our feelings (e.g., glad, sad, mad, scared). Ability to experience emotion appropriate to the situation is vital to a healthy lifestyle.

- ▲ When have you felt and expressed emotion with a good result? Negative emotion? Positive emotion?
- ▲ Can you understand and support another's emotional experience and become attuned to the way this person experiences the world?
- ▲ How do you accept emotional support from others?

Control. People who feel in control of their lives see themselves as making a difference; they are in charge of their own "space." They do not seek to control others.

This is a subjective feeling that you know what is happening, what is going to happen, and that you can control present and future events.

▲ When have you been able to control difficult situations in a positive way?
▲ When have you had a positive sense of self-control? In relation to self? In relation to others?
▲ Provide specific examples of how you are in control of your own destiny. Again, provide positive concrete examples.

Work. We need work to sustain ourselves; it is an activity that takes as much of our time as sleep—or more. Much of our self-worth comes from our ability to contribute to the world through the work we do.

▲ What jobs have you most enjoyed or been most proud of?
▲ What kind of volunteer work do you do?
▲ What do you see as your major contributions or most supportive habits on the job? Please provide specific examples.

Positive Humor. Laughing works! It opens and refreshes the body. Humor is part of creativity and enjoying the moment. Those with a sense of humor can often find something positive in the midst of real problems.

▲ What makes you laugh?
▲ Tell me about your sense of humor.
▲ Is there some specific time when a sense of humor or laughing helped you deal with a difficult situation?

Dimension 5: The Physical Self

The last two aspects of the research on wellness reveal an area that needs far more attention in interviewing and counseling. If a person is not doing well physically, even the best self-concept, ability to handle emotions, or ability to relate effectively with others is not enough. We strongly suggest that you study and bring this dimension into your interviewing and counseling practice.

Nutrition. Eating a good diet is part of a wellness program. If a person is failing to eat well, referral to dietary counseling may be helpful. But focus here on strengths.

▲ How aware of you of the standards of good nutrition?
▲ How well do your present weight and eating habits reflect good nutritional standards?
▲ Could you provide concrete examples of how you have taken care of yourself in terms of nutrition in the past and present?

Exercise. New research appears in newspapers almost daily on the values of exercise and keeping the body moving. For example, recent evidence indicates that general health, memory, and cognitive functioning are all supported by regular exercise. Help your clients keep their bodies moving. One useful treatment for clients who may be depressed is exercise and relaxation training. Make evaluation of exercise part of your interviews and help your clients plan for the future.

- ▲ What do you do for exercise?
- ▲ What types of exercise do you like best?
- ▲ How often do you exercise?
- ▲ Could you provide concrete examples of how exercise has been beneficial for you?
- ▲ How can you start a program of exercise?

INTENTIONAL WELLNESS PLAN

Sweeney and Myers (2005) suggest that counselors need to develop an *Intentional Wellness Plan* with their clients. The first step is a concrete assessment of wellness strengths. The second step is an honest appraisal of areas for improvement. It is particularly important not to overwhelm the client with too many immediate improvements for overall wellness. You could easily lose a discouraged client. Keep it simple; with the client, select one or two items from the wellness assessment and negotiate a contract for action. Check with your client on a regular basis to see how the plan is working. As the client grows and develops, you can move to other dimensions.

We suggest developing an informal wellness plan as part of one session or as a dimension of a longer-term treatment plan. Clients work more effectively on their issues and challenges with a positive wellness approach. The growing interest in positive psychology supports wellness practices in a variety of settings and with clients of all ages. You may ask the client to complete a full wellness assessment as a homework assignment. This will allow you to have a good picture of client strengths that you can draw on during difficult sessions.

MODULE 2.3

SUMMARY

- ▲ Positive psychology has a long history. Leona Tyler in 1961 stressed the exploration of positive resources in the interview to help the client solve problems and build on strengths.
- ▲ Most clients can benefit from a wellness assessment and wellness plan. You can use a wellness assessment and planning in every interview if you work through the areas of wellness step by step.

ATTENDING AND OBSERVATION SKILLS
Basic to Communication

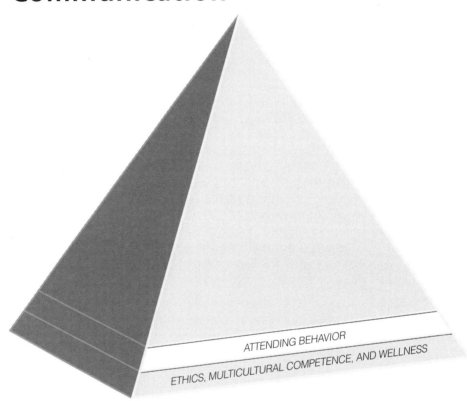

ATTENDING BEHAVIOR

ETHICS, MULTICULTURAL COMPETENCE, AND WELLNESS

How can attending and observation skills be used to help your clients?

CHAPTER GOALS

Attending behavior encourages client talk. You will want to use attending behavior to help clients tell their stories and to reduce your own talk-time. Conversely, the lack of attending behavior can also serve a useful function. Through nonattention you can help others talk less about topics that are destructive or nonproductive.

Observation skills help you understand what is going on between you and your clients verbally *and* nonverbally. This can be vital to establishing a helping relationship. Observation skills will help you to respond appropriately to both individual and multicultural differences.

Awareness, knowledge, and skills developed through the concepts in this chapter will enable you to

▲ Communicate to the client that you are interested in what he or she is saying by your individually and culturally appropriate attending behavior.

▲ Become aware of verbal and nonverbal attending behavior styles in the interview—including the styles of both you and your client.

▲ Modify your patterns of attending to establish rapport with each individual.

▲ Note varying individual and cultural styles of listening and talking.

MODULE 3.1
DEFINING ATTENDING BEHAVIOR

KEY CONCEPT QUESTION

▲ What are the behavioral skills of listening?

Listening is the core of developing a relationship and making *real* contact with our clients. How can we define effective listening more precisely? The following exercise may help you to identify listening in terms of clear observable behaviors.

> One of the best ways to identify and define listening skills is to experience the opposite—poor listening. Think of a time when someone failed to listen to you. Perhaps a family member or friend failed to hear your concerns, a teacher or employer misunderstood your actions and treated you unfairly, or you had that all-too-familiar experience of calling a computer helpline and never getting someone who listened to your problem. Each of these represents the importance of being heard and the frustration that happens when someone does not listen to you.
>
> Find a partner to role-play an interview in which one of you plays the part of the poor listener. The poor listener should feel free to exaggerate, if necessary, in order to identify concrete behaviors of the ineffective interviewer. If no partner is available, think back on a specific time when you felt that you were not heard. What feelings and thoughts occur to you when you recall that someone important did not listen to you?
>
> It will be helpful if you list on a separate piece of paper the specific behaviors of poor listening that you identified. Later, compare your thoughts with the ideas we present in this chapter.

An exaggerated role-play is often humorous. However, on reflection, your strongest memory of it may be disappointment and perhaps even anger at not being heard. Examples of poor listening and other ineffective interviewing behaviors can be numerous—and instructive, because, *if you are to be effective and competent, do the opposite of the ineffective interviewer*. Now let us turn to the key skills of quality listening.

ATTENDING BEHAVIOR: THE SKILLS OF LISTENING

Obviously, you can't learn all the possible qualities and skills of effective listening immediately. It is best to learn important behaviors step by step. The first critical skill of listening is *attending behavior*; it is a necessary part of all interviewing and counseling.

To communicate that you are indeed listening or attending to the client, you need the following "three V's + B":*

1. *Visual/eye contact.* Look at people when you speak to them.
2. *Vocal qualities.* Think of how many ways you can say, "I am really interested in what you have to say," just by altering your vocal tone and speech rate. Moderate your vocal tone and speech rate appropriate to the client and the situation.
3. *Verbal tracking.* Track the client's story; don't change the subject; stay with the client's topic.
4. *Body language.* Be yourself—authenticity is essential to building trust. To show interest, face clients squarely, lean slightly forward with an expressive face, and use encouraging gestures. Especially critical, smile to show warmth and interest in the client.

The definition of each microskill from the Ivey Taxonomy is presented in full detail in Appendix I together with the predicted results of using each skill. These predictions are never 100% perfect. If your client does not respond as expected, try another skill. Below is a definition of attending behavior and its predicted result in client behavior.

Attending Behavior	*Predicted Result*
Support your client with individually and culturally appropriate visuals, vocal quality, verbal tracking, and body language.	Clients talk more freely and respond openly, particularly around topics to which attention is given. Depending on the individual client and culture, anticipate fewer eye contact breaks, a smoother vocal tone, a more complete story (with fewer topic jumps), and a more comfortable body language.

The three V's + B reduce interviewer talk-time and provide clients with an opportunity to tell their stories with as much detail as needed. You will find it helpful to observe your clients' verbal and nonverbal behavior. Note the topics to which your clients attend or those that they avoid. You will find that clients who are culturally different from you may have differing patterns of attending and listening. Use client observation skills and adapt your style to meet the needs of the unique person before you.

MULTICULTURAL AND INDIVIDUAL VARIATIONS IN ATTENDING BEHAVIOR

Each person you work with will have a unique style of communicating. *Furthermore, the multicultural background of each client may modify her or his communication style both verbally and nonverbally.* People with varying disabilities also represent a cultural group with whom you may need to vary your attending style (see Box 3-1). Use your observation skills and be ready to change your style of attending when necessary.

---

*We thank Norma Gluckstern Packard for the three V's acronym.

BOX 3-1   Attending Behavior and People With Disabilities

Attending behaviors may require modification if you are working with people who are disabled. It is your role to learn the clients' unique ways of thinking and being and how they deal with important issues. Focus on the person, not the disability. For example, think of a person with hearing loss rather than "hearing impaired," a person with AIDS rather than "AIDS victim," a person with a physical disability rather than "physically handicapped." So-called handicaps are often societal and environmental rather than personal.

People who are blind or have limited vision	Clients who are blind or partially sighted may not look at you when they speak. Expect clients with limited vision to be more aware of and sensitive to your vocal tone. People who are blind from birth may have unique patterns of body language. It may be helpful to teach the client attending skills such as orienting their face and body to other people. In this way they may communicate more easily with the sighted.
People who are deaf or have hearing loss	Many people who are deaf do not consider themselves impaired in any way. People who were born deaf have their own language (signing) and their own culture that often excludes the hearing. You are unlikely to work with this type of client unless you are skilled in sign language and are trusted among the deaf community.
	You may be skilled in sign language or you may counsel a deaf person through an interpreter. To be effective you will need specific training in the use of an interpreter and a basic understanding of deaf culture. Eye contact is vital in counseling a deaf client or while using an interpreter. It will isolate the client when you speak to the interpreter instead of to the client or use phrases such as, "tell him. . . ."
	For those with moderate to severe hearing loss, speak in a natural way, but not fast. Extensively paraphrase the client's words. Speaking loudly is often ineffective, as ear mechanisms may not equalize for loud sounds. In turn, teaching those with hearing loss to paraphrase what others say to them can help them to communicate with others.
People with physical disabilities	We cannot place people with physical disability in any one group; each person is unique. Consider a person who uses a wheelchair, an individual with cerebral palsy or Parkinson's disease, someone who may have lost a limb or is physically disfigured by a serious burn. They all have the common problem of physical disability, but their body language and speaking style will vary. You must attend to each individual as a complete person from her or his unique perspective.
People who are temporarily able	We suggest that you consider yourself one of the many who are *temporarily able*. Age and life experience will bring most of you some variation of the challenges previously described. For older individuals, the issues discussed here may become the norm rather than the exception. Approach disabled clients with humility and respect.

The National Council on Disability has a helpful search engine for further details (http://www.ncd.gov/).

▲ **MODULE 3.1**
SUMMARY

▲ Demonstrating poor listening skills through role-play is an effective way to identity the importance of listening and the specific skills of attending behavior.

▲ Attending behavior involves the 3V's + B. Visuals, vocal qualities, verbal tracking, and body language.

▲ Be sensitive to clients' multicultural and individual characteristics. Never stereotype.

MODULE 3.2
EXAMPLE INTERVIEWS: Do I Want to Become a Counselor?

KEY CONCEPT QUESTION

▲ How does attending behavior vary in ineffective and effective interviews?

The client, Jared, is a first-semester junior exploring career choice. Like many reading this book, he is considering the helping professions as an alternative. Jared has already stated that he is considering psychology as a major and counseling as a career field. The first example is designed to show ineffective interviewing so that it provides a sharp contrast with the second more positive example.

In both cases, the interviewer, Jerome, is reviewing a form outlining key aspects of career choice. Note how disruptive visual contact and vocal qualities, failure to maintain verbal tracking, and poor body language can lead to an unsatisfactory session.

NEGATIVE EXAMPLE

Interviewer and Client Conversation	Process Comments
1. *Jerome:* The next thing on my questionnaire is your job history. Tell me a little bit about it, will ya?	The vocal tone is overly casual, almost uninterested. The interviewer looks at the form, not at the client. He is slouching in a chair.
2. *Jared:* Well, I guess the job that, uh . . .	Client appears a bit hesitant and unsure as to what to say or do. There is a slight stammer.
3. *Jerome:* Hold it! There's the phone. (Long pause while Jerome talks to a colleague.) Uh, okay, okay, where were we?	The interview is for the client. Avoid phone and other interruptions during the session. Such behavior shows disrespect for Jared. And if a break is necessary, remember what was occurring just before you were called out.
4. *Jared:* The job that really comes to mind is my work as a camp counselor during my senior year of high school. I really liked counseling kids and . . .	The client's eyes brighten and he leans forward as he starts to talk about something he likes.

Interviewer and Client Conversation	Process Comments
5. *Jerome:* (interrupts) Oh, yeah, I did a camp counselor job myself. It was at Camp Itasca in Minnesota. I wasn't that crazy about it, though. But I did manage to have fun. What else have you been doing?	When he is interrupted by the topic jump, Jared looks up with surprise, then casts his eyes downward, as if he realizes he is no longer the focal point of attention. It would have been better if Jerome had asked Jared for specifics about what he liked in his work as a camp counselor.
6. *Jared:* Ah . . . well, I . . . ah . . . wanted to tell you a little bit more about this counseling job, I . . .	Jared is interested in this topic and tries again, but notice the speech hesitations.
7. *Jerome:* (interrupts) I got that down on the form already, so tell me about something else. A lot of counseling types have done peer counseling in school. Have you?	The leading closed question puts Jared on the spot.
8. *Jared:* Ah . . . no, I didn't.	The topic jump now has Jared at a complete standstill. He looks puzzled and confused.
9. *Jerome:* Many effective counselors were peer helpers in school . . .	Jerome is now working on his agenda. One senses that he is not fond of his job and would rather be doing something else.
10. *Jared:* (interrupts) No, I lived in a small town. I never learned about peer counseling until I got to college.	Jared is now interrupting and sits forward and talks a little more loudly. His anger is beginning to show.
11. *Jerome:* Too bad, it might have helped.	Jerome looks away and dismisses Jared's thoughts and feelings.
12. *Jared:* I only had 75 kids in my graduating class. One person that I always admired was my school counselor. He really got along with the kids. . . .	Jared is valiantly trying to focus the conversation on himself and his interest in counseling. He starts to look a bit more enthusiastic, but again is interrupted.
13. *Jerome:* (interrupts) Hmmm, that sounds like something I ought to write down. You came from a small school. My school counselor wasn't so great. I think it was just a job for him.	Jerome does remember he has a job to do. But he is looking intently at his form and still does not look at Jared. He then returns the focus to himself and the client sits back in discouragement and disarray.

This interview is extreme, but not so rare. It illustrates the many ineffective things an interviewer can do. Jerome clearly had poor visuals, vocals, verbal tracking, and body language.

But, let's give Jerome another chance. What differences do you note in the way Jerome handles Jared in the second example below?

POSITIVE EXAMPLE

Interviewer and Client Conversation	Process Comments
1. *Jerome:* Jared, so far, I've heard that you are interested in counseling as a career. You've liked your psychology courses and you find friends come to you to talk about their problems. In this next phase of the session, I'd like to review a form with you that may help us plan together. The next item concerns your job history. Could you tell me a little bit about the jobs you've had in the past?	Jerome leans forward slightly, maintains good eye contact, and his vocal tone is warm and friendly. He personalizes the interview by using the client's name. He summarizes what he has heard and tells the client what is going to happen next. He asks an open question to obtain information from Jared's point of view.
2. *Jared:* Sure, the job that comes to mind is camp counselor at the YMCA during my senior year of high school and my first two years of college.	Jared's vocal tone is confident and relaxed. He seems eager to explore this area.
3. *Jerome:* Sounds like you really liked it. Tell me more.	Jerome observes Jared's enthusiastic words and encourages him to say more.
4. *Jared:* Well, . . . when I was a kid people always asked me what I wanted to be when I grew up. I had no idea, but when I worked at this camp, I realized that I truly liked working with kids, and I was good at it.	Jared smiles and continues.
5. *Jerome:* Uh-huh.	Jerome continues good eye contact and encourages Jared to go on.
6. *Jared:* I like to work with people—maybe that's why I'm thinking of majoring in psychology or maybe human services or social work.	Jerome begins to see the relationship between past jobs Jared has held and possible future majors in college and career choices.
7. *Jerome:* I see. So you really liked helping kids in the camp. You think it might be a good career direction. Could you give me a specific example of what you particularly liked at the camp?	Jerome summarizes Jared's comments. Asking for specific examples moves client talk from general to specific. Jerome uses attending and verbal tracking and gives the lead to his client.
8. *Jared:* Well, there were kids from lots of different racial groups with differing amounts of money in their backgrounds. Yet I seemed to be able to organize them in a way that built on everybody's strengths. I think I helped them feel pretty good about themselves and we seemed to avoid conflicts that way.	Jerome is identifying client wellness strengths, which can serve as a basis for both decision making and problem solving.
9. *Jerome:* Sounds like you really feel good about your work there.	Jerome focuses on Jared's underlying feeling tone.

Interviewer and Client Conversation	Process Comments
10. *Jared:* I feel real good because I helped them and we had lots of fun at the same time. I learned how to play the ukulele and we had some great singing sessions. I thought, you know, that this could be a profession for me.	Jared continues with enthusiasm and verifies good feelings. If feeling tones are correctly identified, the client will often acknowledge these feelings and continue discussion in more depth. Whether a positive or negative feeling, you can anticipate more discussion on that topic.
11. *Jerome:* So, considering counseling as a profession may be important. What are some other things along that line you might want to do?	Jerome pinpoints Jared's enthusiasm, paraphrases Jared's last important words, and then asks an open question to encourage more exploration on the topic.
12. *Jared:* Well, kids came to me a lot to talk about their issues with their families and friends. I might even want to be a camp director. I also thought I might want to become a counselor to help people with real personal problems. I just know I want to work with people, but am not exactly sure how.	Throughout all this discussion Jerome and Jared have a comfortable relaxed relationship with a solid demonstration of the three V's + B. We now have a far better interviewer and client relationship and a basis for further discussion of majors and possible careers.

The focus in this second session was on attending to Jared, drawing out some early dimensions of what his career story has been so far. We now have some positive ideas of where to go with this session. Jerome effectively demonstrated visuals, vocal qualities, verbal tracking, and culturally appropriate body language.

MODULE 3.2

SUMMARY

▲ When the interviewer demonstrates culturally appropriate eye contact, vocal tone, verbal tracking, and body language, it shows interest in the client and promotes greater client talk-time.

MODULE 3.3

INDIVIDUAL AND MULTICULTURAL ISSUES IN ATTENDING BEHAVIOR

KEY CONCEPT QUESTION

▲ What are some of the many individual and multicultural implications of attending behavior?

Listen before you leap! A frequent tendency of the beginning counselor or interviewer is to try to solve the client's difficulties in the first 5 minutes. It is critical that you slow down, relax, and attend to client narratives. Think about it—the client most likely developed her or his concern over a period of time. Attending and giving clients talk-time demonstrates that you truly want to hear their story and major concerns. In addition, each client has varying attending and interacting styles. Through observing

clients' patterns of conversation with you, you are also learning about how they interact with others outside of the session.

VISUAL/EYE CONTACT

Direct eye contact is considered a sign of interest in European–North American
middle-class culture, with more eye contact while listening and less while talking.
However, research indicates that *some* African Americans in the United States may
have reverse patterns—looking more when talking and slightly less when listening.
Among some traditional Native American and Latin groups, eye contact by the young
is a sign of disrespect. Imagine the problems this may cause when the teacher or
counselor contradicts basic cultural values by saying, "Look at me!" Some traditional
Native American, Inuit, or Aboriginal Australian groups generally avoid eye contact,
especially when talking about serious subjects. Cultural differences in eye contact
abound, but we must recall that individual differences are often even greater and we
must not stereotype any client or group with so-called normative patterns.

You want to look at clients and notice breaks in eye contact. Clients often tend to
look away when thinking about a complex issue or discussing topics that particularly
distress them. It may be wise to avoid direct and solid eye contact when the client is
uncomfortable. Also, think about your own breaks in eye contact. You may find yourself avoiding eye contact while discussing certain topics. There are counselors who say
their clients talk about "nothing but sex" and others who say their clients never bring
up the topic. Both types of counselors indicate to their clients whether the topic is
appropriate through their style of eye contact. If you find that your clients are avoiding a topic, look also at your own behavior, not just that of the client. Be sure your
behavior is not encouraging clients to avoid certain subjects.

VOCAL QUALITIES

Your voice is an instrument that communicates much of the feeling you have toward
another person or situation. Changes in its pitch, volume, or speech rate convey specific meaning just as changes in eye contact or body language do.

Keep in mind that different people are likely to respond to your voice differently.
Try the following exercise with a group of three or more people.*

> Ask the group to close their eyes and note your vocal qualities as you speak. Talk for 2
> or 3 minutes in your normal tone of voice on any subject of interest to you. How do
> they react to your tone, your volume, your speech rate, and perhaps even your regional
> or ethnic accent? Ask the group for feedback. What does this feedback say to you?

This exercise reveals a central point of attending—*people differ in their reactions to the
same stimulus.* Some people find one voice interesting; others may find that same
voice boring or even threatening. People differ, and what is successful with one person
or client may not work with another.

Accent is a particularly good example of how different people will react differently
to the same voice. Obviously we need to avoid stereotyping people because their
accent is different from ours. How do you react to the following accents—Australian,
BBC English, Canadian, French, Pakistani, New England U.S., and Southern U.S.?

---

*This exercise was developed by Robert Marx, School of Management, University of Massachusetts, Amherst.

BOX 3-2   National and International Perspectives on Counseling Skills

Use With Care: Culturally Incorrect Attending Can Be Rude
WEIJUN ZHANG

The visiting counselor from North America got his first exposure to cross-cultural counseling differences at one of the counseling centers in Shanghai. His client was a female college student. I was invited to serve as an interpreter. As the session went on I noticed that the client seemed increasingly uncomfortable. What had happened? Since I was translating, I took the liberty of modifying what was said to fit each other's culture, and I had confidence in my ability to do so. I could not figure out what was wrong until the session was over and I reviewed the videotape with the counselor and some of my colleagues. The counselor had noticed the same problem and wanted to understand what was going on. What we found amazed us all.

First, the counselor's way of looking at the client—his eye contact—was improper. When two Chinese talk to one another, we use much less eye contact, especially when it is with a person of the opposite sex. The counselor's gaze at the Chinese woman could have been considered rude or seductive in Chinese culture.

Although his nods were acceptable, they were too frequent by Chinese standards. The student client,

probably believing one good nod deserved another, nodded in harmony with the counselor. That unusual head bobbing must have contributed to the student's discomfort.

The counselor would mutter "uh-huh" when there was a pause in the woman's speech. While "uh-huh" is a good minimal encouragement in North America, it happens to convey a kind of arrogance in China. A self-respecting Chinese would say *er* (oh), or *shi* (yes) to show he or she is listening. How could the woman feel comfortable when she thought she was being slighted?

He shook her hand and touched her shoulder. I told our respected visiting counselor afterward, "If you don't care about the details, simply remember this rule of thumb: in China, a man is not supposed to touch any part of a woman's body unless she seems to be above 65 years old and displays difficulty in moving around."

"Though I have worked in the field for more than 20 years, I am still a lay person here in a different culture," the counselor commented as we finished our discussion.

Are you aware that the person who speaks two or more languages is advantaged? How many languages can you speak?

As you consider the way you tell a story, you will find yourself giving louder volume and increased vocal emphasis to certain words and short phrases; this is known as *verbal underlining*. Clients of course do the same. The key words a person underlines via volume and emphasis are often concepts of particular importance.

Awareness of your voice and observation of the changes in others' vocal qualities will enhance your attending skills. Speech hesitations and breaks and timing of vocal changes can signal distress, anxiety, or discomfort. Clearing one's throat may indicate that words are not coming easily.

VERBAL TRACKING

Verbal tracking is staying with your client's topic. Encourage the full elaboration of the narrative. Just as people make sudden shifts in nonverbal communication, they change topics when they aren't comfortable. In middle-class U.S. communication, direct tracking is appropriate, but in some Asian cultures such direct verbal follow-up may be considered rude and intrusive.

Verbal tracking is especially helpful to both the beginning interviewer and the experienced interviewer who is lost or puzzled about what to say next in response to a client. *Relax;* you don't need to introduce a new topic. Ask a question or make a brief comment regarding whatever the client has said in the immediate or near past. Build on the client's topics, and you will come to know the client very well over time.

Observing yourself and using selective attention. Clients tend to talk about what interviewers are willing to hear. A famous training film has three eminent counselors (Albert Ellis, Fritz Perls, and Carl Rogers) all counseling the same client, Gloria (Shostrum, 1966). Gloria changes the way she talks and responds very differently as she works with each counselor. Research on verbal behavior in the film revealed that Gloria tended to match the language of the varying counselors (Meara et al., 1979, 1981). Each expert indicated, by his nonverbal and verbal behavior, what he wanted Gloria to talk about!

Should clients match the language of the interviewer, or should you, the interviewer, learn to match your language and style with that of the client? Most likely, both approaches are relevant, but in the beginning, you want to draw out client stories from their own language perspective, not yours. What do you consider most important in the interview? Are there topics with which you are less comfortable? Some interviewers are excellent in helping clients talk about vocational issues but shy away from interpersonal conflict and sexuality. Others may find their clients constantly talking about interpersonal issues, excluding critical practical issues such as getting a job.

Consider the following example:

CLIENT: (speaks slowly, seems to be sad and depressed) I'm so fouled up right now. The first term went well and I passed all my courses. But this term, I am really having trouble with chemistry. It's hard to get around the lab in my wheelchair and I still don't have a textbook, yet. (An angry spark appears in her eyes, and she clenches her fist.) By the time I got to the bookstore, they were all gone. It takes a long time to get to that class because the elevator is on the wrong side of the building for me. (looks down at floor) Almost as bad, my car broke down and I missed two days of school because I couldn't get there. (The sad look returns to her eyes.) In high school, I had lots of friends, but somehow I just don't fit in here. It seems that I just sit and study, sit and study. Some days it just doesn't seem worth the effort.

There are several different directions an interviewer could follow from this statement. Where would you go, given the multiple possible directions? List at least three possibilities for follow-up from the client statement above.

One way to respond is to reflect the main theme of the client's story. For example, "You must feel like you're being hit from all directions. Which would you like to talk about first?" Different interviewers place emphasis on different issues. Some interviewers consistently listen attentively to only a few key topics while ignoring other possibilities. Be alert to your own potential patterning of responses. It is important that no issue gets lost, but it is equally important to avoid confusion by not seeking to solve everything at once.

Professor Howard Busby of Gallaudet College has commented on this case in a personal email to Allen and Mary. Dr. Busby, who is deaf, points out that the client's problem could be related to the disability, the issues at school, or both.

> The wheelchair might be the problem as much as how this client is dealing with it. The client obviously has a disability, but it does not have to be disabling unless the client makes it so. Although I am categorized as having a disability due to deafness, I have never allowed it to be disabling.

My interpretation of the client is that this depression, on the surface, could be the result of mobility restriction. However, there are other factors that might have caused the depression, even if there were no need for a wheelchair. It is easy for the client to blame problems on the disability and thus distract from personal issues. The issue could be a poor campus environment, learned helplessness on the part of the client, or a combination of these and other multiple factors.

All of us would do well to consider Dr. Busby's comments. He is pointing out to us the importance of taking a broad and comprehensive view of all cases. We must avoid stereotyping, but we must also be sensitive to individual and cultural differences.

ATTENTIVE AND AUTHENTIC BODY LANGUAGE

The anthropologist Edward Hall once examined film clips of Native Americans of the Southwest and of European North Americans and found more than 20 different variations in the way they walked. Just as cultural differences in eye contact exist, body language patterns differ also.

A comfortable conversational distance for many North Americans is slightly more than arm's length, and the English prefer even greater distances. Many Latin people prefer half that distance, and some from the Middle East may talk practically eyeball-to-eyeball. As a result, the slightly forward lean we recommend for attending is not appropriate all the time.

What determines a comfortable interpersonal distance is influenced by multiple factors. Hargie, Dickson, and Tourish (2004, p. 45) point out the following:

Gender: Women tend to feel more comfortable with closer distances than males.

Personality: Introverts need more distance than extraverts.

Age: Children and the young tend to adopt closer distances.

Topic of conversation: Difficult topics such as sexual worries or personal misbehavior may lead a person to more distance.

Personal relationships: Harmonious friends or couples tend to be closer, while those who have issues may move apart.

A person may move forward when interested and away when bored or frightened. As you talk, notice people's movements in relation to you. How do you affect them? Note your own behavior patterns in the interview. When do you markedly change body posture? A natural, authentic, relaxed body style is likely to be most effective, but be prepared to adapt and be flexible according to the individual client.

Your authentic personhood is a vital presence in the helping relationship. Whether you use visuals, vocal qualities, verbal tracking, or attentive body language, be a real person in a real relationship. Practice the skills, be aware, and be respectful of individual and cultural differences.

THE VALUE OF NONATTENTION

Skilled counselors and interviewers use attending skills to open *and close* client talk, making the most effective use of limited time in the interview. If a client talks insistently about the same topic over and over again or a depressed client endlessly describes how and why the world is wrong, intentional nonattending may be useful. Failure to maintain eye contact, subtle shifts in body posture, vocal tone, and deliberate jumps to more positive topics can facilitate shifts to more appropriate topics and helpful conversation.

THE USEFULNESS OF SILENCE

Sometimes the most useful thing you can do as a helper is to support your client silently. As a counselor, particularly as a beginner, you may find it hard to sit and wait for clients to think through what they want to say. Your client may be in tears, and you may want to give support through your words. However, sometimes the best support may be simply being with the person, and not saying anything.

For a beginning interviewer, silence can be frightening. After all, doesn't counseling mean talking about issues and solving problems verbally? When you feel uncomfortable with silence, look at your client. If the client appears comfortable, draw from her or his ease and join in the silence. If the client seems disquieted by the silence, rely on your attending skills. Ask a question or make a comment about something relevant, mentioned earlier in the session.

Finally, remember the obvious: Clients can't talk while you do. Review your interviews for talk-time. Who talks the most, you or your client? For most adult clients the percentage of client talk-time should generally be more than that of the interviewer. With less verbal clients or young children, however, the interviewer may need to talk slightly more than they do or tell stories to help clients verbalize. A 7-year-old child dealing with parental divorce may not say a word initially. But when you read a children's book on feelings around divorce, he or she may start to ask questions and talk more freely.

▲ **MODULE 3.3**
SUMMARY

- ▲ Expect individual and cultural differences in eye contact and body language.
- ▲ Vocal qualities express emotions, and each client may interpret your voice differently.
- ▲ Verbal tracking is the skill of focusing on client topics and identifying topics of concern.
- ▲ Expect and respect multicultural and individual characteristics in the client's body language. Remain authentic to your own style.
- ▲ Nonattention may help clients shift from negative, nonproductive topics to more appropriate conversation. There are times when silence is the best approach.

MODULE 3.4
OBSERVATION SKILLS

KEY CONCEPT QUESTION

▲ What additional verbal and nonverbal behaviors are important to observe in both interviewer and client?

Some authorities say that 85% or more of communication is nonverbal. Observing verbal and nonverbal behavior is a critical dimension of effective interviewing. Be self-aware and simultaneously aware of client actions and underlying emotional tone, which is often conveyed through nonverbals. *How something is said can sometimes overrule the actual words used by you or your client.*

Client Observation Skills	Predicted Result
Observe your own and the client's verbal and nonverbal behavior. Anticipate individual and multicultural differences in nonverbal and verbal behavior. Carefully and selectively feedback observations to the client as topics for discussion.	Observations provide specific data validating or invalidating what is happening in the session and provide guidance for use of various microskills and strategies. The smoothly flowing interview will often demonstrate movement symmetry or complimentarity. Movement dissynchrony provides a clear clue that you are not "in tune" with the client.

OBSERVE ATTENDING PATTERNS OF CLIENTS

Clients may break eye contact, shift their bodies, and change vocal qualities as their comfort level changes when they talk about varying topics. You may observe clients crossing their arms or legs when they want to close off a topic, using rapid alterations of eye contact during periods of confusion, or exhibiting increased stammering or speech hesitations when topics are difficult. And if you watch yourself carefully on tape, you, as interviewer, will exhibit many of these same behaviors at times.

OBSERVE BODY LANGUAGE

Jiggling legs, making complete body shifts, or suddenly closing one's arms most often indicates discomfort. Hand and arm gestures may give you an indication of how you and the client are organizing things. Random, discrepant gestures may indicate confusion, whereas a person seeking to control or organize things may move hands and arms in straight lines and point fingers authoritatively. Smooth, flowing gestures, particularly those in harmony with the gestures of others, such as family members, friends, or the interviewer, may suggest openness.

Often people who are communicating well "mirror" each other's body language. They may unconsciously sit in identical positions and make complex hand movements together as if in a ballet. This is termed *movement synchrony. Movement complementarity* is paired movements that may not be identical but are still harmonious. For instance, one person talks and the other nods in agreement. You may observe a hand movement at the end of one person's statement that is answered by a related hand movement as the other takes the conversational "ball" and starts talking.

Some expert counselors and therapists deliberately "mirror" their clients. Experience shows that matching body language, breathing rates, and key words of the client can heighten interviewer understanding of how the client perceives and experiences the world.

Particularly important are discrepancies in nonverbal behavior. *Movement dissynchrony* occurs when a client is talking casually about a friend, for example, with one hand tightly clenched in a fist and the other relaxed and open, possibly indicating mixed feelings toward the friend. Lack of harmony in movement is common between people who disagree markedly or even between those who may not be aware they have subtle conflicts. You have likely seen this type of behavior in couples that you know have problems in communicating.

But, be careful with deliberate mirroring. A practicum student reported difficulty with a client, noting that the client's nonverbal behavior seemed especially unusual. Near the end of the session, the client reported, "I know you guys; you try to mirror my nonverbal behavior. So I keep moving to make it difficult for you." You can expect that some clients will know as much about observation skills and nonverbal behavior as you do. What should you do in such situations? Use the skills and concepts in this book with *honesty* and *authenticity*. And talk with your clients about their observations of you without being defensive. Openness works!

INDIVIDUAL AND MULTICULTURAL ISSUES IN NONVERBAL BEHAVIOR

As you engage in observation, recall that each culture has a different style of nonverbal communication. For example, Russians say yes by shaking the head from side to side and no by moving the head up and down. Most Europeans do exactly the opposite.

A study was made of the average number of times in an hour friends of different cultural groups touch each other while talking in a coffee shop. The results showed that English friends did not touch each other at all, French friends touched 110 times, and Puerto Rican friends touched 180 times (cited in Asbell & Wynn, 1991).

Smiling is a sign of warmth in most cultures, but in some situations in Japan, smiling may indicate discomfort. Eye contact may be inappropriate for the traditional Navajo but highly appropriate and expected for a Navajo official who interacts commonly with European American Arizonans.

Be careful not to assign your own ideas about what is "standard" and appropriate nonverbal communication. It is important for the helping professional to begin a lifetime of studying nonverbal communication patterns and their variations. In terms of counseling sessions, you will find that changes in style may be as important as, or more important than, finding specific meanings in communication style. Edward Hall's *The Silent Language* (1959) remains a classic. Paul Ekman's work (2003) is the current standard reference for nonverbal communication. You can also visit several useful websites devoted to nonverbal communication, one of which is http://nonverbal.ucsc.edu/ (or use your search engine with the key words nonverbal communication). Needless to say, the visuals available on the Internet will provide clearer examples of nonverbal communication than we can provide through the written word.

▲ **MODULE 3.4**
SUMMARY

▲ Observing verbal and nonverbal behavior is critical to understanding the client. In addition, watch videos of your own patterns to assess your strengths and areas for improvement.
▲ Movement synchrony, movement complementarity, and mirroring may represent particularly effective moments and close relationships in the interview.
▲ Movement dissynchrony and noncommunicative body movements may indicate that there are issues not being discussed in the here and now of the interview or that the client is uncomfortable with you or the session.
▲ Multicultural impacts on verbal and nonverbal behavior will require a lifetime of learning on the part of the counselor/interviewer.

MODULE 3.5
BECOMING A SAMURAI

KEY CONCEPT QUESTION

▲ What are the advantages of the single skills approach, and what are some key challenges?

Japanese masters of the swords learn their skills through a complex set of highly detailed training exercises.* The process of masterful sword work is broken down into specific components that are studied carefully, one at a time. In this process of mastery, the naturally skilled person often suffers and finds handling the sword more awkward than before training began. The skilled individual may even find his or her performance worsening during the practice of single skills. *Being aware of what one is doing can interfere with coordination and smoothness in the early stages.*

Once the individual skills are practiced and learned to perfection, the Samurai retire to a mountaintop to meditate. They deliberately forget what they have learned. When they return, they find the distinct skills have been naturally integrated into their style or way of being. The Samurai then seldom have to think about skills at all. They have become samurai masters.

Improving and studying our natural communication skills can result in a temporary and sometimes frustrating decrease in competence, just as it does for the Samurai. Intentional and relaxed performance of skills and strategies takes time and practice. You may likely have some discomfort in practicing the single skill of attending. Later you may find the same problem with other skills. This happens to both the beginner and the advanced counselor. Ballet, music, golf, basketball, and many other activities also rely on the single skills approach to learning.

Consider driving. When you first sat at the wheel, you had to coordinate many tasks, particularly if you drove a car with a stick shift. The clutch, the gas pedal, the steering wheel, and the gear ratios had to be coordinated smoothly with what you saw through the windshield. But practice and experience soon led you to forget the specific skills, and you were able to coordinate them automatically and give full attention to the world beyond the windshield. The mastery of single skills led you to achieve your objectives.

Learn the skills of this book, but allow yourself time for meditation and/or integrating these ideas into your own natural authentic being.

△ MODULE 3.5
SUMMARY

- ▲ The Japanese Samurai often learned the specific skills of the sword one by one and practiced them to mastery. They then retired to the mountaintop where learned skills were integrated in a natural fashion.
- ▲ Many highly demanding activities such as driving, golf, dance, music, and others are improved with single skills practice.
- ▲ The microskills approach breaks interviewer skills into single units. When learning single skills one by one, there may be a temporary decrease in competence. However, further practice and experience develops mastery and a natural integration of skills.

---

*We are indebted to Lanette Shizuru, University of Hawai'i, Manoa, for the Samurai story.

HEARING CLIENT STORIES
How to Organize an Interview

Attending behavior is basic to all the communication skills of the microskills hierarchy. Without individually and culturally appropriate attending behavior, there can be no interviewing, counseling, or psychotherapy.

This section presents the *basic listening sequence* that will enable you to draw out the major facts and feelings pertinent to a client's concern. Through the skills of questioning, encouraging, paraphrasing, reflecting feelings, and summarization, you will learn how to draw out your clients and understand their stories more fully.

The basic listening sequence begins with questioning skills (Chapter 4) followed by the clarifying skills of paraphrasing, encouraging, and summarizing (Chapter 5). Perhaps the most important skill for understanding clients is reflecting feelings presented in Chapter 6. Once you become skilled in basic listening, you are prepared to conduct a complete interview (Chapter 7).

It is possible to have a very successful interview using only listening skills. Carl Rogers developed person-centered counseling, and he made it clear that effective interviewing and counseling can be conducted via listening only. Rogers carried this idea even further and rarely used questions as he preferred to have clients carry as much responsibility for the interview as possible.

With sufficient practice, you can reach the following performance objectives:

1. Master the basic listening sequence (open questions, encouraging, paraphrasing, summarizing, and reflection of feeling) and draw out the thoughts, feelings, and behaviors relevant to the clients' concerns.
2. Observe clients' reactions to your skill usage and modify your skills and attending behaviors to complement their uniqueness.
3. Conduct an interview using only listening and observing skills.

When you've accomplished these tasks, you may find that your clients have a surprising ability to solve their own issues and challenges without further intervention on your part. You may also gain a sense of confidence in your own ability as an interviewer. The motto of the first seven chapters is "When in doubt, listen!"

QUESTIONS
Opening Communication

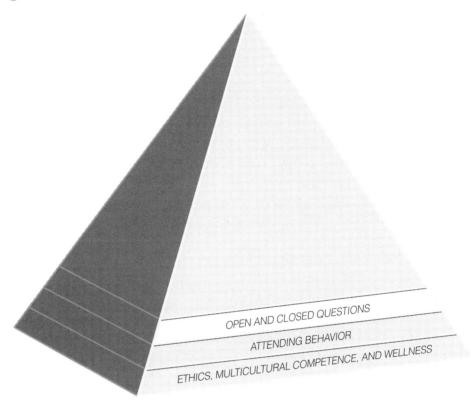

OPEN AND CLOSED QUESTIONS

ATTENDING BEHAVIOR

ETHICS, MULTICULTURAL COMPETENCE, AND WELLNESS

How can questions help you and your clients?

CHAPTER
GOALS

If you use open questions effectively, you can expect the client to talk more freely and openly. Closed questions will elicit shorter responses and may provide you with information and specifics.

Like attending behavior, questions can encourage or discourage client talk. With questions, however, the leadership comes mainly from the interviewer. The client is often talking within your frame of reference. Questions potentially can take away from client self-direction.

Awareness, knowledge, and skills developed through the concepts of this chapter will enable you to

▲ Enrich client stories through bringing out a more complete description, including important specifics.

▲ Choose the question style that is most likely to achieve a useful predicted result. For example, *what* questions often lead to talk about facts, *how* questions to feelings or process, and *why* questions to reasons.

▲ Open or close client talk, intentionally, according to the individual needs of the interview.

MODULE 4.1
DEFINING QUESTIONS

KEY CONCEPT QUESTIONS

▲ **What are open and closed questions and how do they affect client conversation?**

▲ **What are the potential problems of questions in the interview?**

▲ **When are questions essential?**

Benjamin is near completing his junior year of high school, in the middle third of his class. In this school, each student must be interviewed about plans after graduation—work, the armed forces, or college. You are the high school counselor and have called him in to check on his plans after graduation. He is known as a "nice boy"; his grades are average, and he is not particularly verbal and talkative.

What are some questions that you could use to draw him out and help him think ahead to the future? And if you ask too many questions, what potential problems will you face?

You may want to compare your questions and our thoughts on page 73 at the end of this chapter.

Skilled attending behavior is the foundation of the microskills hierarchy; questioning provides a systematic framework for directing the interview. Questions help an interview begin and move along smoothly. They open up new areas for discussion, assist in pinpointing and clarifying issues, and aid in clients' self-exploration.

Open and Closed Questions	*Predicted Result*
Begin open questions with often useful *who, what, when, where,* and *why.* Closed questions may start with *do, is,* or *are. Could, can,* or *would* questions are considered open but have the additional advantage of being somewhat closed, thus giving more power to the client, who can more easily say that he or she doesn't want to respond.	Clients give more detail and talk more in response to open questions. Closed questions provide specific information but may close off client talk. Effective questions encourage more focused client conversations with more pertinent detail and less wandering. *Could, would,* and *can* questions are often the most open of all.

Questions are an essential component in many theories and styles of helping, particularly cognitive-behavioral practice, interviewing around substance abuse, and much of career decision making. The employment counselor, the social worker conducting an assessment interview, and the high school guidance counselor helping a student work on college admissions all need to use questions.

This chapter focuses on two key styles of questioning—open and closed questions:

> *Open questions* are those that can't be answered in a few words. They tend to facilitate deeper exploration of client issues. They encourage others to talk and provide you with maximum information. Typically, open questions begin with *what, how, why,* or *could.* For example, "Could you tell me what brings you here today?"

> *Closed questions* enable you to obtain important specifics and tend to be answered in very few words. They may help you obtain important information, but the burden of guiding the talk remains on the interviewer. Closed questions often begin with *is, are,* or *do.* For example, "Are you living with your family?"

Some theorists and practitioners raise important issues around the use of questions. Excessive use takes the focus from the client and gives too much power to the interviewer. Your central task is to find your own balance using questions in the interview.

Key Issues Around Questions

> Why do some people object to questions? Take a minute to recall and explore some of your own experiences with questions. Perhaps you had a teacher or a parent who used questions in a manner that resulted in your feeling uncomfortable or even attacked—"Why did YOU do that?" What thoughts and feelings did this experience produce in you?

People often respond to this exercise by describing situations in which they were put on the spot or grilled by someone. They may associate questions with anger and guilt as many have had negative experiences with questions. Furthermore, questions may be used to direct and control client talk. School discipline and legal disputes typically use questions to control the person being interviewed. If your objective is to enable clients to find their own way, questions may inhibit your reaching that goal. It is for these reasons that some humanistically oriented helping professionals object to questions in the interview. Additionally, in many non-Western cultures, questions are inappropriate and may be considered offensive or overly intrusive.

Nevertheless, questions remain a fact of life in most cultures and we encounter them everywhere. The physician or nurse, the salesperson, the government official, and many others find questioning clients basic to their profession. Many counseling theories frequently use questions. The issue, then, is how to question wisely and intentionally.

Sometimes Questions Are Essential—"What Else?"

Clients do not always provide you with important information, and sometimes the only way to get at missing data is by asking questions. For example, the client may talk about being depressed and unable to act. As a helper, you could listen to the story carefully but still miss important underlying issues relating to the depression. You could ask an open question, "What important things are happening in your life right now or with your family?" The client's answer might tell you that a separation or divorce is near at hand, that a job has been lost, or that there is some other important dimension underlying the concern. What you first interpreted as a classical clinical depression becomes modified as a shorter-term issue, and treatment takes a different direction.

An incident in Allen's life—when his father became blind after open heart surgery—illustrates the importance of questions. Was the blindness a result of the surgery? No; it was because the physicians failed to ask the basic open question "Is anything else happening physically or emotionally in your life at this time?" If that question had been asked, the physicians would have discovered that Allen's father had developed severe and unusual headaches the week before surgery was scheduled, and they could have diagnosed an eye infection that is easily treatable with medication.

In counseling, a client may speak of tension, anxiety, and sleeplessness. You listen carefully and believe the problem can be resolved by helping the client relax and plan changes in her work schedule. However, you ask the client, "What else is going on in your life?" In response the client shares a story of sexual harassment, and the goals of the session change.

Finally, at the close of any session, consider asking your client something like, "What else should we have discussed today?" or "What have we missed today?"

▲ **MODULE 4.1**
SUMMARY

- ▲ Closed questions focus the interview, provide specific information, and are answered in few words whereas open questions allow more client talk-time and exploration of client concerns.
- ▲ Many people have negative experiences with questions. We may have been "put on the spot" or grilled. It becomes key to determine when and how to use questions effectively.
- ▲ The "What else?" question brings out missing data. It is maximally open and allows the client considerable control.

MODULE 4.2
EXAMPLE INTERVIEW: Conflict at Work

KEY CONCEPT QUESTION

▲ How do open and closed questions appear in the context of an interview?

Virtually all of us have experienced conflict on the job. Angry, difficult customers; insensitive supervisors; lazy colleagues; or challenges from those whom we may supervise give us concern. In the following set of transcripts, we see an employee assistance counselor, Jamila, meeting with Kelly, a junior manager who has a conflict with Peter. The first session illustrates how closed questions can bring out specific facts but can sometimes end in leading the client, even to the point of putting the counselor's ideas into the client's mind.

Closed-Question Example

Interviewer and Client Conversation	Process Comments
1. *Jamila:* Hi, Kelly. What's happening with you today?	Jamila has talked with Kelly once in the past about difficulties she has had in her early experiences supervising others for the first time. She begins the session with an open question that could also be seen as a standard social greeting.

Interviewer and Client Conversation	Process Comments
2. *Kelly:* Well, I'm having problems with Peter again.	Jamila and Kelly have a good relationship. Not all clients are so ready to discuss their issues. More time for developing rapport and trust will be necessary for many clients, even on return visits.
3. *Jamila:* Is he arguing with you?	Jamila appears interested, is listening and demonstrating good attending skills. However, she asks a closed question, is already defining the issue without discovering Kelly's thoughts and feelings.
4. *Kelly:* (hesitates) Not really; he's so difficult to work with.	Kelly sits back in her chair and waits for the interviewer to take the lead.
5. *Jamila:* Is he getting his work in on time?	See Jamila try to diagnose the problem with Peter by asking a series of closed questions. This is much too early.
6. *Kelly:* No, that's not the issue. He's even early.	
7. *Jamila:* Is his work decent? Does he do a good job?	Jamila is starting to grill Kelly.
8. *Kelly:* That's one of the problems, his work is excellent and always there on time. I can't criticize what he does.	
9. *Jamila:* (hesitates) Is he getting along with others on your team?	Jamila frowns and her body tenses as she thinks of what to ask next. Interviewers who rely on closed questions suddenly find themselves having run out of questions to ask. They continue searching for another closed question usually further off the mark.
10. *Kelly:* Well, he likes to go off with Daniel, and they laugh in the corner. It makes me nervous. He ignores the rest of the staff—it isn't just me.	
11. *Jamila:* So, it's you we need to work on. Is that right?	Jamila has been searching for an individual to blame. Jamila relaxes a little as she thinks she is on to something. Kelly sits back in discouragement.
12. *Kelly:* (hesitates and stammers) . . . Well, I suppose so . . . I . . . I . . . really hope you can help me work it out.	Kelly looks to Jamila as the expert. While she dislikes taking blame for the situation, she is also anxious to please and too readily accepts the interviewer's diagnosis.

Closed questions can overwhelm clients and can be used as evidence to force them to agree with the interviewer's ideas. Although the session above seems extreme, encounters like this are common in daily life and even occur in interviewing and counseling sessions. There is a power differential between clients and counselors. It is possible that an interviewer who fails to listen can impose inappropriate decisions on a client.

Open-Question Example

The interview is for the client, not the interviewer. Using open questions, Jamila learns Kelly's story rather than the one she imposed with closed questions in the first example. Again, this interview is in the employee assistance office.

Interviewer and Client Conversation	Process Comments
1. *Jamila:* Hi, Kelly. What's happening with you today?	Jamila uses the same easy beginning as in the closed-question example. She has excellent attending skills and is good at relationship building.
2. *Kelly:* Well, I'm having problems with Peter again.	Kelly responds in the same way as in the first demonstration.
3. *Jamila:* More problems? Could you share more with me about what's been happening lately?	Open questions beginning with "could" provide some control to the client. Potentially a "could" question may be responded to as a closed question and answered with "yes" or "no." But in the United States, Canada, and other English-speaking countries, it usually functions as an open question.
4. *Kelly:* This last week Peter has been going off in the corner with Daniel, and the two of them start laughing. He's ignoring most of our staff, and he's been getting under my skin even more lately. In the middle of all this, his work is fine, on-time, and near perfect. But he is so impossible to deal with.	We are hearing Kelly's story. The predicted result from open questions is that Kelly will respond with information. She provides an overview of the situation and shares how it is affecting her.
5. *Jamila:* I hear you. Peter is getting even more difficult and seems to be affecting your team as well. It's really stressing you out and you look upset. Is that pretty much how you are feeling about things?	When clients provide lots of information, we need to ensure that we hear them accurately. Jamila summarizes what has been said and acknowledges Kelly's emotions. The closed question at the end is termed a perception check or checkout. Periodically checking with your client can help you in two important ways: (a) It communicates to clients that you are listening and encourages them to continue; (b) it allows the client to correct any wrong assumptions you may have.
6. *Kelly:* That's right. I really need to calm down.	

Interviewer and Client Conversation	Process Comments
7. *Jamila:* Let's change the pace a bit. Could you give me a specific example of an exchange you had with Peter last week that didn't work well?	Jamila asks for a concrete example. Specific illustrations of client issues are often helpful in understanding what is really occurring.
8. *Kelly:* Last week, I asked him to review a bookkeeping report prepared by Anne. It's pretty important that our team understand what's going on. He looked at me like, "Who are you to tell *me* what to do?" But he sat down and did it that day. Friday, at the staff meeting, I asked him to summarize the report for everyone. In front of the whole group, he said he had to review this report for me and joked about me not understanding numbers. Daniel laughed, but the rest of the staff just sat there. He even put Anne down and presented her report as not very interesting and poorly written. He was obviously trying to get me. I just ignored it. But that's typical of what he does.	Specific and concrete examples can be representative of recurring problems. The concrete specifics from one or two detailed stories provide better understanding of what is really happening. Now that Jamila has heard the specifics, she is better prepared to be helpful.
9. *Jamila:* Underneath it all, you're furious. Kelly, why do you imagine he is doing that to you?	Will the "why" question lead to the discovery of reasons?
10. *Kelly:* (hesitates) Really, I don't know why. I've tried to be helpful to him.	The intentional prediction did not result in the expected response. This is, of course, not unusual. It is likely too soon for Kelly to know why. This illustrates a common problem with "why" questions.
11. *Jamila:* Gender can be an issue; men do put women down at times. Would you be willing to consider that possibility?	Jamila carefully presents her own hunch. But instead of expressing her own ideas as truth, she offers them tentatively with a "would" question and reframes the situation as "possibility."
12. *Kelly:* Jamila, it makes sense. I've halfway thought of it, but I didn't really want to acknowledge the possibility. But it is clear that Peter has taken Daniel away from the team. Until Peter came aboard, we worked together beautifully. (pause) Yes, it makes sense for me. I think he's out to take care of himself. I see Peter going up to my supervisor all the time. He talks to the female staff members in a demeaning way. Somehow, I'd like to keep his great talent on the team, but how when he is so difficult?	With Jamila's help, Kelly is beginning to obtain a broader perspective. She thinks of several situations indicating that Peter's ambition and sexist behavior are issues that need to be addressed.

Interviewer and Client Conversation	Process Comments
13. *Jamila:* So, the problem is becoming clearer. You want a working team and you want Peter to be part of it. We can explore the possibility of assertiveness training as a way to deal with Peter. But, before that, what do you bring to this situation that will help you deal with him?	Jamila provides support for Kelly's new frame of reference and ideas for where the interview can go next. She suggests that time needs to be spent on finding positive assets and wellness strengths. Kelly can best resolve these issues if she works from a base of resources and capabilities.
14. *Kelly:* First, I need to remind myself that I really do know more about our work than Peter. He is new to it. I worked through a similar issue with Jonathan two years ago. He kept hassling me until I had it out with him. He was fine after that. I know my team respects me; they come to me for advice all the time.	Kelly smiles for the first time. She has sufficient support from Jamila to readily come up with her strengths. However, don't expect it always to be that easy. Clients may return to their weaknesses and ignore their assets.
15. *Jamila:* Could you tell me specifically what happened when you sat down and faced Jon's challenge directly?	This "could" question searches for concrete specifics when Kelly handled a difficult situation effectively. Jamila can identify specific skills that Kelly can later apply to Peter. At this point the interview can move from problem definition to problem solution.

In this excerpt, we see that Kelly has been given more talk-time and room to explore what is happening. The questions that are focused on specific examples clarify what is happening. We also see that question stems such as *why, how,* and *could* have some predictability in expected client responses. The positive asset search is a particularly important part of successful questioning. Issues are best resolved by emphasizing strengths.

You are very likely to work with clients who have similar interpersonal issues wherever you may practice. The previous case examples focus on the single skill of questioning as a way to bring out client stories. Questioning is an extremely helpful skill, but do not forget the dangers of using too many questions.

▲ **MODULE 4.2**
SUMMARY

- ▲ Closed questions can bring out specific data, but if they are overused, the interviewer will run out of things to say and so will the client.
- ▲ Open questions give more control to the client and encourage more client talk-time.
- ▲ Questions used to identify strengths can help clients face their issues with more confidence and ability.

MODULE 4.3
INSTRUCTIONAL READING: Making Questions Work for You

KEY CONCEPT QUESTION

▲ **What are some specific concepts and practices that make questions more useful in the interview?**

Questions can be facilitative, or they can be so intrusive that clients want to say nothing. Use the ideas presented here to help you define your own questioning techniques and strategies and how questioning fits with your natural style.

Questions Help Begin the Interview

With verbal clients and a comfortable relationship, the open question facilitates free discussion and leaves plenty of room to talk. Here are some examples:

"What would you like to talk about today?"

"Could you tell me what prompted you to see me?"

"How have things been since we last talked together?"

"The last time we talked you planned to talk with your partner about your sexual difficulties. How did it go this week?"

The first three open questions provide room for the client to talk about virtually anything. The last question is open but provides some focus for the session, building on material from the preceding week. These types of questions will work well for a highly verbal client. However, such open questions may be more than a nontalkative client can handle. It may be best to start the session with more informal conversation—focusing on the weather, a positive part of last week's session, or a current event of interest to the client. You can turn to the issues for this session as the client becomes more comfortable.

The First Word of Open Questions May Determine Client Response

Key-question stems often, but not always, result in predictable outcomes.

What questions most often lead to facts. "What happened?" "What are you going to do?"

How questions may lead to an exploration of process or feeling and emotion. "How could that be explained?" "How do you feel about that?"

Why questions can lead to a discussion of reasons. "Why did you allow that to happen?" "Why do you think that is so?" Use *why* questions with care. While understanding reasons may have value, a discussion of reasons can also lead to sidetracks. In addition, many clients may not respond well because they associate *why* with a past experience of being grilled.

Could, can, or *would* questions are considered maximally open and also contain some advantages of closed questions. Clients are free to say, "No, I don't want to talk about that." *Could* questions reflect less interviewer control. "Could you tell me more about your situation?" "Would you give me a specific example?" "Can you tell me what you'd like to talk about today?"

Give this a try and you'll be surprised to see how effective this simple guideline can be.

Open Questions Help Clients Elaborate and Enrich Their Story

A beginning interviewer often asks one or two questions and then wonders what to do next. Even more experienced interviewers can find themselves hard-pressed to know what to do next. To help the session start again and keep it moving, ask an open question on a topic the client presented earlier in the interview.

"Could you tell me more about that?"

"How did you feel when that happened?"

"Given what you've said, what would be your ideal solution to the problem?"

"What might we have missed so far?"

"What else comes to your mind?"

Questions Can Reveal Concrete Specifics From the Client's World

The model question "Could you give me a specific example?" is the most useful open question available to any interviewer. Many clients tend to talk in vague generalities, and specific, concrete examples enrich the interview and provide data for understanding action. Some additional open questions that aim for concreteness and specifics follow:

CLIENT: Ricardo makes me so mad!

COUNSELOR: Could you give me a specific example of what Ricardo does?

What does Ricardo do, specifically, that brings out your anger?

What do you mean by "makes me mad"?

Could you specify what you do before and after Ricardo makes you mad?

Closed questions, of course, can bring out specifics as well, but even well-directed closed questions may take the initiative away from the client. However, at the discretion of the interviewer, closed questions may prove invaluable: "Did Ricardo show his anger by striking you?" "Does Ricardo tease you often?" and "Is Ricardo on drugs?" Questions like these may encourage clients to say out loud what they have only hinted at before.

BOX 4-1   National and International Perspectives on Counseling Skills

 Using Questions With Youth at Risk

COURTLAND LEE, PAST PRESIDENT, AMERICAN COUNSELING ASSOCIATION, UNIVERSITY OF MARYLAND

Malik is a 13-year-old African American male who is in the seventh grade at an urban junior high school. He lives in an apartment complex in a lower middle (working) class neighborhood with his mother and 7-year-old sister. Malik's parents have been divorced since he was 6 and he sees his father very infrequently. His mother works two jobs to hold the family together and she is not able to be there when they come home from school.

Throughout his elementary school years, Malik was an honor roll student. However, since he started junior high school, his grades have dropped dramatically and he expresses no interest in doing well academically. He spends his days at school in the company of a group of seventh- and eighth-grade boys who are frequently in trouble with school officials.

This case is one that is repeated among many African American early teens. But this problem also occurs among other racial/ethnic groups as well, particularly those who are struggling economically. And the same pattern occurs frequently even in well-off homes. There are many teens at risk for getting in trouble or using drugs.

While still a boy, Malik has been asked to shoulder a man's responsibilities as he must pick up things his mother can't do. Simultaneously, his peer group discounts the importance of academic success and wants to challenge traditional authority. And Malik is making the difficult transition from childhood to manhood without a positive male model.

I've developed a counseling program designed to empower adolescent Black males that focuses on personal and cultural pride. The full program focuses on the central question, *"What is a strong Black man?"* (Lee, 1992). While this question is designed for group discussion, it is an important one for adolescent males in general, who might be engaging in individual work. The idea is to use this question to help the youth redefine, in a more positive sense, what it means to be strong and powerful. Some of the related questions that I find helpful include these:

What makes a man strong?
Who are some strong Black men that you know personally? What makes these men strong?
Do you think that you are strong? Why?
What makes a strong body?
Is abuse of your body a sign of strength?
Who are some African heroes or elders that are important to you? What did they do that made them strong?
How is education strength?
What is a strong Black man?
What does a strong Black man do that makes a difference for his people?
What can you do to make a difference?

Needless to say, you can't ask an African American adolescent or a youth of any color these questions unless you and he are in a positive and open relationship. Developing sufficient trust to ask these challenging questions may take time. You may have to get out of your office and into the school and community to become a person of trust.

My hope for you as a professional counselor is that you will have a positive attitude when you encounter challenging adolescents. They are seeking models for a successful life and you may become one of those models yourself. I hope you think about establishing group programs to facilitate development and that you'll use some of these ideas with adolescents to help move them toward a more positive track.

Questions Have Potential Problems

Questions can have immense value in the interview, but we must not forget their potential problems.

Bombardment/grilling. Too many questions may give too much control to the interviewer and tend to put many clients on the defensive.

Multiple questions. Another form of bombardment, throwing out too many questions at once, may confuse clients. However, it may enable clients to select which question they prefer to answer.

Questions as statements. Some interviewers may use questions to sell their own points of view. "Don't you think it would be helpful if you studied more?" This question clearly puts the client on the spot. On the other hand, "What do you think of trying relaxation exercises when you are tense?" might be helpful to get some clients thinking in new ways. Consider alternative and more direct routes of reaching the client. A useful standard is this: If you are going to make a statement, do not frame it as a question.

Why questions. *Why* questions can put interviewees on the defensive and cause discomfort. As children, most of us experienced some form of "Why did you do that?" Any question that evokes a sense of being attacked can create client discomfort and defensiveness.

In Cross-Cultural Situations, Questions Can Promote Distrust

If your life background and experience are similar to your client, you may be able to use questions immediately and freely. If you come from a significantly different cultural background, your questions may be met by distrust and given only grudging answers. Questions place power with the interviewer. A poor client, who is in clear financial jeopardy, may not come back for another interview after receiving a barrage of questions from a clearly middle-class interviewer. If you are African American or White and working with an Asian American or a Latino/a, an extreme questioning style can produce mistrust. If the ethnicities are reversed, the same problem could occur.

Allen was conducting research and teaching in South Australia with Aboriginal social workers. He was seeking to understand their culture and their special needs for training. Allen is naturally inquisitive and sometimes asks many questions. Nonetheless, the relationship between him and the group seemed to be going well. But one day, Matt Rigney, whom Allen felt particularly close to, took him aside and gave some very useful corrective feedback:

You White fellas! . . . Always asking questions! Let me tell you what goes on in my mind when a White person asks me a question. First, my culture considers many questions rude. But, I know you and that's what you do. But, this is what goes on in my mind when you ask me a question. First, I wonder if I can trust you enough to give you an honest answer. Then, I realize that the question you asked is too complex to be answered in a few words. But I know you want an answer. So I chew on the question in my mind. Then, you know what? Before I can answer the first question, you've moved on to the next question!

Allen was lucky he had developed enough trust and rapport that Matt was willing to share his perceptions. Many People of Color have said that the Australian Aboriginal feedback represents how they felt about many interactions with White people. Moreover, disabled individuals, gays/lesbians/bisexuals, spiritually conservative persons, and many others, anyone in fact, may be distrustful of the interviewer who uses too many questions.

Questions Can Help Clients Search for Positive Assets and Patterns of Wellness

Stories presented in the helping interview are often negative and full of problems. Carl Rogers, the founder of client-centered counseling, was always able to find something positive in the interview. He considered positive regard and respect for the client essential for future growth. Once again, people grow from strength, not from weakness.

The positive asset search and wellness review are concrete ways to approach positive regard and respect for the client. As you listen to the client, constantly search for strengths and positives, and share your observations. Of course, you do not want to become overly optimistic and minimize the seriousness of the client's situation. However, it is increasingly clear that if you listen to only the sad and negative parts of the client's story, progress and change will be slow and painful.

Clients are "off-balance" when they tend to talk about their problems and what they can't do. The effective interviewer can help them center and feel better about themselves through a strength inventory, discovering what the client is doing right. Some specific, concrete examples of how to engage in a positive asset search include the following:

"Could you tell me a success story that you have had? What was it that you did right?"

"Tell me about a time in the past when someone supported you and what he or she did. What are your currently available support systems?"

"Can you share a time when you helped someone else?"

"What are some things you have been proud of in the past? Now?"

"What do you do well or what do others say you do well?"

You could search for external strengths in culture and family:

"Taking your ethnic/racial/spiritual history, can you identify some positive strengths, visual images, and experiences that you have now or have had in the past?"

"Can you recall a friend or family member of your own gender who represents some type of hero in the way he or she dealt with adversity? What did that person do? Can you develop an image of her or him?"

"We all have family strengths despite frequent family concerns. Family can include our extended family, our stepfamilies, and even those who have been special to us over time. For example, some people talk about a special teacher, a neighbor, or an older person who was helpful. Could you tell me concretely about them and what they mean to you?"

Review the wellness dimensions outlined in Chapter 2 as an additional approach to the search for strengths and positive assets.

Using Open and Closed Questions With Less Verbal Clients

Generally in the interview, open questions are preferred over closed questions. Yet it must be recognized that open questions require a verbal client, one who is willing to share with you. Here are some suggestions to encourage clients to talk with you more freely.

Build trust at the client's pace. A central issue with hesitant clients is trust. Extensive questioning too early can make trust building a slow process with some clients. If the client is required to meet with you or is culturally different from you, he or she may be less willing to talk. Trust building and rapport need to come first, and your own natural openness and social skills are particularly important. With some clients, trust building may take a full session or more.

Search for concrete specifics. Some interviewers and many clients talk in vague generalities. We call this "talking high on the abstraction ladder." This may be contrasted with concrete and specific language where what is said immediately makes sense. If your client is talking in very general terms and is hard to understand, it often helps to ask, "Could you give me a *concrete, specific* example?"

As the examples become clearer, ask even more specific questions. "You said that you are not getting along with your teacher. What specifically did your teacher say (or do)?" Your chances for helping the client talk will be greatly expanded when you focus on concrete events and avoid evaluation and opinion in a nonjudgmental fashion. Examples of concrete questions focusing on specifics include the following:

Draw out the linear sequence of the story. What happened first? What happened next? What was the result?

Focus on observable concrete actions. What did the other person say? What did he or she do? What did you say or do?

Help clients see the result of an event. What happened afterward? What did you do afterward? What did he or she do afterward? Sometimes clients are so focused on the event that they don't yet realize it is over.

Focus on emotions. What did you feel or think just before it happened? During? After? What do you think the other person felt?

Note that each of the preceding questions requires relatively short answers. These are open questions that are more focused and can be balanced with some closed questions. Do not expect your less verbal client to give you full answers to these questions. You may need to ask closed questions to fill in the details and obtain specific information. "Did he say anything?" "Where was she?" "Is your family angry?" "Did they say 'yes' or 'no'?"

A *leading* closed question is dangerous, particularly with children. In the previous examples, you can see that a long series of closed questions can bring out the story, but it may provide only the client's limited responses to *your* questions rather than what the client really thought or felt. Worse, the client may end up adopting your way of thinking or may simply stop coming to see you.

▲ **MODULE 4.3**
SUMMARY

- ▲ Questions help begin the interview, elaborate the client's story, and bring out concrete specifics of the client's world.
- ▲ Key sentence stems of certain open questions may predict client response. *What* tends to lead to facts, *how* to process and feelings, *why* to reasons, while *could/can/would* were described as maximally open.
- ▲ Potential difficulties with questions include client grilling and bombardment, the use of questions to make statements, and defensiveness from *why* questions.
- ▲ Questions may be seen as rude and intrusive and may be inappropriate. Sufficient trust needs to be present for questions to work effectively, particularly when multicultural differences are present.
- ▲ With less verbal clients, be particularly careful not to lead the client into your own frame of reference.

Our Thoughts About Benjamin (from p. 60)

We would likely begin by asking Benjamin what he is thinking about his future after he completes school. We would start with informal conversation about current school events, or something personal we know about Ben. The first question might be, "You'll soon be starting your senior year; what have you been thinking about doing after you graduate?" We would likely ask him to elaborate on his responses. If he focuses on indecision about volunteering for the army, enrolling in a local community college, or attending the state university, we might ask him some of the following questions:

"What about each of these appeals to you?"

"Could you tell me about some of your strengths?"

"If you went to college, what might you like to study?"

"How do finances play a role in these decisions?"

"Are there any negatives about any of these possibilities?"

"How do you imagine your ideal life 10 years from now?"

On the other hand, Benjamin just might look to you for guidance and say, "I don't know, but I guess I better start thinking about it." We might ask him to review his past likes and dislikes for possible clues to the future. Out of these questions, we might see patterns of ability and interest that suggest actions for the future.

"What courses have you liked best in high school?"

"What have been some of your activities?"

"Could you tell me about the jobs you've had in the past?"

"Tell me about your hobbies and what you do in your spare time."

"What gets you most excited and involved?"

"What did you do that made you feel most happy in the past year?"

If Benjamin is uncomfortable in the counseling office, all of these questions might put him off. He might feel that we are grilling him and perhaps even see us as intruding in his world. Usually, getting this type of information and organizing it requires the use of questioning. But questions are only effective if you and the client have a good relationship and are working together.

ENCOURAGING, PARAPHRASING, AND SUMMARIZING

Skills of Active Listening

CHAPTER

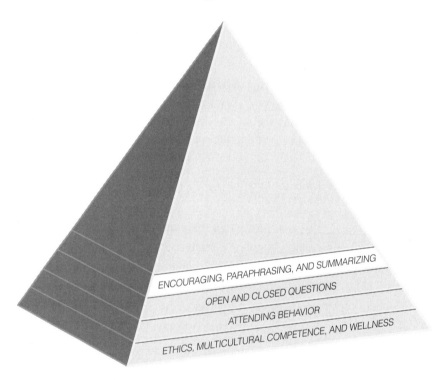

ENCOURAGING, PARAPHRASING, AND SUMMARIZING

OPEN AND CLOSED QUESTIONS

ATTENDING BEHAVIOR

ETHICS, MULTICULTURAL COMPETENCE, AND WELLNESS

How can these active listening skills help you and your clients?

CHAPTER GOALS

Clients need to know that the interviewer *hears* what they say, sees their point of view, and *feels* their world as they experience it. Encouragers and restatements, paraphrases, and summarizations are basic to empathy and helping a client feel understood. When clients feel their story is heard, they open up and become more ready for change.

Awareness, knowledge, and skills developed through the concepts of this chapter will enable you to

- ▲ Help clients talk in more detail about their issues of concern. In addition, you can stop the overly talkative client from repeating the same facts.
- ▲ Clarify for the client and you, the interviewer, what is really being said during the session.
- ▲ Check on the accuracy of what you hear by saying back to clients the essence of their comments.

MODULE 5.1
DEFINING ACTIVE LISTENING

KEY CONCEPT QUESTION

▲ What is active listening?

Active listening requires actions and decisions on our part. What we listen to (selective attention) will have a profound influence on how clients talk about their concerns. When a client comes in full of information and talks rapidly, we can find ourselves confused and even overwhelmed by the complexity of the story. You need to pay very close attention to hear this type of client accurately.

JENNIFER: (enters the room and starts talking immediately) I really need to talk to you. I don't know where to start. I just got my last exam back and it was a disaster, maybe because I haven't studied much lately. I was up late drinking at a party last night and I almost passed out. I've been sort of going out with a guy for the last month, but that's over as of last night. . . . (pause) But what really bothers me is that my mom and dad called last Monday and they are going to separate. I know that they have fought a lot, but I never thought it would come to this. I'm thinking of going home, but I'm afraid to. . . .

> Jennifer continues for another three minutes in much the same vein, repeating herself somewhat, and seems close to tears. The data are coming so fast that it is hard to follow her. Finally she stops and looks at you expectantly.
>
> Imagine you are listening to Jennifer's detailed and emotional story. What are you thinking about her at this moment? Using the ideas of active listening, write what you could say and do to help her feel that you understand her and empathize? Compare your ideas with ours, below.

If our work was personal counseling, we would most likely focus on the separation of Jennifer's parents and restate and paraphrase some of her key ideas, helping her focus on what may be the most central issue—Mom and Dad are separating. By doing this, we are likely to help her focus on one key issue before turning to the others. On the other hand, if we were academic counselors, not engaging in personal issues, we'd likely selectively attend to the study issues (the area of our expertise) and refer Jennifer to an outside source for personal counseling.

Another possibility would be to summarize the essence of Jennifer's several points and say them back to her. Use the check-out (e.g., "Have I heard you correctly?") to see how close you are to what she thinks and feels. Follow by asking her, "You've talked about many things. Where would *you* like to start today?"

How do our thoughts in the preceding paragraphs compare to what you would do?

Active listening demands that you participate fully in the interview by encouraging, paraphrasing, or summarizing and helping clients enlarge and enrich their stories. Active listening demands serious attention to empathy. You seek to "walk in the client's shoes" and hear small changes in thoughts, feelings, and behaviors. All this will enable you to enter the client's world and worldview more completely.

Encouraging, paraphrasing, and summarizing are basic to empathic understanding and enable you to communicate to clients that they have been heard.

Using empathic listening skills, you do not mix your own ideas with what the client has been saying. You say back to clients what you have heard, using their key words. You help clients by distilling, shortening, and clarifying what has been said. Accurate empathic listening is not as common nor as easy as it may sound, but its impact is often profound.

Encouraging	*Predicted Result*
Encourage with short responses that help clients keep talking. They may be verbal (repeating key words and short statements) or nonverbal (head nods and smiling).	Clients elaborate on the topic, particularly when encouragers and restatements are used in a questioning tone of voice.
Paraphrasing	*Predicted Result*
Shorten, clarify the essence of what has just been said, but be sure to use the client's main words when you paraphrase. Para-phrases are often fed back to the client in a questioning tone of voice.	Clients will feel heard. They tend to give more detail without repeating the exact same story. If a paraphrase is inaccurate, the client has an opportunity to correct the interviewer.
Summarizing	*Predicted Result*
Summarize client comments and integrate thoughts, emotions, and behaviors. Sum-marizing is similar to paraphrasing but used over a longer time span.	Clients will feel heard and often learn how the many parts of important stories are integrated. The summary tends to facilitate a more centered and focused dis-cussion. The summary also provides a more coherent transition from one topic to the next or as a way to begin and end a full session.

EXERCISE

Ask your friend or family member to tell you a story (e.g., a conflict, a positive experience, a current challenge). Simply sit and listen to what is said, perhaps asking a few questions to enrich and enlarge the story. Say back, as accurately as possible, what you have heard. Ask your friend how accurate your summary was and how it felt to be listened to. Write your observations and the other person's reactions.

△ **MODULE 5.1**

SUMMARY

▲ Listening is active; and how you selectively attend to clients impacts how they tell their stories or discuss their concerns.
▲ Empathy means to experience the client's world and to see things as the client does without mixing in your own thoughts and feelings. "Walk in the other person's shoes."
▲ Encouraging, paraphrasing, and summarizing are key active listening skills that keep the client talking.

BOX 5-1   Listening Skills and Children

Using the listening and observing skills with children is just as important as using them with adults. Children too often go through life being told what to do. If we listen to them and their singular constructions of the world, we can reinforce their unique qualities and help them develop belief in themselves and their own value. Here are a few key comments on the listening skills and children:

Attending	Talk to children at their level whenever possible; avoid looking down at them. This may mean sitting on the floor or in small chairs. Be prepared for more topic jumps with children; use attending skills to bring them back to critical issues. They may need to expend excess energy by doing something with their hands; allow them to draw or play with clay as they talk to you.
Questions and Concreteness	Seek to get the child's perspective, not yours. Children may have difficulty with a general open question, such as "Could you tell me what happened?" Use short sentences, simple words, and a concrete language style. Break down abstract questions into concrete and situational language using a mix of closed and open questions: "Where were you when the fight occurred?" "What was going on just before the fight?" "Then what happened?" "How did he feel?" "Was she angry?" "What happened next?" "What happened afterward?" In questioning children on touchy issues, be especially careful of closed, leading questions.
Encouraging, Paraphrasing, and Summarizing	These three skills, coupled with good attending and questioning, help children tell their stories. Effective elementary teachers consistently use these skills, especially paraphrasing and encouraging. Observe a competent teacher and identify these distinct microskills.
Other Issues	Provide an atmosphere that is suitable for children by using small chairs, interesting objects, and games. Warmth, humor, a smile, an active style, and an actual liking for children are essential. Under stress, children (and many adults) become confused; use names rather than pronouns.

MODULE 5.2
EXAMPLE INTERVIEW: They Are Teasing Me About My Shoes

KEY CONCEPT QUESTION

▲ How can the active listening skills be used with children?

All clients have an equal need to know they have been heard. Counseling children is much like counseling adolescents and adults. You will use the same microskills, but there tends to be more emphasis on encouraging, paraphrasing, and summarization skills. You will note that many effective elementary teachers constantly say back to students what they have just said. These skills reinforce the conversation and help the children keep talking from their own frame of reference. Telling your story to someone who hears you accurately is clarifying, comforting, and reassuring.

The following sample interview is an edited version of a videotaped interview conducted by Mary Bradford Ivey with Damaris, a child actor, role-playing the problem. Damaris is an 11-year-old sixth grader. The session below presents a child's problem, but all of us, regardless of age, have experienced nasty teasing and put-downs, often in our closest relationships. Mary first draws out the child's story about teasing and then Damaris's thoughts and feelings about the teasing. Mary follows with a focus on the child's strengths, an example of the wellness approach.

Mary uses many encouragers and restatements. A review of the entire video transcript reveals nine minimal encouragers ("oh . . . ," "uh, huh," and single word utterances), three positive encouragers ("that's great," "nice"), four additional brief restatements, and numerous smiles and head nods. Children demand constant involvement, and showing your interest and good humor is even more essential with them. Active listening is especially important with children, as they tend to respond more briefly than adults.

Interviewer and Client Conversation	Process Comments
1. *Mary:* Damaris, how're you doing?	The relationship between Mary and Damaris is already established; they know each other through school activities.
2. *Damaris:* Good.	She smiles and sits down.
3. *Mary:* I'm glad you could come down. You can use these markers if you want to doodle or draw something while we're talking. I know—you sort of indicated that you wanted to talk to me a little bit.	Mary welcomes the child and offers her something to do with her hands. Many children get restless just talking. Damaris starts to draw almost immediately. You may do better with an active male teen by taking him to the basketball court while you discuss issues. It can also help to have things available for adults to do with their hands.
4. *Damaris:* In school, in my class, there's this group of girls that keep making fun of my shoes, just 'cause I don't have Nikes.	Damaris looks down and appears a bit sad. She stops drawing. Children, particularly the "have-nots," are well aware of their economic circumstances. Some children have used sneakers; Damaris, at least, has newer sneakers.
5. *Mary:* They "keep making fun of your shoes"?	Encourage in the form of a restatement using Damaris's exact key words.
6. *Damaris:* Well, they're not the best; I mean—they're not Nikes, like everyone else has.	Damaris has a slight angry tone mixed with her sadness. She starts to draw again.
7. *Mary:* Yeah, they're nice shoes, though. You know?	It is sometimes tempting to comfort clients rather than just listen. Mary offers reassurance; a simple "uh-huh" would have been more effective. However, reassurance later in the interview may be a very important intervention.
8. *Damaris:* Yeah. But my family's not that rich, you know. Those girls are rich.	Clients, especially children, hesitate to contradict the counselor. Notice that Damaris says, "But. . . ." When clients say, "Yes, but . . . ," interviewers are off track and need to change their style.

Interviewer and Client Conversation	Process Comments
9. *Mary:* I see. And the others can afford Nike shoes, and you have nice shoes, but your shoes are just not like the shoes the others have, and they tease you about it?	Mary backs off her reassurances and paraphrases the essence of what Damaris has been saying using her key words.
10. *Damaris:* Yeah. . . . Well, sometimes they make fun of me and call me names, and I feel sad. I try to ignore them, but still, the feeling inside me just hurts.	If you paraphrase or summarize accurately, a client will usually respond with *yeah* or *yes* and continue to elaborate the story.
11. *Mary:* It makes you feel hurt inside that they should tease you about shoes.	Mary reflects Damaris's feelings. The reflection of feeling is close to a paraphrase and is elaborated in the following chapter.
12. *Damaris:* Mmm-hmm. (pause) It's not fair.	Damaris thinks about Mary's statement and looks up expectantly as if to see what happens next. She thinks back on the basic unfairness of the whole situation.
13. *Mary:* So far, Damaris, I've heard how the kids tease you about not having Nikes and that it really hurts. It's not fair. You know, I think of you, though, and I think of all the things that you do well. I get . . . you know . . . it makes me sad to hear this part because I think of all the talents you have, and all the things that you like to do and—and the strengths that you have.	Mary's brief summary covers most of the important points and Mary also discloses some of her own feelings. Sparingly used self-disclosure can be helpful. Mary begins the positive asset search by reminding Damaris that she has strengths to draw from.
14. *Damaris:* Right. Yeah.	Damaris smiles slightly and relaxes a bit.
15. *Mary:* What comes to mind when you think about all the positive things you are and have to offer?	An open question encourages Damaris to think about her strengths and positives.
16. *Damaris:* Well, in school, the teacher says I'm a good writer, and I want to be a journalist when I grow up. The teacher wants me to put the last story I wrote in the school paper.	Damaris talks a bit more rapidly and smiles.
17. *Mary:* You want to be a journalist, 'cause you can write well? Wow!	Mary enthusiastically paraphrases positive comments using Damaris's own key words.
18. *Damaris:* Mmm-hmm. And I play soccer on our team. I'm one of the people that plays a lot, so I'm like the leader, almost, but . . . (Damaris stops in mid-sentence.)	Damaris has many things to feel good about; she is smiling for the first time in the session.

Interviewer and Client Conversation	Process Comments
19. *Mary:* So, you are a scholar, a leader, and an athlete. Other people look up to you. Is that right? So how does it feel when you're a leader in soccer?	Mary has added *scholar* and *athlete* for clarification and elaboration of the positive asset search. She knows from observation on the playground that other children do look up to Damaris. Counselors may add related words to expand the meaning. Mary wisely avoids leading Damaris and uses the checkout, "Is that right?" Mary also asks an open question about feelings. And we note that Damaris used that important word "but." Do you think that Mary should have followed up on that or should she continue with her search for strengths?
20. *Damaris:* (small giggle, looking down briefly) Yeah. It feels good.	Looking down is not always sadness! The spontaneous movement of looking down briefly is termed the "recognition response." It most often happens when clients learn something new and true about themselves. Damaris has internalized the good feelings.
21. *Mary:* So you're a good student and you are good at soccer and a leader, and it makes you feel good inside.	Mary summarizes the positive asset search using both facts and feelings. The summary of feeling *good inside* contrasts with the earlier feelings of *hurt inside*.
24. *Damaris:* Yeah, it makes me feel good inside. I do my homework and everything (pause and the sad look returns), but then when I come to school, they just have to spoil it for me.	Again, Damaris agrees with the paraphrase. She feels support from Mary and is now prepared to deal from a stronger position with the teasing. Here we see what lies behind the "but" in 18 above. We believe Mary did the right thing in ignoring the "but" the first time. Now it is obvious that the negative feelings need to be addressed. When Damaris's wellness strengths are clear, Mary can better address those negative feelings.
25. *Mary:* They just spoil it. So you've got these good feelings inside, good that you're strong in academics, good that you're, you know, good at soccer and a leader. Now, I'm just wondering how we can use those good feelings that you feel as a student who's going to be a journalist someday and a soccer player who's a leader. Now the big question is how you can take the good, strong feelings and deal with the kids who are teasing. Let's look at ways to solve your problem now.	Mary restates Damaris's last words and again summarizes the many good things that Damaris does well. Mary changes pace and is ready to move to the problem-solving portion of the interview.

BOX 5-2   Accumulative Stress: When Do "Small" Events Become Traumatic?

At one level, being teased about the shoes one wears doesn't sound all that serious—children will be children! However, some poor children are teased and laughed at throughout their life for the clothes they wear. At a high school reunion, Allen talked with a classmate who recalled painful memories, still immediate, of teasing and bullying during school days. Later life did not get much better for her partially because of the difficult time in school.

Small slights become big hurts if repeated again and again. Athletes and "popular" students may talk arrogantly and dismissively about the "nerds," "townies," "hicks," or other out-group. Teachers, coaches, and even counselors sometimes join in the laughter. Over time, these slights mount inside the child or adolescent. Some people internalize their issues in psychological distress; others may act them out in a dramatic fashion—witness the shootings at Columbine High School in Colorado and at other schools throughout the country.

Discrimination and prejudice are other examples of accumulative stress and trauma. One of Mary's interns, a young African American woman, spoke of a recent racial insult. At a restaurant she overheard two White people talking loudly about the "good old days" of segregation. Perhaps the remark was not directed at her, but still, it hurt. She related how common racial insults were in her life, directly or indirectly. She could tell how bad things were racially by the size of her phone bill. When an incident occurred that troubled

her, she needed to talk to her sister or parents and seek support. Out of continuing indignities can come feelings of underlying insecurity about one's place in the world (internalized oppression and self-blame) and/or tension and rage about unfairness (externalized awareness of oppression). Either way, the person who is ignored or insulted feels tension in the body, the pulse, and heart rate increase, and—over time—hypertension and high blood pressure may result. The psychological becomes physical and accumulative stress becomes traumatic.

Soldiers at war, women who suffer sexual harassment, those who are short or overweight, the physically disfigured through birth or accident, gays and lesbians, and many others are all at risk for accumulative stress building to real trauma or posttraumatic stress.

Be alert for signs of accumulative stress in your clients. Are they internalizing the stressors by blaming themselves? Or are they externalizing and building a pattern of explosive rage and anger? All these people have important stories to tell and at first, these stories may sound routine. The occurrence of posttraumatic stress responses in later life may be alleviated or prevented by your careful listening and support.

Finally, social work's position on social justice is that the interviewer has the responsibility to act and intervene, where possible, to combat oppression and injustice. The counseling and psychology position on social action is not as clear. Where do you stand?

Mary had a good relationship and was able to draw out Damaris's story fairly quickly. She moved to positive assets and wellness strengths that make it easier to address client problems and challenges.

Using these same skills with an adult, you could expect to follow a similar interviewing structure. However, most adults will provide longer verbal responses. And you would usually not need to use as many verbal and nonverbal encouragers.

Informed Consent and Working With Children

When you work with children, the ethical issues around informed consent become especially important. Depending on state laws and practices, it is often necessary to obtain written parental permission before interviewing a child or before sharing information about the interview with others. The child and family should know exactly how the information is to be shared, and interviewing records should be available to them for their comments and evaluation. An important part of informed consent is stating that both child and parents have the right to withdraw their permission at any point.

▲ **MODULE 5.2**
SUMMARY

▲ Children, adolescents, and some adults will be more comfortable if you provide something for them to do with their hands. Avoid towering over small children; sit at their level. Avoid abstractions, use short sentences and simple words, and focus on concrete, observable issues and behaviors.

▲ Note that the case demonstrates effective verbal attending through encouraging, paraphrasing, and summarizing, which help the client explore the issues more effectively. Effective questions are used to bring in new data, organize the discussion, and point out positive strengths.

▲ When you conduct a practice interview, particularly with a child, follow all pertinent informed consent guidelines (Chapter 2).

MODULE 5.3

INSTRUCTIONAL READING: The Active Listening Skills of Encouraging, Paraphrasing, and Summarizing

KEY CONCEPT QUESTIONS

▲ **How do we define the skills of encouraging, paraphrasing, and summarizing, and how do they relate to active listening?**

▲ **What is the relationship between active listening and diversity issues in the interview?**

Encouraging, paraphrasing, and summarizing help the client clarify issues and move into deeper exploration of concerns. These skills help you make sure that you accurately hear what the client is saying. A proficient demonstration of active listening skills requires you to listen intently, with a nonjudgmental attitude, and clarify what clients have to say.

A real challenge for most interviewers is to remain nonjudgmental and accepting as we listen to clients, particularly when our internal beliefs and values disagree with them. It is all too easy for interviewer behavior to convey judgment and negative attitudes. Moreover, a *nonjudgmental attitude* is key to all interviewing, counseling, and psychotherapy. Listen to clients without evaluating them, either as "good" or "bad." Simply try to hear and accept what they say. You convey your ability to be both neutral and supportive with eye contact (visuals), vocal quality, verbal tracking, and body language (3 Vs + B).

Social justice ethics (Chapter 2) and the multicultural movement suggest that interviewers and counselors need to speak up and make judgments. For example, if a woman denies obvious abuse, the interviewer may have to decide to make a report. If a person has been racially or sexually harassed and blames herself or himself for the problem, again the counselor must do more than pure listening. When a client shows clear racism, sexism, anti-Semitism, or other oppressive thinking in the interview, the interviewer is faced with a challenge. There is an increasing move in the field toward interviewer responsibility to instruct clients who may need to learn more tolerance and respect. What are you going to do when faced with these challenges?

Encouraging

Encouragers are a variety of verbal and nonverbal expressions the counselor or therapist can use to prompt clients to continue talking. Encouragers are minimal verbal utterances ("Ummm"and"Uh-huh"), head nods, open-handed gestures, and positive facial expressions that encourage the client to keep talking. Silence, accompanied by appropriate nonverbal communication, can be another type of encourager. These encouragers are not meant to direct client talk; rather, they simply encourage clients to keep talking.

Repetition of key words can encourage a client and has more influence on the direction of client talk. Consider the following client statement:

> "And then it happened again. The grocery store clerk gave me a dirty look and I got angry. It reminded me of my last job, where I had so much trouble getting along. Why are they always after me?"

The counselor could use a variety of short encouragers in a questioning tone of voice ("Angry?" "Last job?" "Trouble getting along?" "After you?"), and in each case the client would likely talk about a different topic. These short encouragers are a form of interviewer selective attention and direct the interview much more than casual observation would suggest. It is important that you note your selection of single-word encouraging responses; you may direct clients more than you think.

A *restatement* is another type of extended encourager in which the counselor or interviewer repeats short statements, two or more words *exactly* as used by the client. "The clerk gave you a dirty look." "You got angry." "You had trouble getting along in your last job." "You wonder why they are always after you."Restatements can be used with a questioning tone of voice; they then function much like the single-word encourager. Like short encouragers, different types of restatements lead the client in different directions.

Well-timed encouragers maintain flow and continually communicate to the client that you are listening. Some have observed that use of too many encouragers can seem wooden and unexpressive, and too few encouragers may suggest to clients that you are not interested. Single-word encouragers often facilitate client talk toward deeper meanings. All types of encouragers facilitate client talk unless they are overused or used badly. Excessive head nodding or gestures and too much parroting can annoy and frustrate some clients.

EXERCISE

Reread the paragraphs above; say the suggested encouragers and restatements aloud. Use different vocal tones and note how your verbal style can facilitate others' talking or stop them cold.

Paraphrasing

At first glance, paraphrasing appears to be a simple skill, only slightly more complex than encouraging. In restatement and encouraging, exact words and phrases are fed back to the client. Paraphrasing covers more of what the client has just said, usually several sentences. Paraphrasing continues to feed back key words and phases, but catches and distills the essence of what the client has just said. Paraphrase clarifies a confusing client story.

The tone of your voice and your body language, when you paraphrase, indicate to the client whether you are interested in listening in more depth or you wish for the client to move on to another topic. Accurate paraphrasing will help the client stop repeating a story unnecessarily. Some clients have complex problems that no one has ever bothered to hear accurately, and they literally need to tell their story over and over until someone indicates they have been heard clearly. If you are able to give an accurate paraphrase to a client, you are likely to be rewarded with a "That's right" or "Yes . . . ," and the client will go on to explore the issue in more depth. Once clients know they have been heard, they are often able to move on to new topics. The goal of paraphrasing is the facilitation of client exploration and the clarification of issues.

How do you paraphrase? Observe the client, hear the client's important words, and use them in your paraphrase much as the client does. You may use your own words, but the main ideas and concepts must reflect the client's view of the world, not yours!

An accurate paraphrase, then, usually consists of four dimensions:

1. A *sentence stem* sometimes using the client's name. Names help personalize the session. Examples are: "Damaris, I hear you saying . . . ," "Luciano, sounds like . . . ," "Looks like the situation is. . . ." A stem is not always necessary and, if overused, can make your comments seem like parroting. Clients have been known to say in frustration, "That's what I just said; why do you ask?"
2. The *key words* used by the client to describe the situation or person. Include main ideas and exact words that come from clients. This aspect of the para-phrase is sometimes confused with the encouraging restatement. A restatement, however, covers a very limited amount of client talk and is almost entirely in the client's own words.
3. The *essence of what the client has said* in briefer and clearer form. Identify, clarify, and feed back the client's sometimes confused or lengthy talk into succinct and meaningful statements. The counselor has the difficult task of staying true to the client's ideas but not repeating them exactly.
4. A *check-out* for accuracy. The check-out is a brief question at the end of the par-aphrase, the summary, reflection of feelings, the interpretation/reframe, or other microskills. Here you ask the client for feedback on whether the paraphrase (or other skill) was correct and useful. Some example check-outs include "Am I hearing you correctly?" "Is that close?" "Have I got it right?" It is also possible to paraphrase with an implied check-out by raising your voice at the end of the sentence as if the paraphrase were a question.

The example below shows a brief client statement followed by key word encouragers, restatements, and a paraphrase that could be selected by an interviewer to encourage client talk.

> "I'm really concerned about my wife. She has this feeling that she has to get out of the house, see the world, and get a job. I'm the breadwinner and I think I have a good income. The children view Yolanda as a perfect mother, and I do too. But last night, we really saw the problem differently and had a terrible argument."

- ▲ Key-word encouragers: "Breadwinner?" "Terrible argument?" "Perfect mother?"
- ▲ Restatement encouragers: "You're really concerned about your wife." "You see yourself as the breadwinner." "You had a terrible argument."
- ▲ Paraphrase: "You're concerned about your picture-perfect wife who wants to work even though you have a good income, and you've had a terrible argument. Is that how you see it?"

The key-word encourager, the restatement, and the paraphrase are all different points on a continuum. In every case the goal is hearing the client and feeding back what has been said. Both short paraphrases and longer key-word encouragers will resemble restatements. A long paraphrase is close to a summary. All can be helpful in an interview; or they can be overdone.

Summarizing

Summarizing falls along the same continuum as the key-word encourager, restatement, and paraphrase. Summarizing, however, encompasses an even longer period of conversation than paraphrasing; at times it may cover an entire interview or even issues discussed by the client over several interviews.

In summarizing, the interviewer attends to verbal and nonverbal comments from the client over a period of time and selectively attends to key concepts and dimensions, restating them for the client as accurately as possible. A check-out at the end for accuracy is an important part of the summarizing. See the following examples:

To begin a session: "Let's see, last time we talked about your feelings toward your mother-in-law, and we discussed the argument you had with her when the new baby arrived. You saw yourself as guilty and anxious. Since then you haven't gotten along too well. We also discussed a plan of action for the week. How did that go?"

Midway in the interview: "So far, I've seen that you felt guilty again when you saw the action plan as manipulative. Yet one idea did work. You were able to talk with your mother-in-law about her garden, and it was the first time you had been able to talk about anything without an argument. You visualize the possibility of following up on the plan next week. Is that about it?"

At the end of the session: "In this interview we've reviewed more detail about your feelings toward your mother-in-law. Some of the following things seem to stand out: First, our plan didn't work completely, but you were able to talk about one thing without yelling. As we talked, we identified some behaviors on your part that could be changed. They include better eye contact, relaxing more, and changing the topic when you start to see yourself getting angry. Does that sum it up?"

BOX 5-3   National and International Perspectives on Counseling Skills

 Developing Skills to Help the Bilingual Client
AZARA SANTIAGO-RIVERA

It wasn't that long ago that counselors considered bilingualism a "disadvantage." We now know that a new perspective is needed. Let's start with two important assumptions: *the person who speaks two languages is able to work and communicate in two cultures and, actually, is advantaged. The monolingual person is the one at a disadvantage!* Research actually shows that bilingual children have more fully developed capacities and a broader intelligence (Power & Lopez, 1985).

If your client was raised in a Spanish-speaking home, for example, he or she is likely to think in Spanish at times, even though having considerable English skills. We tend to experience the world nonverbally before we add words to describe what we see, feel, or hear. For example, Salvadorans who experience war or other forms of oppression *felt* that situation in their own language.

You are very likely to work with clients in your community who come from one or more language backgrounds. Your first task is to understand some of the history and experience of these immigrant groups. Then, we suggest that you learn some key words and phrases in their original language. Why? Experiences that occur in a particular language are typically encoded in memory in that language. So certain memories containing powerful emotions may not be accessible in a person's second language (English) because they were originally encoded in the first language (for example, Spanish). And if the client is talking about something that was experienced in Spanish, Khmer, or Russian, the *key words* are not English; they are in the original language.

Here is an example of how you might use these ideas in the session:

Social worker:	Could you tell me what happened for you when you lost your job?
Maria (Spanish-speaking client):	It was hard; I really don't know what to say.
Social worker:	It might help us if you would say what happened in Spanish and then you could translate it for me.
Maria:	*Es tan injusto! Yo pensé que perdi el trabajo porque no hablo el ingles muy bien. Me da mucho coraje cuando me hacen esto. Me siento herido.*
Social worker:	Thanks; I can see that it really affected you. Could you tell me what you said now in English?
Maria:	(more emotionally) I said, "It all seemed so unfair. I thought I lost my job because I couldn't speak

Diversity and Active Listening

Periodic encouraging, paraphrasing, and summarizing are basic skills that seem to have wide cross-cultural acceptance. Virtually all your clients like to be listened to accurately. It may take more time to establish a relationship with a client who is culturally different from you.

North American and European counseling theory and style generally expect the client to get at the problem immediately and may not allow enough emphasis on relationship building. Some traditional Native American Indians, Dene, Pacific Islanders, Aboriginal Australians, and New Zealand Maori may want to spend a full interview getting to know and trust you before you begin.

Building trust requires visiting the other person's world from time to time. Actively involving yourself in positive community activities will be noticed. If you are seen enjoying yourself in a natural way in the village, the community, and at pow-wows

BOX 5-3   (Continued)

	English well enough for them. It makes me really angry when they do that to me. It hurts."
Social worker:	I understand better now. Thanks for sharing that in your own language. I hear you saying that *injusto* hurts and you are very angry. Let's continue to work on this and, from time to time, let's have you talk about the really important things in Spanish, OK?

The above brief example provides a start. The next step is to develop a vocabulary of key words in the language of your client. This cannot happen all at once, but you can gradually increase your skills. Here are some Spanish key words that might be useful with many clients:

Respecto:	Was the client treated with respect? For example, the social worker might say, "Your employer failed to give you *respecto*."
Familismo:	Family is very important to many Spanish-speaking people. You might say, "How are things with your *familia?*"

Emotions (see next chapter) are often experienced in the original language. When reflecting feeling, you could learn and use these key words with clients:

Aguantar: endure	*Miedo:* fear
Amor: love	*Orgullo:* proud
Carino: like	*Sentir:* feel
Coraje: anger	

We also recommend learning key sayings, metaphors, and proverbs in the language(s) of your community. *Dichos* are Spanish proverbs, like the following examples:

Al que mucho se le da, mucho se le demanda.	The more people give you, the greater the expectations of you.
Vale mas tarde que nunca.	Better late than never.
No hay peor sordo que el no quiere oir.	There is no worse deaf person than someone who doesn't want to listen.
En la unión está la fuerza.	Strength is found in unity.

Consider developing a list like this, learn to pronounce them correctly, and you will find them useful in counseling Spanish-speaking clients. Indeed, you are giving them *respecto*. You may wish to learn key words in several languages.

---

or other cultural celebrations, this will be helpful in trust building. The same holds true for a Person of Color. It will be helpful for you to visit a synagogue or all White church, understand the political/power structure of a community, and view White people as a distinct cultural group with many variations. Each of these activities may help you to avoid stereotyping those who are culturally different from you. And keep in mind the multiple dimensions of the RESPECTFUL model—virtually all interviewing and counseling are cross-cultural in some fashion.

When you are culturally different from your client, self-disclosure and an explanation of your methods may be helpful. For example, if you use only questioning and listening skills, the client may view you as suspicious and untrustworthy. The client may want directions and suggestions for action. A young adolescent may expect reaction from you before he or she has even finished the story.

A general recommendation for working cross-culturally is to discuss differences early in the interview. For example, "I'm a White European American and we may need to discuss whether this is an issue for you. And if I miss something, please let me know." "I know that some gay people may distrust heterosexuals. Please let me know if anything bothers you." "Some White people may have issues talking with an African American counselor. If that's a concern, let's talk about it up front." "You are 57 and I (the counselor) am 26. How comfortable are you working with someone my age?" There are no absolute rules here for what is right. However, a highly acculturated Jamaican, Native American Indian, or Asian American might be offended by the same statements.

Some Asian (Cambodian, Chinese, Japanese, Indian) clients from traditional backgrounds may be seeking direction and advice. They are likely to be willing to share their stories, but you may need to tell them why you want to wait a bit before coming up with answers. To establish credibility, there may be times when you have to commit yourself and provide advice earlier than you wish. If this becomes necessary, be assured and confident; just let them know you want to learn more, and that the advice may change as you get to know them better.

It is important to consider differences in gender. Even though there are many exceptions to this "rule," women tend to use more paraphrasing and related listening skills; men tend to use questions more frequently. You may notice in your own classes and workshops that men tend to raise their hands faster at the first question and interrupt more often.

▲ **MODULE 5.3**
SUMMARY

- ▲ Encouragers help clients elaborate their stories and include exact words they spoke, uh-huh's, smiles, a warm style, and short comments.
- ▲ The restatement is a form of encourager, but repeats key words or short phrases back to the client.
- ▲ The paraphrase includes (1) a sentence stem, often with the client's name; (2) key words used by the client; (3) the essence of what a client has said in briefer and clarified form; and (4) a check-out for accuracy. The accurate paraphrase will catch the essence of and clarify what the client says. The paraphrase is similar to the restatement but covers more client interview time.
- ▲ The summary covers a longer period of the interview. It is also often used to begin or end a session or repeat back to the client what was said in the last session(s).
- ▲ Trust is critical when working with clients, particularly those who may be culturally different from you. The same active listening skills are required, but more participation and self-disclosure on your part may be necessary. Trust building occurs when you visit the client's community and learn about cultures different from your own. But best of all is having a varied multicultural group of friends.

OBSERVING AND REFLECTING FEELINGS

A Foundation of Client Experiencing

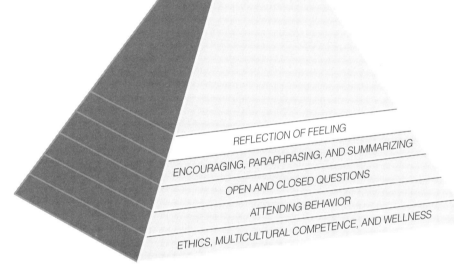

REFLECTION OF FEELING

ENCOURAGING, PARAPHRASING, AND SUMMARIZING

OPEN AND CLOSED QUESTIONS

ATTENDING BEHAVIOR

ETHICS, MULTICULTURAL COMPETENCE, AND WELLNESS

How can observing and reflection of feeling help you and your clients?

CHAPTER GOALS

Feelings and emotions are underneath the words, thoughts, and behaviors of all people. The purpose of reflection of feeling is to make these implicit, sometimes hidden, emotions explicit and clear. Becoming proficient at reflection of feelings is essential to being fully with the client.

Awareness, knowledge, and skills developed through the concepts of this chapter will enable you to

- ▲ Bring out the richness of the client's emotional world.
- ▲ Note that most clients have mixed feelings toward significant others or events.
- ▲ Help clients sort through complex feelings and thoughts.
- ▲ Focus the counselor and client in the basic experience of deeper feelings and goals.

MODULE 6.1
DEFINING REFLECTION OF FEELING

KEY CONCEPT QUESTIONS

▲ **How is reflection of feeling defined?**

▲ **How are reflection of feeling and paraphrasing skills similar and how are they different?**

Reflection of Feeling	*Predicted Result*
Identify the key emotions of a client and feed them back to clarify affective experience. With some clients, the brief acknowledgment of feeling may be more appropriate. Often combined with paraphrasing and summarizing.	Clients experience and understand their emotional state more fully and talk in more depth about feelings. They may correct the interviewer's reflection with a more accurate descriptor.

Paraphrasing feeds back to the client the key points of what has just been said. Reflection of feeling involves observing emotions, naming them, and repeating them back to the client. Paraphrasing and reflection of feeling are closely related and will often be found together in the same statement. The important distinction is emphasis on content (paraphrase) and emotion (reflection of feeling). Note the content and the feelings expressed by Thomas below:

THOMAS: My Dad drank a lot when I was growing up, but it didn't bother me so much until now. (pause) But I was just home and it *really hurts* to see what Dad's starting to do to my Mum—she's awful quiet, you know. (looks down with brows furrowed and tense) Why she takes so much, I don't figure out. (looks at you with a puzzled expression) But, like I was saying, Mum and I were sitting there one night drinking tea, and he came in, stumbled over the doorstep, and then he got angry. He started to hit my mother and I moved in and stopped him. I almost hit him myself, I was so *angry*. (Anger flashes in his eyes.) I *worry* about Mum. (A slight tinge of fear seems to mix with the anger in the eyes, and you notice that his body is tensing.)

EXERCISE

Paraphrase Thomas's main ideas, the content of his conversation; then focus on emotion and reflect his feelings. Use your intuition and note the main feeling words. Here are two possible sentence stems for your consideration:

Paraphrase: Thomas, I hear you saying . . .

Reflection of feeling: Thomas, sounds like you feel . . .

Paraphrasing focuses on the content and clarifies the essence of what the client is saying. The content from the case above includes the drinking history, Mum being quiet and taking it, and the difficult situation when the client was last home. The paraphrase indicates to Thomas that you hear what is said and encourages him to move the discussion further.

Paraphrase: Thomas, your father has been drinking a long time, and your Mum takes a lot. But now he's started to be violent, and you've been tempted to hit him yourself. Have I heard you right?

In this example, we are focusing on what is happening and seeking to understand the total situation. The key content issue is escalation of violence and the need to protect Thomas's Mum. It will not help the situation if Thomas becomes part of the violence. At this point, the issue is to listen and learn more about the situation; with a joint understanding, we can plan actions for the future. Later in the session, we can focus on emotion in depth and help him work through issues.

The first step in eliciting and reflecting feelings is to recognize the *key emotional words* expressed by the client. When you reviewed Thomas's case, you may have recorded *really hurts, angry,* and *worry.* You know with some certainty that the client has these feelings; they have been made explicit. The most basic reflections of feeling would be "It really hurt," "You felt angry," and "You are worried." These reflections of feelings use the client's exact main words.

Next the interviewer must observe the many *unspoken* feelings expressed by the client, even if the client is not fully aware of them. These unspoken or implicit feelings are often, but not always, expressed nonverbally. For example, Thomas looked down with brows furrowed and body tense (a likely indication of tension and confusion); anger and fear flashed in his eyes as he was talking about hitting his Dad.

Feelings are also layered, like an onion. Clients may talk about emotional tones such as confused, lost, or frustrated; or they may be direct and forthright with a single clear emotion. Further listening and reflection often reveal underlying complex and sometimes conflicting emotions. For example, maybe a client is frustrated with her or his partner. When the interviewer reflects that frustration, the client may talk about anger at lack of attention, being afraid of being alone if the relationship breaks up, and lingering deep caring for the partner. As counseling continues, you may discover that the partner is trying to control your client. When the client learns of this control he or she will most likely experience deep anger at the partner's controlling behavior. Should the relationship end, the client may experience feelings of relief and anticipation of better times. And during all this, the hurt will likely remain constant.

To acknowledge the client's emotions, combine the paraphrase with reflection of feelings by repeating the client's exact stated key feeling words. For example, "Thomas, you're *really hurting* right now," "You're *angry* because your Dad hit your Mum," "You're *worried* that your Dad's drinking is getting worse." Feeding back the feeling words may encourage more detail in the telling of the story.

After the story is told more completely through your listening, you may help the client sort through many and often conflicting emotions. There are obvious emotions here such as Thomas's anger and worry. In addition, the nonverbals and the complexity of the situation suggest that less obvious, implicit emotions are also present. There are many possibilities for reflecting implicit emotions that we observe. In each of the following we suggest a check-out so that the accuracy of your observations can be tested with the client. Here are three reflections of feeling for your consideration.

I hear your anger, but also now, you're *hurting* and almost *fearful* about the situation. Am I close to what you are feeling right now? (Explicit anger and accompanying implicit emotions are reflected followed by a check-out for accuracy, thus allowing Thomas to follow up with his own reactions.)

BOX 6-1   National and International Perspectives on Counseling Skills

Does He Have Any Feelings?
WEIJUN ZHANG

Illustration: A student from China comes in for counseling, referred by his American roommate. According to the roommate, the client quite often calls his wife's name out loud while dreaming, which usually wakes the others in the apartment, and he was seen several times doing nothing but gazing at his wife's picture. Throughout the session the client is quite cooperative in letting the counselor know all the facts concerning his marriage and why his wife is not able to join him. But each time the counselor tries to identify or elicit his feelings toward his wife, the client diverts these efforts by talking about something else. He remains perfectly polite and expressionless until the end of the session.

No sooner had the practicing counselor in my practicum class stopped the videotape machine, than I heard comments such as "inscrutable," and "He has no feelings!" escape from the mouths of my European American classmates. I do not blame them, for the Chinese student did behave strangely, judged from their frame of reference.

"How do you feel about this?" "What feelings are you experiencing when you think of this?" How many times have we heard questions such as these? The problem with these questions is that they stem from a European American counseling tradition, which is not always appropriate.

For example, in much of Asia, the cultural rationale is that the social order doesn't need extensive consideration of personal, inner feelings. We make sense of ourselves in terms of our society and the roles we are given within the society. In this light, in China, individual feelings are ordinarily seen as lacking social

significance. For thousands of years, our ancestors have stressed how one behaves in public, not how one feels inside. We do not believe that feelings have to be consistent with actions. Against such a cultural background, one might understand why the Chinese student was resistant when the counselor showed interest in his feelings and addressed that issue directly.

But I am not suggesting here that Asians are devoid of feelings or strong emotions. We are just not supposed to telegraph them as do people from the West. Indeed, if feelings are seen as an insignificant part of an individual and regarded as irrelevant in terms of social importance, why should one send out emotional messages to casual acquaintances or outsiders (the counselor being one of them)?

What is more, most Asian men still have traditional beliefs that showing affection toward one's wife while others are around, even verbally, is a sign of being a sissy, being unmanly, or weak. I can still vividly remember when my child was four years old, my wife and I once received some serious lecturing on parental influence and social morality from both our parents and grandparents, simply because our son reported to them that he saw "Dad give Mom a kiss." You can imagine how shocking it must be for most Chinese husbands, who do not dare even touch their wives' hands in public, to see on television that American presidential candidates display such intimacy with their spouses on the stage! But the other side of the coin is that not many Chinese husbands watch television sports programs while their wives are busy with household chores after a full day's work. They show their affection by sharing the housework!

You look very tense. Stopping your Dad from hitting your Mum brought out a lot of emotion—I see some anger, perhaps even a little fear. Am I right? (The focus here is on nonverbal expression, unspoken feelings. The check-out is particularly important.)

Your Dad has been drinking for many years. I hear many different feelings—anger, sadness, confusion—and I also hear that you care a lot about both your Mum and your Dad. Am I close to how you feel about what's been going on a long time? (This is a broader reflection of feeling that summarizes several explicit and implicit feelings and encourages the client to think more broadly.)

Which of the several *possibilities* suggested for a reflection of feeling is "right"? Any of them could be suitable, if you demonstrate empathy, good listening skills, and are intentionally attuned to your client. Generally, we recommend that you first focus on explicit feelings and use the client's actual emotional words. Later, you can explore the implicit, unspoken feelings.

▲ MODULE 6.1
SUMMARY

- ▲ Both paraphrasing and reflection of feeling feed back to clients what they have been experiencing.
- ▲ A paraphrase focuses on the verbal content of what the client says while reflection of feelings centers on both verbal and nonverbal emotional underpinnings.
- ▲ Unspoken feelings may be seen in client's nonverbal expression, may be heard in client's vocal tone, or may be implied from the language of the client.
- ▲ Feelings are layered like an onion. Words like frustration, mixed up, and confused represent conflicting emotions underneath surface words.

MODULE 6.2
THE LANGUAGE OF EMOTION

KEY CONCEPT QUESTION

▲ What is the vocabulary of emotion?

People are constantly expressing verbal and nonverbal emotions. General social conversation usually ignores feelings unless they are especially prominent. Prior to interviewing training, we tend to ignore or pay little attention to someone else's emotional experience; we may fail to observe what is happening before our eyes and ears.

EXERCISE

As a first step toward naming and understanding emotions, it is helpful to establish your own vocabulary of emotions. Focus on four basic feelings—*sad, mad, glad,* and *scared.* These four emotions are considered the primary emotions, and their commonality, in terms of facial expression and language, has been validated throughout the world in all cultures (Ekman, 2004). In the blanks below, brainstorm emotional words associated with each primary emotion. Think of related emotional words with different intensities. For example, *mad* might lead you to think of *annoyed, angry,* and *furious.* Try this exercise and then continue to brainstorm and build your vocabulary list of emotions.

Sad	*Mad*	*Glad*	*Scared*
_____	_____	_____	_____
_____	_____	_____	_____
_____	_____	_____	_____

Clients will often express emotions in unclear ways demonstrating mixed and conflicting emotions. This is where you can be especially helpful as they sort through these more complex feelings. Clients may experience caring, anger, and fear, and even more feelings all at once. A client going through a difficult separation or divorce may express feelings of love toward the partner at one moment and extreme anger the next. Words such as puzzled, sympathy, embarrassment, guilt, pride, jealousy, gratitude, admiration, indignation, and contempt are *social emotions* that come from primary emotions. How we deal with emotional experience, of course, depends very much on our learning history. Basic emotions appear to be universal across all cultures, but the social emotions appear to be learned from family members and our peers. They are made more complex by the multifaceted and challenging world that surrounds us.

You can be especially helpful to clients as they sort out social emotions. Think of how the word "guilt" combines anger toward oneself, sadness, and perhaps even some fear. The feeling of guilt has been learned through social interaction in the family and culture. You have the opportunity through active listening and reflection of feeling to aid the client in sorting through mixed emotions. You can enable clients to bring positive thoughts and a wellness attitude. This is particularly important when you work with clients who use negative thinking.

▲ MODULE 6.2
SUMMARY

▲ People constantly feel and express emotion. The proficient interviewer will hear explicit emotions, observe implicit emotions, and feed these emotions back to the client.

▲ Sad, mad, glad, and scared are *primary emotions* used as root words for building a vocabulary of emotion. They appear to be universal across cultures.

▲ *Social emotions* (embarrassment, guilt, pride) are modified and built on primary emotions. They are learned in family and cultural context.

MODULE 6.3
EXAMPLE INTERVIEW: My Mother Has Cancer

KEY CONCEPT QUESTION

▲ How is reflection of feeling integrated into the interview?

Difficult life situations bring us face to face with many emotions. Whether you are dealing with clients who experience physical illness, interpersonal conflict, alcohol or drug abuse, or challenges in the work or school setting, it is central that you learn the way they feel about the situation and themselves. The intentional interviewer or counselor is always alert to clients' expression of emotions and knows how to identify and clarify these emotions for them.

The discovery of cancer, AIDS, or other major physical illness brings with it an immense emotional load. Busy physicians and nurses may fail to deal with emotions in their patients or the family members of those who are ill. Illness can be a frightening experience, and family, friends, and neighbors may also have trouble dealing with it.

The following transcript illustrates reflection of feeling in action. This is the second session and Jennifer has just welcomed the client, Stephanie, into the room. They had a brief personal exchange of greetings, and it was clear, nonverbally, that the client was ready to start immediately.

Interviewer and Client Conversation	Process Comments
1. *Jennifer:* So, Stephanie, how are things going with your mother?	Jennifer knows what the main issue is likely to be, so she introduces it with her first open question.
2. *Stephanie:* Well, the tests came back and the last set looks pretty good. But, I'm upset. With cancer, you never can tell. It's hard . . . (pause)	Stephanie speaks quietly and as she talks, she talks in an even softer tone of voice. At the word "cancer," she looks down.
3. *Jennifer:* You're really upset and worried right now.	Jennifer uses the emotional word ("upset") used by the client, but adds the unspoken emotion of worry. With "right now," she brings the feelings to here-and-now immediacy. She did not use a check-out. Was that wise?
4. *Stephanie:* That's right. Since she had her first bout with cancer . . . (pause), I've been really concerned and worried. She just doesn't look as well as she used to, she needs a lot more rest. Colon cancer is so scary.	Often if you help clients name their unspoken feelings, they will verbally affirm or nod their head. Naming and acknowledging emotions helps clarify the total situation.
5. *Jennifer:* Scary?	Repeating the key emotional words used by clients often helps them elaborate in more depth.
6. *Stephanie:* Yes, I'm scared for her and for me. They say it can be genetic. She had Stage 2 cancer and we really have to watch things carefully.	Stephanie confirms the intentional prediction and elaborates on the scary feelings. She has a frightened and physically exhausted look on her face.
7. *Jennifer:* So, we've got two things here. You've just gone through your mother's operation, and that was scary. You said they got the entire tumor, but your Mom really had trouble with the anesthesia, and that was frightening. You had to do all the care giving and you felt pretty lonely and unsupported. And the possibility of inheriting the genes is pretty terrifying. Putting it all together, you feel overwhelmed. Is that the right word to use, overwhelmed?	Jennifer summarizes what has been said. She repeats key feelings. She uses a new word, *overwhelmed*, which comes from her observations of the total situation.
8. *Stephanie:* (immediately) Yes, I'm overwhelmed, I'm so tired, I'm scared, and I'm furious with myself. (pause) But I can't be angry; my mother needs me. It makes me feel guilty that I can't do more. (starts to sob)	Stephanie is now talking about her issues at the here-and-now level. Stephanie has not cried in the interview before, and she likely needs to allow herself to cry and let the emotions out. Caregivers often burn out and need care themselves.

Interviewer and Client Conversation	Process Comments
9. *Jennifer:* (sits silently for a moment) Stephanie, you've faced a lot and you've done it alone. Allow yourself to pay attention to you for a moment and experience the hurt. (As Stephanie cries, Jennifer comments.) Let it out . . . that's OK.	Stephanie has held it all in and needs to experience what she is feeling. If you are personally comfortable with emotional experience, this ventilation of feelings can be helpful. There will be a need to return to a discussion of Stephanie's situation from a less emotional frame of reference.
10. *Stephanie:* (continues to cry, but the sobbing lessens)	See Box 6-2 for ideas in helping clients deal with deeper emotional experience.
11. *Jennifer:* Stephanie, I really sense your hurt and aloneness. I admire your ability to feel—it shows that you care. Could you sit up now and take a breath?	The client sits up, the crying almost stops, and she looks cautiously at the interviewer. She wipes her nose and takes a deep breath. Jennifer did three things here: (a) She reflected Stephanie's here-and-now emotions; (b) she identified a positive asset and strength; and (c) she suggested that Stephanie take a breath. Conscious breathing often helps clients pull themselves together.
12. *Stephanie:* I'm OK. (pause)	She wipes her eyes and continues to breathe. She seems more relaxed now that she has let out some of her emotions. At this point, she can explore the situation more fully—both emotionally and content wise—as she moves toward decisions.

The major skill Jennifer used in this session was reflection of feelings, with a few questions to draw out emotions. Because human change and development are rooted in emotional experience, reflection of feelings is important in all theories of counseling and therapy. Humanistic counselors consider eliciting and reflecting feelings the central skill and strategy of interviewing.

You are most likely beginning your work and starting to discover the importance of reflecting feelings. It may take you some time before you are fully comfortable using this skill because it is seldom a part of daily communication. We suggest you start by first simply noting emotions and then acknowledging them through short reflections indicating that the emotions have been observed. As you gain confidence and skill, you will eventually decide the extent and place of emotional exploration in your helping repertoire.

Before moving further, it is important for you to reflect on yourself and your own personal style. How comfortable are you with emotional expression? If discussing feelings was not common in your past experience, you may have difficulty helping clients explore their issues in depth. Reflect on your own personal history and ability to deal with emotions as you learn how to reflect client feelings. The exercises throughout this text may help you gain greater access to your own experiential and emotional world.

When you practice reflection of feeling, attempt to use the skill as frequently as possible. In the early stages of mastery it is wise to combine the skill with questioning, encouraging, and paraphrasing as most people find it awkward to use a single skill by itself. You will achieve full mastery of a skill when you can conduct a long interview segment effectively by almost constantly using a single skill. The most effective interviewer or counselor—consciously or subconsciously—develops proficiency so that it makes relatively little difference which specific skill he or she is using. Effectiveness and competence do not necessarily depend on the particular skill, but on the art of effective use. Facilitate your general personal and professional development as an interviewer; become aware of and competent in each of the microskills and gradually integrate them naturally.

▲ **MODULE 6.3**
SUMMARY

- Because human change and development are rooted in emotional experience, reflection of feelings is important in all theories of counseling and therapy.
- Reflection of feelings clarifies the client's emotional state, leads clients in new directions, and results in new discoveries.
- It is important to identify positive qualities and emotions to help clients deal more effectively with negative emotions.
- In the case, Jennifer reflects the main emotional words actually used by the client. She also points out unspoken feelings and checks out with the client whether the identified feeling is accurate. For example, "Is that close to what you feel?"

BOX 6-2   Helping Clients Increase or Decrease Emotional Expressiveness

Observe nonverbals   Breath directly reflects emotional content. Rapid or frozen breath indicates a contact with intense emotion. Also note facial flushing, eye movement, body tension, and changes in vocal tone. Especially, note hesitations. At times you may also find apparent absence of emotion when discussing a difficult issue. This might be a clue that the client is avoiding dealing with feelings or that the expression of emotion is culturally inappropriate for this client.

You can pace clients and then lead them to more expression and awareness of affect. Many people get right to the edge of a feeling, and then back away with a joke, change of subject, or intellectual analysis. Some of the things you can do are the following:

Pace clients
- Say to the client that she looked as though she was close to something important. "Would you like to go back and try again?"
- Discuss some positive resource that the client has. This base can free the client to face the negative. You as counselor also represent a positive asset yourself.
- Consider asking questions. Used carefully, questions may help some clients explore emotions.
- Use here-and-now strategies, especially in the present tense: "What are you feeling right now—at this moment?" "What's occurring in your body as you talk about this?" Use the word *do* if you find yourself uncomfortable with emotion: "What do you feel?" or "What did you feel then?" starts to move the client away from here-and-now experiencing.

(Continued)

BOX 6-2 Helping Clients Increase or Decrease Emotional Expressiveness (Continued)

When tears, rage, despair, joy, or exhilaration occur	Your comfort level with your own emotional expression will affect how a client faces emotion. If you aren't comfortable with a particular emotion, your client will likely avoid it also and you may handle the issue less effectively. It is important to keep a balance between being very present with your own breathing and showing culturally appropriate and supportive eye contact but still allowing room for the client to sob, yell, or shake.

You can also use phrases such as these:

I'm here.
I've been there, too.
Let it out . . . that's OK.
These feelings are just right.
I hear you.
I see you.
Breathe with it.

Sometimes it is helpful to keep emotional expression within a fixed time; two minutes is a long time when you are crying. Afterward, helping the person reorient is important. Tools for reorienting the interview include these:

▲ Help the client use slowed, rhythmic breathing.

▲ Discuss the client's positive strengths.

▲ Discuss direct, empowering, self-protective steps that the client can take in response to the feelings expressed.

▲ Stand and walk or center the pelvis and torso in a seated position.

▲ Reframe the emotional experience in a positive way.

▲ Comment that it helps to tell the story many times.

Caution	As you work with emotion, there is the possibility of reawakening issues in a client who has a history of painful trauma. When you sense this possibility, decide with the client in advance and obtain permission for the desired depth of emotional experiencing. The beginning interviewer needs to seek supervision and/or refer the client to a more experienced professional.

This box is adapted from a presentation by Leslie Brain, a graduate student at the University of Massachusetts, Amherst.

MODULE 6.4

INSTRUCTIONAL READING: Becoming Aware of and Skilled With Emotional Experience

KEY CONCEPT QUESTIONS

▲ *Acknowledgement of feeling.* Do we always need to explore emotion in depth?

▲ *Techniques.* What specific verbal skills go with reflection of feeling?

▲ *Emotional complexity.* **What are mixed emotions and where might they come from?**

▲ *Observing emotional experience.* **How do we observe clients' feelings?**

▲ *Positive emotions.* **How can positive emotions help clients deal with challenging issues?**

▲ *Caution.* **What care should we use with reflection of feeling?**

At the most elementary level, the brief encounters we have with people throughout the day involve our emotions. Some are pleasant; others can be fraught with tension and conflict. The interaction may only be with a telemarketer desperate to make a sale, a hurried clerk in a store, or the police as they stop you for speeding. Feelings undergird these situations and more complex feelings underlie more intimate relationships with those close to us. Awareness of your own and others' feelings can help you move through the tensions of the day gracefully and may enable you to be helpful in many small ways.

Sometimes a simple, brief acknowledgment of feeling is just as helpful as a full reflection of feeling. In acknowledging feelings, you state the feeling briefly ("You seem to be sad about that" or "It makes you happy") and move on with the rest of the conversation. The same structure is used in an acknowledgment as in a full reflection, but there is much less emphasis and time given to feeling. Acknowledgment of feelings may be especially helpful with children, particularly when they are unaware of what they are feeling. Children also respond well to the classic reflection of feeling, "You feel (sad, mad, glad, scared) because. . . ."

A basic feeling we have toward our parents, family, and best friends is love and caring. This is a deep-seated emotion in most individuals. At the same time, over years of close contact, negative feelings about the same people may also appear. These negative feelings may be buried and overwhelm and hide positive feelings. Many people want a simple resolution and want to run away from complex mixed emotions. A common task of counselors is to help clients sort out mixed feelings toward significant people in their lives. Ideally the counselor helps the client discover and sort out both positive and negative feelings.

Trust between counselor and client is necessary for full emotional exploration, but in some cultures expression of feelings is discouraged (see Box 6-1). However, do not use individual or cultural uniqueness as an excuse to avoid talking about emotion in the interview. All clients have vital emotional lives, whether they are aware of their emotions or not.

The Techniques of Reflecting Feelings

Somewhat like the paraphrase, reflection of feeling involves a typical set of verbal responses that can be used in a variety of ways. The classic reflection of feeling consists of the following dimensions:

1. *Sentence stem:* Choose a sentence stem such as "I hear you are feeling . . . ," "Sounds like you feel . . . ," "I sense you are feeling. . . ." Unfortunately, these sentence stems have been used so often they can sound like comical stereotypes. As you practice, you will want to vary sentence stems and sometimes omit them completely. Using the client's name and the pronoun *you* help soften and personalize the sentence stem.

2. *Feeling label:* Add an emotional word or feeling label to the stem ("Jonathan, you seem to feel *bad* about . . . ," "Looks like you're *happy*," "Sounds like you're *discouraged* today; you look like you *feel really down*"). For mixed feelings, more than one emotional word may be used ("Maya, you appear both glad and sad . . .").

3. *Context or brief paraphrase:* You may add a brief paraphrase to broaden the reflection of feeling. The words *about, when,* and *because* are only three of many that add context to a reflection of feeling ("Jonathan, you seem to feel bad about *all the things that have happened in the past two weeks,*" "Maya, you appear both glad and sad *because you're leaving home*").

4. *Tense and immediacy:* Reflections in the present tense ("Right now, you *are* angry") tend to be more useful than those in the past ("You felt angry then"). Some clients have difficulty with the present tense and talking in the "here and now." Occasionally, "there and then" review of past feelings can be helpful and feel safer for the client.

5. *Check-out:* Check to see whether your reflection of feelings is accurate. This is especially helpful if the feeling is unspoken ("You feel angry today—am I hearing you correctly?").

You need to respect individual and cultural diversity in the way one expresses feelings. The student from China discussed in Box 6-1 is an example of cultural emotional control. Emotions are obviously still there, but they are expressed differently. Do not expect all Chinese or Asians to be emotionally reserved, however. Their style of emotional expression will depend on their individual upbringing, their acculturation, and other factors. Many New England Yankees may be fully as reserved in emotional expression as the Chinese student described by Weijun Zhang. But again, it would be unwise to stereotype all New Englanders in this fashion.

Observing Client Verbal and Nonverbal Feelings

When a client says "I feel sad"—or "glad" or "frightened"—and supports this statement with appropriate nonverbal behavior, identifying emotions is easy. However, many clients present subtle or discrepant messages, for they may not be sure how they feel about a person or situation. The counselor may have to identify and label the implicit feelings, but with skilled listening you can help clients label their own emotions.

The most obvious technique for identifying client feelings is simply to ask the client an open question, "How do you feel about that?" "Could you explore any emotions that come to mind about your parents?" "What feelings come to mind when you talk about the loss?" With less verbal clients, a closed question in which the counselor supplies the missing feeling word may be helpful, "Does that feel hurtful to you?" "Could it be that you feel angry at them?" "Are you glad?"

At other times the counselor will want to infer, or even guess at, the client's feelings through observation of verbal and nonverbal cues. Discrepancies offer vital clues; they may include discrepancies between what the client says about a person and a slight body movement contradicting the client's words. As many clients have mixed feelings about the most significant events and people in their lives, inference of unstated feelings becomes one of the important observational skills of the counselor. A client may be talking about caring for and loving parents while holding his or her fist closed. The mixed emotions may be obvious to the observer though not to the client.

Stephanie, in the interview about cancer, used the following feeling words during the session: *upset, worried, concerned, scared, tired, guilty,* and *anger.* Jennifer, the counselor, reflected those words, but also integrated her own observations. We saw Stephanie's reaction to the word *overwhelmed.* The interviewer also emphasized positive emotions such as caring and the strengths that the client demonstrated. Stephanie needs to be encouraged to talk through the worries and problems. As the interview moves on, we can anticipate that Stephanie will express fewer difficult emotions and will move to more awareness of positive feelings and strengths.

The intentional counselor does not necessarily respond to every noted emotion, congruent or discrepant; reflection of feeling must be timed to meet the needs of the individual client. Sometimes it is best simply to note the emotion and keep it in mind for possible comment later.

The Place of Positive Emotions in Reflecting Feelings

Positive emotions, whether joyful or merely contented, are likely to color the ways people respond to others and their environments. Research shows that positive emotions broaden the scope of people's attention, expand their repertoires for action, and increase their capacities to cope in a crisis. Research also suggests that positive emotions produce patterns of thought that are flexible, creative, integrative, and open to new information (Gergen & Gergen, 2005).

"Sad, mad, glad, scared." This is one way to organize the language of emotion. But perhaps we need more attention to glad words such as pleased, happy, contented, together, excited, delighted, pleasured, and the like. Take a moment and think of specific situations when you experienced each of these positive emotions. It is very likely that you would smile, your body tension would be reduced, and likely even your blood pressure would change in a more positive direction.

When you experience emotion, your brain signals bodily changes. When you feel sad or angry, a set of chemicals floods your body and usually these changes will show nonverbally. Emotions change the way your body functions and are a foundation for all our thinking experience (Damasio, 2003). As you help your clients experience more positive emotions, you are also facilitating wellness and a healthier body. The route toward health, of course, often entails confronting negative emotions.

Searching for wellness strengths and positive assets will likely be helpful to you and your clients. Obviously, we need to explore negative and troubling emotions, but if your clients can start from a positive base of emotion, they may be better able to cope with the negative. Following are four examples of how to help clients focus more on positive emotions.

▲ *Wellness assessment.* Be sure that you reflect the positive feelings associated with aspects of wellness. For example, your client may feel safety and strength in spirituality, pride in gender and/or cultural identity, caring and warmth from past and/or present friendships, and the intimacy and caring of a love relationship. It would be possible to anchor these emotions early in the interview and draw on these positive emotions during more stressful moments. Out of a wellness inventory can come a "backpack" of positive emotions and experiences that are always there and can be drawn on as needed.

▲ *What's right in the relationship?* Couples with relationship difficulties can be helped if they focus more on the areas where things are going well. What remains good about the relationship? Many couples focus on the 5% of times when they disagree and fail to note the 95% when they have been successful or enjoyed each other. Some couples respond well when asked to focus on the reasons they got together in the first place. These positive strengths can help them deal with very difficult issues.

▲ *Positive homework.* When providing your clients with homework assignments, have them engage daily in activities associated with positive emotions. For example, it is difficult to be sad and depressed while running or walking at a brisk pace. Meditation and yoga are often useful in generating more positive emotions and calmness. Seeing a good movie when one is down can be useful as can going out with friends for a meal. In short, help clients remember that they have access to joy, even when things are at their most difficult.

▲ *Service to others.* Helping others often makes individuals feel good about themselves. When people are discouraged and feeling that they are inadequate, volunteering for a church work group, working on a Habitat for Humanity home, or volunteering to work with animal rights can all help them develop a more positive sense of self.

Important caution: But please do not use these examples as a way to tell your clients that "everything will be OK." Some interviewers and counselors are so afraid of negative emotions that they never allow their clients to express what they really feel. Do not minimize difficult emotions by too quickly focusing on the positive.

Some Limitations of Reflecting Feeling

Reflection has been described as a basic skill of the counseling process, yet it can be overdone. Many times a short and accurate reflection may be the most helpful. With friends, family, and fellow employees, a quick acknowledgment of feelings ("If I were you, I'd feel angry about that . . ." or "You must be tired today") followed by continued normal conversational flow may be most helpful in developing better relationships. In an interaction with a harried waiter or salesperson, an acknowledgment of feelings may change the whole tone of a meal or business interchange. Similarly, with many clients a brief acknowledgment of feeling may be more useful. However with complex issues, identifying unspoken feelings can be helpful. Sorting out mixed feelings is key to successful counseling, be it vocational interviewing, personal decision making, or in-depth individual counseling and therapy.

Remember, not all clients will appreciate your comments on their feelings. Exploring the emotional world can be uncomfortable to those who have avoided looking at feelings in the past. Be aware that an empathic reflection can have a confrontational quality that causes clients to look at themselves from a different perspective; therefore, it may seem intrusive to some clients. Timing is particularly important with reflection of feeling. Clients tend to disclose feelings only after rapport and trust have been developed. Less verbal clients may find reflection puzzling or may say, "Of course I'm angry; why did you say that?" Some men may believe that expression of feelings is "unmanly," yet a brief acknowledgment of feelings may be received with appreciation. Brief attention to feelings early on can lead to deeper exploration in later interviews.

▲ **MODULE 6.4**

SUMMARY

▲ Everyone has complex emotions associated with people and events in their lives. Helping clients sort out these feelings is an important part of counseling.

▲ Proficient interviewers must be able to observe and reflect emotional dimensions accurately.

▲ The components of reflection of feeling are (1) a sentence stem, (2) the feeling word, (3) some context, (4) present tense, and (5) a check-out. Beginning with the client's name is helpful, and present tense, here-and-now reflections are often more powerful than a review of past emotions.

▲ Research and clinical experience reveal that special attention to positive emotions can provide clients with strengths to better address their emotional challenges.

▲ Not all clients are comfortable discussing emotion. Reflection of feeling can be overdone, particularly if the client comes from a family or culture that believes emotional expression is inappropriate. A brief acknowledgment of feeling may be more helpful.

How to Conduct an Interview Using Only Listening Skills

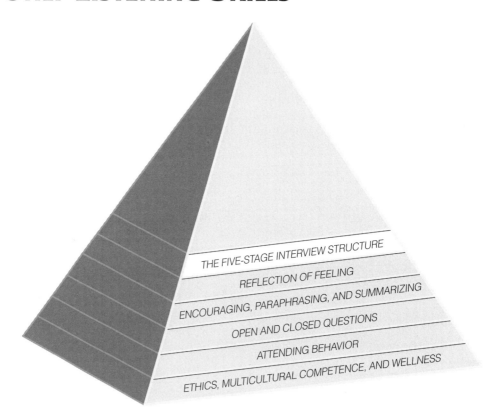

THE FIVE-STAGE INTERVIEW STRUCTURE

REFLECTION OF FEELING

ENCOURAGING, PARAPHRASING, AND SUMMARIZING

OPEN AND CLOSED QUESTIONS

ATTENDING BEHAVIOR

ETHICS, MULTICULTURAL COMPETENCE, AND WELLNESS

How can listening skills and a well-formed interview help you and your clients?

CHAPTER GOALS

The tasks are to integrate the ideas and skills previously covered in this text and to examine your intentional competence as you conduct a full interview. Define the several listening skills and predict how clients are likely respond to your personal interviewing style.

Awareness, knowledge, and skills developed through the concepts of this chapter will enable you to

▲ Predict the client's response to your use of each microskill.
▲ Demonstrate fluid responsiveness to clients, whether or not your predictions are successful.
▲ Understand and use the basic listening sequence.
▲ Define the concept of empathy and rate interviews for empathic understanding.

▲ Define the five stages/dimensions of the well-formed interview.

▲ Conduct a complete interview using only listening skills.

▲ Recognize that each interview and each client are unique and that the interview is a holistic experience.

MODULE 7.1

DEFINING THREE KEY CONCEPTS FOR EFFECTIVE INTERVIEWING:
Predicting Interview Skill Results, the Basic Listening Sequence, and Empathic Understanding

KEY CONCEPT QUESTIONS

▲ **What is the Ivey Taxonomy and how can it help me in the interview?**

▲ **How can we understand and empathize with clients if we have not had similar experiences?**

▲ **What are the three levels of empathic understanding and how do they relate to the basic listening sequence?**

▲ **How do the listening skills relate to other professions?**

▲ **How does diversity impact empathic understanding?**

This module examines the listening skills from several perspectives. First, we will examine how we can predict client responses from the several listening skills and what we need to do when our predictions are not fully accurate. With practice, these skills will become a natural part of your interviewing. The basic listening sequence and empathic understanding are next reviewed, followed by the implications of all this for diversity issues.

The Ivey Taxonomy: Predictability and Flexibility

The boxes at the beginning of each skill chapter are all part of the *Ivey Taxonomy,* a systematic breakdown of the key microskills from the microskills hierarchy. Each box contains a definition of the skill on the left; on the right is the predicted result that follows from using the skill effectively. The full Ivey Taxonomy is presented in Appendix I and there you can review the list of microskills previously covered. Refer to the full taxonomy to solidify your understanding and expertise as you integrate the basic listening skills. For example, in the chapter of reflection of feeling, you may recall the following:

Reflection of Feeling	*Predicted Result*
Identify the key emotions of a client and feed them back to clarify affective experience. With some clients, the brief acknowledgment of feeling may be more appropriate. Often combined with paraphrasing and summarizing.	Clients experience and understand their emotional state more fully and talk in more depth about feelings. They may correct the interviewer's reflection with a more accurate descriptor.

Interviewing is not a chance process. With study, interviewing practice, and experience, you will automatically anticipate what happens as a result of your actions. This anticipation of results is basic to intentionality and is an example of the Samurai effect discussed in Chapter 3. Skills that once had to be studied now have become part of you. *However, remain aware that predictions of what the client is going to do next are always tentative. Be ready to flex intentionally when the unexpected occurs.* Again, as you gain experience, flexibility with the skills described here will become an automatic and natural part of your work.

The Basic Listening Sequence

Basic Listening Sequence	*Predicted Result*
Select and practice all elements of the basic listening sequence, open and closed questions, encouraging, paraphrasing, reflection of feeling, and summarization. These are supplemented by attending behavior and client observation skills.	Clients discuss their stories, problems, or concerns, including the key facts, thoughts, feelings, and behaviors. Clients feel that their stories have been heard.

The *basic listening sequence* (BLS) integrates several key skills. Many successful interviewers begin their sessions with an open question followed by closed questions for diagnosis and clarification. The paraphrase catches the essence of what the client is saying, and the reflection of feeling examines key emotions. These skills are followed by a summary of the concern expressed by the client. Encouragers may be used throughout the interview to help evoke details, while attending and observation remain an underlying part of the entire process.

The BLS, used effectively, is predicted to bring out client stories, including facts, thoughts, feelings, and behaviors. The summarization is particularly useful in bringing order and making sense of client conversation. The skills of the BLS need not be used in any specific sequence, although the sequence does appear regularly in effective interviews. Each person needs to adapt these skills to meet the requirements of the client and the situation. The effective interviewer uses client observation skills to note client reactions and intentionally *flexes* to provide the support the client needs.

For the beginning counselor or interviewer, mastery of the BLS is critical as these skills can be used in many different situations. It is not unusual for a person knowledgeable in the concepts of intentional interviewing to be conducting career counseling at a college in the morning, training parents in communication skills in the afternoon, and working as a management consultant on group meeting skills in the evening (see Table 7-1).

Counseling and the interview can be difficult experiences for some clients. They have come to discuss their problems and resolve conflicts, so the session can rapidly become a depressing litany of failures and fears. It becomes important to use the BLS to help the client identify assets and resources. To ensure a more optimistic and directed interview, use the positive asset search and wellness approach. Rather than just ask about problems, the intentional interviewer seeks to point out the client's positives and strengths. Even in the most difficult situation, it is possible to find good

▲ **TABLE 7-1** Three Examples of the Basic Listening Sequence

Skill	Counseling	Management	Medicine
Open question	"Could you tell me what you'd like to talk to me about . . ."		
Closed question	"Did you graduate from high school?" "What specific careers have you looked at?"	"Who was involved with the production line problem?" "Did you check the main belt?"	"Is the headache on the left side or on the right? How long have you had it?"
Encouragers	Repetition of key words and restatement of longer phrases.		
Paraphrases	"So you're considering returning to college."	"Sounds like you've consulted with almost everyone."	"It looks like you feel it's on the left side and may be a result of the car accident."
Reflection of feeling	"You feel confident of your ability but worry about getting in."	"I sense you're upset and troubled by the supervisor's reaction."	"It appears you've been feeling very anxious and tense lately."
Summarization	In each case the effective counselor, manager, or physician summarizes the story from the client's point of view *before* bringing in the interviewer's point of view.		

things about the client and resources for later problem resolution. Emphasizing positive assets also gives the client a sense of personal worth as he or she talks with you.

Empathic Understanding

The basic listening sequence contains the building blocks of empathy and empathic understanding. Carl Rogers (1957, 1961) first brought the importance of empathy to our attention through his person-centered interviewing. He made clear how vital it is to listen carefully, to enter the world of the client, and to communicate that we understand the client's world *as the client sees and experiences it.* Empathy is often defined as experiencing the world as if *you* were the client, but with awareness that the client remains separate from you. Many others have elaborated on Rogers's influential definition of empathy (cf. Carkhuff, 2000; Egan, 2002; Ivey & Ivey, 2007).

Empathy is important in all areas of interviewing. Observations of interviews in many settings outside of counseling have revealed a common thread. Empathic understanding and careful listening are important in all fields where human communication is central. Effective managers, physicians and nurses, teachers, peer helpers, and many others all have revealed the importance of empathy. It is vital to use the listening skills, but we also need to use them with a desire to understand the client and the way the client experiences the world.

Part of empathy is *communicating that you understand,* and the paraphrase, reflection of feeling, and summarization are particularly important skills to show clients that you are with them. Review audio- or videotaped interviews and assess the level

BOX 7-1 Empathy and Brain Research

Empathy is not just an abstract idea—empathy is identifiable and measurable in the physical brain. Fascinating research on brain activity validates what the helping field has been saying for years. "The basic building blocks (of empathy) are hardwired into the brain and await development through interaction with others. . . . Empathy (is) an intentional capacity" (Decety & Jackson, 2004, pp. 71, 93).

Volunteer couples experienced a painful electric shock and then observed their loved ones experiencing the same shock. When the shock was delivered, brain scans revealed the painful stimulus showed in the cognitive pain-processing network of *both* participants. However, only the shocked partner's brain registered actual physical pain (Singer et al., 2004). This finding has been replicated in several other experiments.

What we learn here is that the empathic person's brain responds to another's experience, even though the observer does not physically feel the other's pain. Many studies over the years back up this central point. For example, children around their second year indicate concern for others cognitively, emotionally, and behaviorally when they notice another child having a problem and often try to help (Zhan-Waxler et al., 1992). You may have seen two young children playing together. One falls and starts crying. Even though the second child has not been hurt, he or she also cries. This ability to observe the feelings of others could be considered the developmental roots of empathic understanding.

Awareness of self, awareness of others, and the ability to differentiate you from the client are essential for empathic understanding. Young children may empathize, but in the situations described above, they have not yet separated themselves from what they have seen. Our task as counselors and therapists is to resonate or empathize with the client's story, but we also need to separate ourselves from that client. In addition, we need to work intentionally with an array of skills and strategies that can help that client to grow further. And that client growth will be shown not only in behavior but also in measurable aspects of brain functioning.

We should also mention that brain research reveals that the antisocial, criminal personality has a reduced ability to appreciate the emotions of others, a counseling fact that is well known (Blair, 2001).

of empathic understanding demonstrated by the interviewer. In addition, examine your own tapes or discs and consider how accurately you are listening. Rate yourself and other interviews you observe on the following three-level empathy scale.

Level 1. Subtractive empathy: The interviewer response gives back to the client less than what the client has said and perhaps even distorts or misunderstands the client. In this case, the listening skills are used inappropriately and take the client off track. Focusing solely on the negative also leads to subtractive empathy.

Level 2. Basic empathy: Interviewer responses are roughly interchangeable with those of the client. The interviewer is able to say back accurately what the client has said. Skilled and intentional use of the basic listening sequence is a way to demonstrate basic empathy.

Level 3. Additive empathy: Interviewer responses add a link to something the client has said earlier or a new idea or frame of reference that helps the client see a new perspective. Wellness and the positive asset search can be vital parts of additive empathy. Skilled use of listening skills and/or influencing skills (see Appendix I) enable an interviewer to become additive.

It is easier to be empathic if you have experienced similar issues in your own life. If you come from a family that experienced alcohol or substance abuse, you may have a special understanding of where this type of client is "coming from." Women in rape support groups find empathy and understanding when they hear others tell a story similar to their own. Cancer survivors may feel more trust and understanding from someone who has parallel experiences to their own. But someone else's experience, even if similar, is not your experience. Just because you have "been there" does not necessarily mean that you are automatically empathic. For example, each soldier's experience of war will be unique.

Empathy requires two things. The first requirement is to be with the client; listening is your key to entering the client's experience as fully as possible. But it is equally important to be aware that the client's world is not your world. Do not lay "your thing" on the client.

Box 7-2 speaks to one aspect of life experience that is seldom considered—the culture of those who have experienced infertility. The question needs to be raised—"If you haven't *been there*, how empathic can you really be?" And if you have not had similar experiences to those of the client, how can you still be an effective helper?

BOX 7-2   National and International Perspectives on Counseling Skills

Is Empathy Always Possible?
KATHRYN QUIRK, Graduate Student in Counseling Program at Cambridge College

As beginning students in counseling, one of the first concepts we run into is empathy—experiencing and understanding the world of the client. Certainly this is core to the helping interview.

But, as I read my text (not this one), I felt increasingly uncomfortable. Was this almost magical concept really possible? I'll tell you why. First the happy ending. I am now the happy mother of a lovely child, the darling of my life. But, Ryan did not come easily and my husband and I needed the help of two fertility clinics.

The "simpler" strategies of getting pregnant failed for three years. Those years were agonizing, but only a sample of the trauma we were to face (yes, dear reader, going through fertility procedures meets the full definition of trauma). We then moved to complicated in vitro procedures involving Petri dishes and surgery. The first three procedures failed and the fourth resulted in a pregnancy that ended when twins died after three months. I don't like the word "fetus"—and grieving for lost babies was horrible. We moved to a new clinic and our fifth try was fantastically successful.

How does all this relate to empathy? I recall a pleasant and expert nurse who counseled a group of us experiencing primary infertility. She was helpful and had good suggestions, but when things got emotional and we cried, she simply didn't get it. She would say that she understood and knew what we were going through. But, let's face it; *she hadn't been there herself.* How could she truly understand the physical pain or the feelings of failure, shame and hopelessness? She didn't understand our loneliness and, perhaps worst of all, the crushed hopes? How can she understand what we were really feeling? I resented it when she said she understood when she clearly did not and could not. Fortunately, those in the group who had "been there" supplied the needed empathy and support.

Does this mean that if you haven't experienced the inner world and actual experience of the client that you can't be empathic? At first I thought that understanding of my experience was impossible except for those who experienced what I had gone through. However, I've softened my thoughts somewhat as I learn about and think about good counseling. I still

(Continued)

feel that *being there* is what serves as a foundation for the deepest empathy. But, the nurse could have provided a deeper empathy than she did if she had admitted openly that she understood our feelings and experience only partially. She did, after all, have more experience listening to people with pregnancy challenges than we did. She did have something to offer.

By failing to discuss and admit that she was different from us suggested to me and to others in the group that she did not understand. What could she have done? First, I think she should have said early in her work with us that she herself had not experienced the difficulties that we went through and, as such, she could have admitted that her understanding and empathy were only partial. But, she could have pointed out that she understood pain and loss and perhaps even shared some of her own difficult experience. Saying this and also outlining her experience and knowledge would have developed more trust and given us all a deeper feeling that she was an empathic person.

As I've gone through my counseling program, I increasingly become aware that I too will have

problems with being truly empathic and communicating the understanding I do have. When I meet clients who are different from me multiculturally (e.g., race, sexual orientation, religious commitment), I now know that I need to discuss these issues upfront. And, I have the obligation to learn as much about the cultural background of these clients as I can. To maximize my empathic potential, I need to read, get out in the community where these people live, and participate with them when I can.

This also holds true for me when I work with alcoholics, cancer survivors, and those who have been raped. I haven't been there, but I have a responsibility to learn more about those whose life experience is different from mine.

Empathy is clearly important, but it is not learned just from classes and books. We all need to examine the human experience and become more fully aware of the life of those around us. And a special P.S. needs to be added—our wonderful second child, Charles, shown on the dedication page of this book, arrived on July 20, 2006.

The Impact of Diversity on Empathic Understanding and the Basic Listening Sequence

A critical issue in interviewing is that the same skills may have different effects on people with varying individual and cultural backgrounds. Diversity will always characterize the mainstream of interviewing and counseling. For every interview, you will encounter people with varying life experiences, and you must factor in the many issues of multiculturalism (e.g., ethnicity/race, people with disabilities, sexual orientation, spirituality/religion). In effect, all interviewing is multicultural.

Individual differences must be added to diversity. A special joy and opportunity we have in the helping fields is discovering the richness of individual and human diversity. Cultural and intentional competence will give you many responses to help the constantly varying individuals with whom you will work.

One Arab American, African American, or European American/Canadian/Australian client cannot be expected to behave the same as the next. Veterans from the Gulf War and the war in Iraq are not the same. And you will find that the individual client will behave differently from one interview to the next. Almost as soon as you think you understand a client, a new side of the client's personality will appear.

Intentional competence requires flexibility and the ability to move and change with constantly shifting client needs. But we must always be aware that anticipating specific results from our interventions is also potentially dangerous. Our wide-ranging clientele will constantly vary. What "works" as expected one time may not the next.

You have already covered the basic sections of the taxonomy—ethics, multicultural competence, wellness, attending behavior, and the basic listening sequence. In addition, we suggest that you examine the summary of the five-stage interview discussed in more detail in the following section.

▲ **MODULE 7.1**

SUMMARY

- ▲ The Ivey Taxonomy (Appendix I) is an expansion of the microskills hierarchy. When we use a specific microskill, we can anticipate what the client may do or say.
- ▲ Clients will often say or do something unexpected. Intentional competence requires you to flex and generate a new alternative for helping when the first skill or strategy produces an unexpected result.
- ▲ Empathy is defined as experiencing the world as if you were the client, but with awareness that the client remains separate from you. Be with the client, but be aware that the client's world is not your world.
- ▲ The basic listening sequence (BLS) is built on attending and observing the client, but the key skills are open and closed questions, encouraging, paraphrasing, reflecting feelings, and summarization.
- ▲ When we listen to clients, using the BLS, we want to obtain the overall background of the client's story, and learn about the facts, thoughts, feelings, and behaviors that go with that story.
- ▲ Three levels of empathic understanding are subtractive (where you fail to hear the client's story fully), basic empathy (where your responses are accurate and interchangeable with what the client says), and additive (where you contribute to client understanding at a new and deeper level).
- ▲ Diversity includes multiple dimensions. To remain effective when you are culturally different from the client, it is important to demonstrate empathic understanding while simultaneously being aware that you cannot enter the full world of the client's experience.

MODULE 7.2

INSTRUCTIONAL READING: Decisional Counseling and the Five Stages/Dimensions of the Well-Formed Interview

KEY CONCEPT QUESTIONS

- ▲ **What is decisional counseling and how does it relate to the structure of the interview?**
- ▲ **What are the five stages of the well-formed interview?**
- ▲ **Do we always need to follow the same five-stage order when conducting an interview?**
- ▲ **What are some multicultural issues in the five-stage interview?**

You are about to be asked to complete a full decisional interview using only the attending, observation, and listening skills stressed thus far in this chapter. Here, you will see how the skills are integrated in a full interview.

Decision Making as a Basis for Structuring the Interview

> Virtually any human activity can be viewed
> as the solving of a problem.
> (Kurt VanLehn, 1998)

The decisional counseling or problem-solving structure can be used in virtually all types of interviewing and counseling, as well as psychotherapy. This framework may be used in individual, family, and group counseling (Ivey & Ivey, 2007; Ivey & Matthews, 1984). When you are asked to integrate both listening and influencing skills in Chapter 13, the decisional counseling model will be outlined in further detail.

The classic decisional or problem-solving model was first identified by Benjamin Franklin:

1. Define the problem
2. Define goals
3. Generate alternative solutions and select an effective approach

The five-stage model of the interview was developed out of the decision-making model but adds to this basic triad. First, it is critical to establish a relationship with the client and keep the client informed about basic issues throughout counseling. It is important to structure the session so that both you and the other person know what is likely to happen. However, this is a road map and the interview may be expected to take unforeseen turns, so be flexible and ready to shift to another skill or even move to an entirely new interviewing stage, if necessary.

Defining the problem and client goals plus generating alternative solutions are close to the five-stage interview model. But just defining the problem misses the wellness approach and potential positive resources available to the client. Generalizing new ideas to one's home setting is as critical as any stage of the interview. *If the client takes home and actually practices the thoughts, feelings, and behaviors discovered in the session, your interview has clearly made a difference.* Finally, each session must conclude, and longer series of interviews face the issue of termination of the relationship.

The five stages/dimensions of the interview follow with a brief description of each.

1. Initiate the session—Develop rapport and structuring.
2. Gather data—Define the problem by drawing out stories, concerns, problems, or issues plus client strengths.
3. Set mutual goals—What does the client want to happen? What is your role in this process?
4. Explore and create—Generate alternatives, confront client incongruities and conflict, and help the client create a new story, way of thinking, feeling, or behaving.
5. Conclude—Plan for generalization of learning to "real life" and eventual termination of the interview or series of interviews

After you have mastered the five stages in a linear fashion, consider them an important checklist to ensure that you have covered all the issues. Although all five dimensions need to be considered in the interview and treatment plan, it is not always necessary to follow them in a specific order. Not all clients will feel comfortable with the stages as presented, regardless of cultural background. Rapport and structuring are important throughout the interview. New information revealed in later interviewing

FIGURE 7-1 The circle of interviewing stages

stage may result in the need for more data gathering (Stage 2) and redefining client concerns in a new way.

The circle of interviewing in Figure 7-1 reminds us that helping is a mutual endeavor between client and counselor. We need to be flexible in our use of skills and strategies. A circle has no beginning or end and is a symbol of an egalitarian relationship in which interviewer and client work together. The hub of the interviewing circle is wellness and the positive asset search, important in all stages and dimensions.

Stage 1: Initiate the Session

Introducing the interview and building rapport are most important in the first interview, but they will remain important in all subsequent sessions. Most interviews begin with some variation on "Could you tell me how I might be of help?" or "What would you like to talk about today?" "Hello, Lynette." "Its good to meet you, Marcus." A prime rule for establishing rapport is to use the client's name and repeat it periodically through the session. Some interviewing situations require extensive attention and time to the rapport stage, whereas others can assume rapport and start the session immediately. Rapport building can be quite lengthy and blend into treatment. For example, in reality therapy with a delinquent youth, playing Ping-Pong or basketball and getting to know the client on a personal basis may be part of the treatment. It may take several sessions before those who are culturally different from you develop real trust. In most Western counseling and interviewing, however, this stage is quite short. After a brief "Hello" the interviewer may immediately move to a discussion of what the client wants.

What is most important is that the interviewer is open, authentic, and congruent with the client, and flexibly meets the needs expressed by the client. The most important microskills for building rapport are attending and client observation. Basic attending demonstrates that you are interested and understand the client and is furthered by use of the basic listening sequence. You can help maintain continuity in a series of continuing sessions, by summarizing and integrating past interviews with the current session. Observe when the client starts talking spontaneously about concerns. You may note that you and the client have a natural mirroring of body language. This indicates that the client is clearly ready to move on to gathering data (Stage 2).

Interviewer self-disclosure, used judiciously, may be helpful with some clients. Be willing to answer questions posed by the client. If the client is culturally different from you, this can be especially helpful. Wellness and the positive asset search may be an important part of rapport building. With a nervous or insecure client, taking time to outline specific and concrete strengths provides the client with a secure base from which to confront difficult problems.

As part of building rapport and trust, some clients need to have the interview explained for them through structuring. This may be their first interview, and they may not know how to behave. The interviewer explains the purpose of the interview and what he or she can or cannot do. Welfare interviewers, for example, find that they can better assist clients if they indicate very early in the session what they really can do, rather than frustrating the client who has high expectations.

Other issues in structuring the session may include informed consent and ethical issues. When you conduct an interview using only attending and listening skills, inform your client that you are going to listen to him or her carefully. As counseling continues, you will want to keep the client informed of the progress toward goals and the possibility of defining new goals.

What about cross-cultural counseling when your race and ethnicity differ significantly from the client's? Authorities increasingly agree that cultural and ethnic differences need to be addressed in a straightforward manner relatively early in counseling, often in the first interview (for example, see Kim et al., 2003). Your ability to recognize and respect differences is essential for the success of the interview or counseling series.

Different cultural groups develop relationships in varying ways. In traditional Native American, Australian Aboriginal, Maori, or Dene culture, for example, almost the entire first helping session may need to be devoted to relationship building. In Latin cultures, the concepts of respect and dignity are particularly important. The more experienced your client is in English-speaking cultures, the more likely he or she will be to understand traditional counseling and interviewing theory and approaches.

Stage 2: Gather Data on Both Issues and Resources

"What's your concern?" The first task of the interviewer is to find out why the client is there and what the problem is. Bring out the story with the basic listening sequence. Open and closed questions will help define the issue as the client views it. Encouragers and paraphrases will provide additional clarity and an opportunity for you to check out whether you heard correctly. Reflection of feeling will provide understanding of the emotional underpinnings. And finally, summarization provides a good way to put the client's conversation into an orderly format.

Next, define the issues as the client describes them. Gather information and data about clients and their perceptions. The basic *who, what, where, when, how,* and *why* series of questions as mentioned in journalism classes provides one short and often useful framework to make sure you have covered the most important aspects of information gathering and problem definition. In your attempts to define the central client concerns, always ask yourself, what is the real world of the client? What problem seeks resolution, or what opportunity needs to be actualized? Failure to clearly answer these questions often results in an interview that wanders and lacks purpose.

Failure to treat is one of the most common causes of malpractice suits. Failure to treat issues most often occurs when counselors and clients are unclear about counseling outcomes. Clients and counselors who agree on goals in a clear fashion can work toward them and revise the goals as the sessions continue. Clients who participate in goal setting and understand the reasons for your helping interventions may be more likely to participate in the process and be more open to change.

Clients grow from strength. Don't focus just on problems. The positive asset search should be part of this stage of the interview. This might be the place for a comprehensive wellness search as described in Chapter 2.

Stage 3: Set Goals Mutually

The word *mutual* is included as part of the goal-setting process. Your active involvement in client goal setting is important. *If you and the client don't know where the interview is going, you may end up somewhere else!* Too often the client and counselor assume they are working toward the same outcome when actually each of them wants something different. A client may be satisfied with sleeping better at night, but the counselor wants complete personality reconstruction. The client may want brief advice about how to find a new job, whereas the counselor wants to give extensive vocational testing and suggest a new career. Blanchard and Johnson (1981), in their long-term best seller on effective management, *The One-Minute Manager,* summarize the issue succinctly: "If you can't tell me what you'd like to be happening . . . you don't have a problem yet. You're just complaining. A problem only exists if there is a difference between what is actually happening and what you desire to be happening" (p. 3).

Authorities on brief counseling (Chapter 14) favor setting goals in the first part of the interview, along with rapport and structuring. With high school discipline problems, less verbal clients, and those of some cultural groups, moving quickly to define a clear outcome may help rapport development. Some clients dislike lengthy analysis of their concerns and want action *now.* If you adapt your interviewing style to meet obvious need, you will achieve counseling success with many clients that more traditional problem-focused methods cannot reach.

Once the goal has been established, a brief summary of the original presenting concern as contrasted with the defined goals can be very helpful. Consider the model sentence below as a basic beginning to working through client issues.

> "On one hand, your problem/concern/issue is (summarize the situation briefly), but on the other hand, your goal is (summarize the goal). What occurs to you as possibilities for resolution?"

Define both the problem and desired outcome in the client's language. The summary confrontation should list several alternatives that the client has considered. The client ideally should generate more than one answer or possibility before moving on to Stage 4. You may want to use hand movements, as if balancing the scales, to present the real and the ideal. Using such physical movements can add clarity to the summary confrontation of key issues.

A maxim for the confused interview—be it discipline, career, or even marital counseling—is "Define a goal, make the goal explicit, search for assets to help facilitate goal attainment, and only then return to examine the nature of the concern." At times, clear goal definition and a solid asset search can make problem identification unnecessary.

Stage 4: Explore and Create

How does the interviewer help the client work through new solutions? First, summarize the client conflict as just described in the model sentence in the preceding section, "On the one hand. . . ." Use the basic listening sequence to facilitate the client's resolution of the issue(s). Second, the interviewer could summarize the client story about the problem or set of issues with newer frames of reference through influencing skills (feedback, self-disclosure, instruction, directives, interpretation) and/or apply alternative helping theories (e.g., person-centered, cognitive-behavioral, brief counseling).

Imagine a school counselor talking with a teen who just had a major showdown with the principal. Establish rapport, but expect the teen to challenge you; he or she likely expects you to support the principal. Do not judge, but gather data from the teen's point of view. If you have developed rapport (Stage 1) and listened during data gathering (Stage 2), the teen will search for solutions in a more positive way. Follow by asking what he or she would like to have happen in terms of a positive change. Work with the teen to find a way to "save face" and move on.

Your first goal in explore and create (Stage 4) is to encourage your clients to find their own resolution. To explore and create with this teen, listen well and use summarization—"On one hand, you see the situation as . . . and your goal is. . . . The principal tells a different story and his goal is likely to be. . . ." If you have developed rapport and listened well, many teens will be able to generate ideas to help resolve the situation.

The basic listening sequence and skilled questioning are useful in facilitating client exploration of answers and solutions. Here are some useful questions to assist client problem solving. The last two focus on a wellness approach and would be common in brief counseling.

"Can you brainstorm ideas—just anything that occurs to you?"

"What other alternatives can you think of?"

"Tell me about a success that you have had."

"What has worked for you before?"

"What part of the problem is workable if you can't solve it all right now?"

"Which of the ideas that we have generated appeals to you most?"

"What are the consequences of taking that alternative?"

Interviewing, counseling, and psychotherapy all try to resolve issues in clients' lives in a similar fashion. The counselor needs to establish rapport, define the problem, and help the client identify desired outcomes. The distinction between the problem and the desired outcome is the major incongruity that may be resolved in three basic ways. First, the counselor uses attending skills to clarify the client's frame of reference and then feeds back a summary of client concerns and the goal. Often clients generate their own synthesis and resolve their challenges. Second, if clients do not generate their own answers, the interviewer can use interpretation, self-disclosure, and other influencing skills to resolve the conflict. Finally, in systematic problem solving and decision making, counselor and client generate and brainstorm alternatives for action and set priorities among the most promising possibilities.

During this stage it is particularly important to keep the issue, or challenge, in view while generating alternatives for a solution and an eventual decision for action. However, a decision for action is not enough. You also need to generalize feelings, thoughts, and behaviors and plan for action beyond the interview itself.

Stage 5: Conclude—Generalization and Eventual Termination of the Interview or Series of Sessions

"Will you do it?" The complexities of the world are such that taking a new behavior back to the home setting is difficult. How do we generalize to daily life the ideas and behaviors learned in the interview? Some counseling theories work on the assumption that behavior and attitude change will come out of new unconscious learning; they "trust" that clients will change spontaneously. This indeed can happen, but there is increasing evidence that planning for change greatly increases the likelihood that it will actually happen.

Consider the situation with the teen in conflict with the principal. Some good ideas may have been generated, but unless the teen follows up on them, nothing is likely to change in the conflict situation. Find something "that works" and leads to changes in the repeating behavioral problems. As you read through the list of generalization suggestions below, consider what you would do to help this teen and other clients restory and change their thoughts, feelings, and behavior.

Change does not come easily and many clients revert to earlier, less intentional behaviors. Work to help the client plan for change. More and more interviewers, therapists, and counselors are using some variation of this form to help ensure that the hard work done in the session has relevance and impact in the "outside world." Here are examples that interviewers and counselors have used to facilitate the transfer of learning from the interview.

Homework and Journaling. Assigning homework so that the effect of the interview continues after the session ends has become an important part of interviewing and counseling. Negotiate specific tasks for the client to try during the week after the session ends. Use very specific behavioral assignments such as, "To help your shyness, you agreed to approach one person after church/synagogue/mosque and introduce yourself." Ask the client to keep a journal of key thoughts and feelings during the week and this can become the basis of the follow-up session. Another is paradoxical intention: "Next week, I want to you engage in the same self-defeating behavior that we have talked about. But take special notice of how others react and how you feel." This helps the client become much more aware of what he or she is doing and its self-defeating aspects.

Role-Playing. The client can practice the new behavior in a role-play with the interviewer. This emphasizes the specifics of learning and increases the likelihood that the client will recognize the need for the new behavior after the session is over. In the case of the teen, you could become the principal and role-play the forthcoming meeting with the principal.

Family or Group Counseling. Sometimes individual problems are deeply merged within difficult marriage, family, or work-group arrangements. An increasing number of counselors involve spouses and families in the counseling process. If the problem is job related, you may find yourself meeting with a work group and helping them become a more effective team.

Follow-up and Support. Ask the client to return for further sessions, each with a specific goal. Use telephone and email support for behavior maintenance checks. The counselor can provide social and emotional support through difficult periods.

These are only a few of the possibilities for developing and maintaining client change. Each individual will respond differently to these techniques, and client observation skills will help determine which technique or set of techniques is most likely to be helpful. For maximal impact and behavior transfer, a combination of several techniques is suggested. Behavior and attitudes learned in the interview do not necessarily transfer to daily life without careful planning. Ask your client at the close of the interview, "Will you do it?" as a form of contract between the two of you for the future. Sometimes a written contract or plan can be helpful.

▲ MODULE 7.2

SUMMARY

▲ Regardless of varying counseling and therapy theories, most interviews involve making some sort of decision including defining the problem, defining the goal, and selecting from alternatives.

▲ The five stages of the well-formed interview include these: (1) initiate the session; (2) gather data; (3) set goals mutually; (4) explore and create; and (5) conclude, generalize, and terminate the session(s).

▲ Following the five stages in order is often helpful to you and the client, but be flexible and move with the client's needs and interests. Consider the five stages a checklist to be covered in each session.

▲ **TABLE 7-2** The Five Stages/Dimensions of the Microskills Interview

Recall that the core of the five-stage structure is the positive asset search and the wellness approach (Chapter 2).			
Stage/Dimension	*Function and Purpose*	*Commonly Used Skills*	*Predicted Result*
1. Initiate the session. Develop rapport and structuring. "Hello, what would you like to talk about today?"	Build a working alliance and enable the client to feel comfortable with the interviewing process. Explain what is likely to happen in the session or series of interviews including informed consent and ethical issues.	*Attending, observation skills, information giving* to help *structure* the interview. If the client asks you questions, you may use *self-disclosure.*	The client feels at ease with an understanding of the key ethical issues and the purpose of interview. The client may also know you more completely as a person and professional.
2. Gather data. Draw out client stories, concerns, problems, or issues. "What's your concern?" "What are your strengths and resources?"	Discover and clarify why the client has come to the interview and listen to the client stories and issues. Identify strengths and resources as part of a wellness approach.	*Attending* and *observation* skills, especially *the basic listening sequence* and the *positive asset search.*	The client shares thoughts, feelings, and behaviors, and tells the story in detail as well as presenting strengths and resources.

(Continued)

▲ **TABLE 7-2** (Continued)

Recall that the core of the five-stage structure is the positive asset search and the wellness approach (Chapter 2).			
Stage/Dimension	*Function and Purpose*	*Commonly Used Skills*	*Predicted Result*
3. Set goals mutually. "What do you want to happen?"	Discover and outline ideal solutions— how would the client like things to be? What does the client want? Clearly defined goals keep the interview from wandering with little or no direction. In brief counseling (Chapter 14), goal setting is fundamental, and this stage may be part of the first phase of the interview.	*Attending skills, especially the basic listening sequence,* certain *influencing skills,* especially *confrontation* (Chapter 8), may be useful.	The client will discuss directions in which he or she might want to go, new ways of thinking, desired feeling states, and behaviors that might be changed. The client might also seek to learn how to live more effectively with situations or events that cannot be changed at this point (rape, death, an accident, an illness). A more ideal story ending might be defined.
4. Explore and create. Explore alternatives, confront client incongruities and conflict, restory. "What are we going to do about it?" "Can we generate new ways of thinking, feeling, and behaving?"	Generate at least *three* alternatives that may resolve the client's issues. Creativity is useful here and seek to find at least three alternatives so that the client has a choice. One choice at times may be to do nothing but accept things as they are.	*Summary* of major discrepancies with a supportive *confrontation.* More extensive use of *influencing skills,* depending on theoretical orientation *(e.g., interpretation, reflection of meaning, feedback).* But this is also possible using only *listening skills.* Use *creativity* to solve problems.	The client may re-examine individual goals in new ways, solve problems from at least those alternatives, and start the move toward new stories and actions.
5. Conclude. Plan for generalizing interview learning to "real life" and eventual termination of the interview or series of sessions. "Will you do it?"	Generalize new learnings and facilitate client changes in thoughts, feelings, and behaviors in daily life. Commit the client to homework and action. As appropriate, plan for termination of sessions.	*Influencing skills,* such as *directives* and *information/ explanation,* plus *attending and observation skills and the basic listening sequence.*	The client demonstrates changes in behavior, thoughts, and feelings in daily life outside of the interview.

MODULE 7.3
EXAMPLE INTERVIEW: I Can't Get Along With My Boss

KEY CONCEPT QUESTIONS

▲ **How is a five-stage interview conducted?**

▲ **What about taking notes in the interview?**

It requires a verbal, cooperative client to work through a complete interview using only listening skills. This interview has been edited to show portions that demonstrate skill usage and levels of empathy. Robert, the client, is 20 and a part-time student who is in conflict with his boss at work. Machiko, the counselor, finds him relatively verbal and willing to work on the problem with her assistance.

Stage 1: Rapport/Structuring

Counselor/Client Statement	Process Comments
1. *Machiko:* Robert, do you mind if we tape this interview? It's for a class exercise in interviewing. I'll be making a transcript of the session, which the professor will read. Okay? We can turn the recorder off at any time. I'll show you the transcript if you are interested. I won't use the material if you decide later you don't want me to use it.	Machiko opens with a closed question followed by structuring information. It is critical to obtain client permission and offer client control over the material before taping. As a student you cannot legally control confidentiality, but it is your responsibility to protect your client.
2. *Robert:* Sounds fine; I do have something to talk about.	Robert seems at ease and relaxed. As the taping was presented casually, he is not concerned about the use of the recorder. Rapport was easily established.
3. *Machiko:* What would you like to share?	The open question, almost social in nature, is designed to give maximum personal space to the client.
4. *Robert:* My boss. He's pretty awful.	Robert indicates clearly through his nonverbal behavior that he is ready to go. Machiko observes that he is comfortable and decides to move immediately to gather data (Stage 2). With some clients, several interviews may be required to reach this level of rapport.

Stage 2: Gather Data

Counselor/Client Statement	Process Comments
5. *Machiko:* Could you tell me about it?	This open question is oriented toward obtaining a general outline of the problem the client brings to the session.
6. *Robert:* Well, he's impossible.	Instead of the expected general outline of the concern, Robert gives a brief answer. The predicted consequence didn't happen.
7. *Machiko:* Impossible?	Encourager. Intentional competence requires you to be ready with another response.
8. *Robert:* Well, he's impossible. Yeah, really impossible. It seems that no matter what I do he is on me, always looking over my shoulder. I don't think he trusts me.	Clients often elaborate on the specific meaning of a problem if you use the encourager. In this case the prediction holds true.
9. *Machiko:* Could you give me a more specific example of what he is doing to indicate he doesn't trust you?	Robert is a bit vague in his discussion. Machiko asks an open question eliciting concreteness.
10. *Robert:* Well, maybe it isn't trust. Like last week, I had this customer lip off to me. He had a complaint about a shirt he bought. I don't like customers yelling at me when it isn't my fault, so I started talking back. No one can do *that* to me! And of course the boss didn't like it and chewed me out. It wasn't fair.	As events become more concrete through specific examples, we understand more fully what is going on in the client's life and mind.
11. *Machiko:* As I hear it, Robert, it sounds as though this guy gave you a bad time and it made you angry, and then the boss came in.	Machiko's response is relatively similar to what Robert said. Her paraphrase and reflection of feeling represents basic interchangeable empathy.
12. *Robert:* Exactly! It really made me angry. I have never liked anyone telling me what to do. I left my last job because the boss was doing the same thing.	Accurate listening often results in the client's saying "exactly" or something similar.
13. *Machiko:* So your last boss wasn't fair either?	Machiko's vocal tone and body language communicate nonjudgmental warmth and respect. She brings back Robert's key word *fair* by paraphrasing with a questioning tone of voice, which represents an implied check-out. This is an interchangeable empathic response (Level 2).

The interview continues to explore Robert's conflict with customers, his boss, and past supervisors. There appears to be a pattern of conflict with authority figures over the past several years. This is a common pattern among young males in their early careers. After a detailed discussion of the specific conflict situation and several other examples of the pattern, Machiko decides to conduct a positive asset search.

Counselor/Client Statement	Process Comments
14. *Machiko:* Robert, we've been talking for a while about difficulties at work. I'd like to know some things that have gone well for you there. Could you tell me about something you feel good about at work?	Paraphrase, structuring, open question, and beginning positive asset search.
15. *Robert:* Yeah; I work hard. They always say I'm a good worker. I feel good about that.	Robert's increasingly tense body language starts to relax with the introduction of the positive asset search. He talks more slowly.
16. *Machiko:* Sounds like it makes you feel good about yourself to work hard.	Reflection of feeling, emphasis on positive regard (Level 2 empathy).
17. *Robert:* Yeah. For example, . . .	

Robert continues to talk about his accomplishments. In this way Machiko learns some of the positives Robert has in his past and not just his problems. She has used the basic listening sequence to help Robert feel better about himself. Machiko also learns that Robert has positive assets such as determination and willingness to work hard to help him resolve his own problems.

Stage 3: Set Mutual Goals

Counselor/Client Statement	Process Comments
18. *Machiko:* Robert, given all the things you've talked about, could you describe an ideal solution? How would you like things to be?	Open question. The addition of a new possibility for the client represents additive empathy (Level 3). It enables Robert to think of something new.
19. *Robert:* Gee, I guess I'd like things to be smoother, easier, with less conflict. I come home so tired and angry.	
20. *Machiko:* I hear that. It's taking a lot out of you. Tell me more specifically how things might be better.	Paraphrase, open question oriented toward concreteness.
21. *Robert:* I'd just like less hassle. I know what I'm doing, but somehow that isn't helping. I'd just like to be able to resolve these conflicts without always having to give in.	Robert is not as concrete and specific as anticipated. But he brings in a new aspect of the conflict—giving in.
22. *Machiko:* Give in?	Encourager.

Machiko learns another dimension of Robert's conflict with others. Subsequent use of the basic listening sequence brings out this pattern with several customers and employees. As new data emerge in the goal-setting process, you may find it necessary to change the problem definition and perhaps even return to Stage 2 for more data gathering.

Counselor/Client Statement	Process Comments
23. *Machiko:* So, Robert, I hear two things in terms of goals. One, that you'd like less hassle, but another, equally important, is that you don't like to give in. Have I heard you correctly?	Machiko uses a summary to help Robert clarify his problem, even though no resolution is yet in sight. She checks out the accuracy of her hearing (Level 3 additive empathy).
24. *Robert:* You're right on, but what am I going to do about it?	

Stage 4: Explore and Create

Counselor/Client Statement	Process Comments
25. *Machiko:* So, Robert, on the one hand I heard you have a long-term pattern of conflict with supervisors and customers who give you a bad time. On the other hand, I also heard just as loud and clear your desire to have less hassle and not give in to others. We also know that you are a good worker and like to do a good job. Given all this, what do you think you can do about it?	Machiko remains nonjudgmental and appears to be very congruent with the client in terms of both words and body language. In this major empathic Level 3 summary, she distills and clarifies what the client said.
26. *Robert:* Well, I'm a good worker, but I've been fighting too much. I let the boss and the customers control me too much. I think the next time a customer complains, I'll keep quiet and fill out the refund certificate. Why should I take on the world?	Robert talks more rapidly. He, too, leans forward. However, his brow is furrowed indicating some tension. He is "working hard."
27. *Machiko:* So one thing you can do is keep quiet. You could maintain control in your own way, and you would not be giving in.	Paraphrase, Level 3 additive empathy. Machiko is using Robert's key words and feelings from earlier in the interview to reinforce his present thinking. But she waits for Robert's response.
28. *Robert:* Yeah, that's what I'll do, keep quiet.	He sits back, his arms folded. This suggests that the "good" response above was in some way actually subtractive. There is more work to do.
29. *Machiko:* Sounds like a good beginning, but I'm sure you can think of other things as well, especially when you simply can't be quiet. Can you brainstorm more ideas?	Machiko gives Robert brief feedback. Her open question is a Level 3 response adding to the interview. She is aware that his closed nonverbals suggest more is needed.

Clients are often too willing to seize the first idea as a way to agree and avoid looking fully at issues. It is helpful to use a variety of questions and listening skills to further draw out the client. Later in the interview, Robert was able to generate two other useful suggestions: (a) to talk frankly with his boss and seek his advice; and (b) to plan an exercise program to blow off steam and energy. In addition, Robert began to realize that his problem with his boss was only one example of a continuing problem with anger. He and Machiko discussed the possibilities of continuing their discussions or for Robert to visit a professional counselor to work with him on anger management. Robert decided he'd like to talk with Machiko a bit more. A contract was made: If the situation did not improve within 2 weeks, Robert would seek professional help.

Stage 5: Conclude—Generalization and Transfer of Learning

Counselor/Client Statement	Process Comments
30. *Machiko:* So you've decided that the most useful step is to talk with your boss. But the big question is "Will you do it?"	Paraphrase, open question.
31. *Robert:* Sure, I'll do it. The first time the boss seems relaxed.	
32. *Machiko:* As you've described him, Robert, that may be a long wait. Could you set up a specific plan so we can talk about it the next time we meet?	Paraphrase, open question. To generalize from the interview, it is important to encourage specific and concrete action in your client.
33. *Robert:* I suppose you're right. Okay, occasionally he and I drink coffee in the late afternoon at Rooster's. I'll bring it up with him tomorrow.	
34. *Machiko:* What, specifically, are you going to say?	Open question, again eliciting concreteness.
35. *Robert:* I could tell him that I like working there, but I'm concerned about how to handle difficult customers. I'll ask his advice and how he does it. In some ways, it worries me a little; I don't want to give in to the boss . . . but maybe he will have a useful idea.	Robert is able to plan something that might work. With other clients, you may role-play, give advice, actually assign homework. You will also note that Robert is still concerned about "giving in."
36. *Machiko:* Would you like to talk more about this the next time we meet? Maybe through your talk with your boss we can figure out how to deal with this in a way that makes you feel more comfortable. Sounds like a good contract. Robert, you'll talk with your boss and we'll meet later this week or next week.	Open question, structuring. If Robert does talk to his boss and listens to his advice—and actually changes his behavior—then this interview could be rated holistically at Level 3. If not, then a lower rating is obvious.

It would have been wise to specify the follow-up contract even more precisely, but this would most likely entail the use of influencing skills, prescribing homework, and so forth. Again, you'll find that concreteness is very important in assisting clients to make and act on decisions. It was an especially important response when Machiko asked Robert what he was specifically going to do.

You may find it challenging to work through the systematic five-stage interview using only attending, observation, and the basic listening sequence, yet it can be done. It is a useful format to use with individuals who are verbal and anxious to resolve their own issues. You will also find this decisional structure useful with resistant clients who want to make their own decisions. By acting as a mirror and asking questions, you can encourage many of your clients to find their own direction. More information on decisional counseling will be presented in Chapter 13.

Theoretically and philosophically, this interview style, using only listening skills, is related to Carl Rogers's person-centered counseling (Rogers, 1957). Rogers developed guidelines for the "necessary and sufficient conditions of therapeutic personality change," and the empathic constructs described in this chapter are derived from his thinking. Rogers originally was opposed to the use of questions but in later life modified his position. In this example, you saw a decisional model combined with a modified person-centered approach. Respect for the client's ability to find her or his own unique direction is implicit in conducting an interview without using information, advice, and influencing skills.

Taking Notes in the Interview

Avoid note taking that takes precedence over listening. You and your client can usually work out an arrangement suitable for both of you. If you personally are relaxed about note taking, it will seldom become an issue. If you are worried about taking notes, it likely will be a problem. When working with a new client, obtain permission early about taking notes. We suggest that any case notes be made available to clients and in practice sessions. Volunteer client feedback on the interview can be most helpful in thinking about your own style of helping. Using your own natural style, you may begin:

> I'd like to take a few notes while you talk. Would that be OK? I write down your exact key words for important reference points for both of us. I'll make a copy of the notes before you leave, if you wish. As you know, all notes in your file are open to you at any time.

In-session note taking is often most helpful in the initial portions of interviewing and counseling and less important as you get to know the client better. Audiotaping and videotaping the session follow the same guidelines. If you are relaxed and share on an equal basis with your client, making this type of record of the interview generally goes smoothly. Some clients find it helpful to take audio recordings of the session home and listen to them, thus enhancing learning from the interview. There is nothing wrong with *not* taking notes in the session, but records are very important and you will need to write session summaries shortly after the interview finishes.

▲ **MODULE 7.3**

SUMMARY

▲ Machiko was able to complete a full interview with some success using only the basic listening skills.

▲ She was able to maintain her skills at basic interchangeable empathy (Level 2), but she also had several additive (Level 3) responses. When her responses did not achieve predicted results, she was able to flex intentionally and try another skill.

▲ Helping the client make specific plans for generalization of new learning is particularly important. Often interviewers and clients are tired at the end of the session and fail to take this final step.

▲ Detailed note taking in which the writing takes precedence over listening is to be avoided. If you personally are relaxed about note taking, it will seldom become an issue. If you are worried about taking notes, it likely will be a problem.

▲ When you wish to take notes or audiotape or videotape a session, obtain permission from the client early in the session. Make all records available to the clients, even volunteer clients.

HELPING CLIENTS GENERATE NEW STORIES THAT LEAD TO ACTION

Influencing Skills and Strategies

The listening skills and the five-stage interview structure form the foundation of intentional interviewing. Our goal is to draw out the client's story, find positive strengths, and help generate new stories that lead to change and action. The five-stage interview provides a structure that, for many clients, will be complete in itself—simply telling the story in a positive, supportive atmosphere is often sufficient for positive change to occur.

Influencing skills and strategies of Section III represent another way to help a client develop new ways of thinking, feeling, and behaving. Confrontation (Chapter 8) may be the most important agent of change in the interview after the listening skills. When confronting, observe discrepancies and conflict in the client and facilitate resolving the client's issues. Included in this chapter is the Client Change Scale that enables you to assess your client's responses and evaluate larger developmental change over a series of interviews.

Focusing (Chapter 9) extends the concept of confrontation and illustrates how multiple frameworks for examining stories and personal issues can result in breakthroughs in client understanding. Too many counselors and interviewers focus narrowly on their clients' problems and miss contextual issues such as impact of family, significant others, and multicultural and social factors.

Reflection of meaning and the interpretation/reframe (Chapter 10) are complex and rich. These related skills provide a deeper understanding of each client's issues and history. Both skills are concerned with finding new perspectives on life and its meaning. Reflection of meaning tends to focus more on values and critical issues underlying overt behavior, and these discoveries come from the client rather than the interviewer. Interpretation and reframing tend to come from the interviewer's personal or theoretical perspective and provide clients with a new way to understand themselves and their situations.

Additional strategies of interpersonal influence (Chapters 11 and 12) are explored with specific suggestions for facilitating client restorying and action. These skills are logical consequences, self-disclosure, feedback, directives, and information/advice. All of these involve active participation by the interviewer.

Awareness, knowledge, and skills developed through the concepts of this section will enable you to

- ▲ Master the art of confrontation and gain the ability to assess your client's developmental change in response to your interventions.
- ▲ Demonstrate the ability to focus the interview and facilitate client exploration of the full complexities of the story.
- ▲ Use the skills of reflection of meaning and interpretation/reframing to help clients move to deeper levels of self-exploration and self-understanding.
- ▲ Use an array of influencing skills and strategies to assist client developmental progress, particularly when the more reflective listening skills are insufficient to produce change and understanding.

If you are a beginning counseling and interviewing student, do not expect to achieve intentional competence in all the concepts of this section in your first course. Confrontation, for example, is a complex skill that even the most experienced counselor or therapist can always improve. Assessing client change in the *here and now* is a new concept in the helping field and likely to be challenging even for experienced interviewers. The learning in interviewing and counseling never ends. *Be patient, listen, learn new things constantly, and practice new skills and ideas until you can use them easily in the interview.*

SUPPORTING WHILE CHALLENGING
Confrontation

C H A P T E R

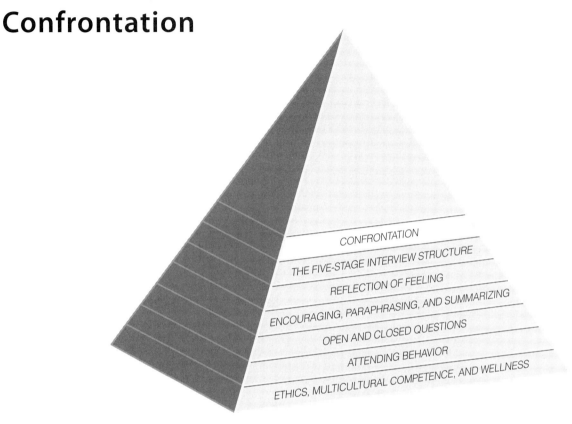

CONFRONTATION

THE FIVE-STAGE INTERVIEW STRUCTURE

REFLECTION OF FEELING

ENCOURAGING, PARAPHRASING, AND SUMMARIZING

OPEN AND CLOSED QUESTIONS

ATTENDING BEHAVIOR

ETHICS, MULTICULTURAL COMPETENCE, AND WELLNESS

How can confrontation help you and your clients?

CHAPTER
GOALS

Confrontation of discrepancies acts as a lever for the activation of human potential. Most clients come to an interview seeking some sort of movement or change in their lives. However, they may resist your efforts to bring about the very transformation they seek. Your task is to help them move beyond their issues and problems to realize their potential as human beings. An understanding of confrontation is basic to helping clients restory their lives.

Awareness, knowledge, and skills developed through the concepts of this chapter will enable you to

▲ Identify incongruity, discrepancies, or mixed messages in behavior, thought, feelings, or meanings.
▲ Increase client talk with a view toward explanation and/or resolution of conflict and discrepancies.
▲ Identify client change processes occurring during the interview and throughout the treatment period, using the Client Change Scale.

MODULE 8.1
DEFINING CONFRONTATION

KEY CONCEPT QUESTION

▲ What is a confrontation and how it is structured?

Confrontation	Predicted Result
Supportively challenge the client: 1. Listen, observe, and note client conflict, mixed messages, and discrepancies in verbal and nonverbal behavior. 2. Point out internal and external discrepancies by feeding them back to the client, usually through the listening skills. 3. Evaluate how the client responds and whether the confrontation leads to client movement or change. If the client does not change, the interviewer flexes intentionally and tries another skill.	The client responds to the confrontation of discrepancies and conflict with new ideas, thoughts, feelings, and behaviors and these will be measurable on the five-point Client Change Scale. Again, if no change occurs, *listen*. Then try an alternative style of confrontation.

Cultural intentionality is not just a goal for interviewers; it is also a goal for clients. A client comes to an interview "stuck"—having either no alternatives for solving a problem or a limited range of possibilities. The task of the interviewer is to eliminate stuckness and substitute intentionality. *Stuckness* is an inelegant, but highly descriptive, term coined by Fritz Perls, to describe the opposite of intentionality. Other words that represent the same condition include *immobility, blocks, repetition compulsion, inability to achieve goals, lack of understanding, limited behavioral repertoire, limited life script, impasse,* and *lack of motivation.* Stuckness may also be defined as an inability to resolve conflict, reconcile discrepancies, and deal with incongruity. In short, clients often come to the interview because they are stuck for a variety of reasons and seek intentionality—they need a new story.

Our clients often become stuck because of internal and/or external conflict. *Internal conflict* or incongruity occurs when they have difficulty making important decisions, they feel confusion or sadness, or they have mixed feelings and thoughts about themselves. *External conflict* could be with others (friends, family, coworkers, or employers) or with a difficult situation such as coping with failure, living effectively with success, or having difficulty in achieving an important goal financially or socially. External conflict inevitably leads to internal feelings of incongruity. And internal conflict can lead to conflict with others—for example, the inability to make a decision may also result in conflict with a significant other who needs to know what is going to happen.

Effective confrontation of conflict and incongruity leads clients to new ways of thinking and increased intentionality. Confrontation may be defined as follows:

> Confrontation is *not* a direct, harsh challenge but is a more gentle skill that involves listening to clients carefully and respectfully and helping them examine themselves or their situations more fully. Confrontation is not "going against" the client; it is "going with" the client; seeking clarification and the possibility of a new resolution of difficulties. Think of confrontation as a supportive challenge.

Confrontation is the word that helping professions have chosen for challenging clients to think in new ways, to examine themselves more fully, and to consider themselves and their relations with others more carefully. Confrontation is not a skill that you use frequently, but it is a powerful tool when it is needed. Clients often need challenges to increase their motivation to change, and a supportive confrontation helps them reach core issues of their problem, conflict, or issue more quickly and with greater precision. Your skill in listening is vital in helping the client identify conflicts, incongruities, and discrepancies.

Once you have established sufficient rapport, developed a working relationship, and heard the client's story, you will identify instances of internal and external conflict. Questions, coupled with paraphrasing, reflecting feeling, and summaries, will help clarify the conflict issues, but eventually you will want to provide a supportive challenge/confrontation to reach the next step of personal growth. Positive growth and development occur with the resolution of conflict and incongruity. Through this process of transformation and change, clients learn new ways to manage their lives.

▲ **MODULE 8.1**
SUMMARY

- ▲ Confrontation is based on effective listening and observation of client conflict, discrepancies, incongruity, and mixed feelings and thoughts.
- ▲ Effective confrontation leads to increased client intentionality.
- ▲ Confrontation is a supportive challenge to client incongruity that helps bring a clearer understanding of core issues.

MODULE 8.2
INSTRUCTIONAL READING: The Specific Skills of Confrontation

KEY CONCEPT QUESTIONS

▲ **What are the specific skills of confrontation?**

▲ **How does a theory of death and dying relate to client change?**

▲ **What are some multicultural issues related to confrontation?**

▲ **What is the Client Change Scale and how can we evaluate client change in the here and now in the interview or over a series of sessions?**

First, confrontation is different in a major way from all skills previously discussed. Confrontation does not stand alone as a skill but rather appears as a dimension of other skills. For example, imagine that a client talks to you about possibly leaving a job because of interpersonal conflict but also speaks of real anxiety about what this action might mean for the future. After hearing the full story, you might provide a brief summary confrontation as follows:

> Shavon, sounds as if you really have mixed feelings about this choice. On one hand, I hear some anger with your boss and a real desire to get out and move on. But, on the other hand, I sense that you feel a bit confused and anxious about where you'd go next. Have I got that right?

In this summary, the interviewer confronts Shavon with the essence of her conflict and implicitly challenges her to think through what she really wants. A more forceful challenge would be "We've gone through this for some time. What do *you*, Shavon, *really* want?" If Shavon understands the challenge, she will generate her own ideas for possible resolution. The words "on one hand . . . but on the other hand . . ." are a classic way to respond to client conflict and incongruity. Amplifying the alternatives with hand and arm movements helps illustrate conflict even more clearly.

Thus, one of the most powerful influencing skills is based on careful listening. Paraphrasing is particularly useful when the conflict or incongruity is around decisions and the pluses and minuses of the decision need to be outlined. Reflection of feeling is important for emotional issues, particularly when clients have mixed feelings ("on one hand, you feel . . . , but on the other, you also feel . . ."). A summary is a good choice for bringing together many strands of thoughts, feelings, and behaviors.

Confrontation, Step 1: Identify Conflict by Observing Mixed Messages, Discrepancies, and Incongruity

This session, while abbreviated and edited, illustrates the fundamentals of confrontation—supporting while challenging.

Interviewer and Client Conversation	Process Comments
Client: (the body language shows excitement) I found this wonderful friend on the Internet. We're emailing at least four times a day. It feels great. I think I'd like to meet him. But it means I may have to go out of town. (Her body language becomes more hesitant and she breaks eye contact.) I wonder what my partner would think if he found out. I'm a little bit anxious, but I really want to meet this guy.	The client demonstrates conflict or incongruity between desire and excitement about meeting the Internet friend and internal anxiety and hesitation. There is the inevitable external conflict of being involved with two people at once. Which discrepancy might you discuss first? Clients who discuss mixed feelings and conflicts usually show them nonverbally as well through vocal tone and/or body language.
Counselor: You really want to meet him, but you're a little bit anxious.	This paraphrase and reflection of feeling confront the mixed feelings in the client. This catches both verbal and nonverbal observations. Note that a confrontation always occurs as part of other microskills.
Client: Yes, but what would happen if my partner found out? It scares me. I've got so much involved with him over the past two years. But, wow, this guy on the Internet . . .	The client responds and turns her focus to the discrepancy with her partner. There are at least two issues in this situation.

Your ability to observe verbal and nonverbal incongruities and mixed messages is fundamental to effective confrontation. The words *conflict, discrepancy, incongruity,* and *mixed message* are used interchangeably in this chapter.

What Are Example Internal Conflicts?

Discrepancies internal to the client include mixed messages observed in nonverbal behavior, incongruities between two verbal statements, and discrepancies between what the person says and what he or she does. A vital part of counseling is helping clients sort out mixed and confused feelings, thoughts, and behaviors. The client's thoughts and feelings about her present partner against the excitement of the new Internet friend clearly represent an internal conflict. The client has discrepancies within herself that need to be resolved.

What Are Example External Conflicts?

Discrepancies between the client and the external world highlight conflict with other individuals ranging from friends and family to those at work or contacts in the community. Another type of conflict is between the client and challenging situations such as college choice, a major purchase, or dealing with sexism or racism. Much of your counseling and interviewing work will focus on discrepancies that clients have with their external world. In the Internet example, the client likely has several conflicts with her partner. The basic listening sequence will be important in drawing out the underlying nature of the relationship conflict. Beyond that, the client may have difficulties at work, problems with her parents, or other situational issues that relate to external discrepancies.

Discrepancies between you and the client can be challenging. Interviewers and counselors may need to hide differences they have with clients. If you sense difference or feel a conflict between you and your client, support the client by listening. If you listen carefully, most discrepancies between you and your clients will disappear as you understand how they came to think and behave as they do. Note your own or the client's discomfort with differences between you, question yourself silently, draw out the client's perceptions, and work to understand them. Keeping one's thoughts and feelings to oneself is part of being nonjudgmental. However, there are times when carefully sharing your differences with clients is important. For example, the client may be making an unwise decision that you see will lead to even more difficulty. Summarizing the client's point of view and then sharing your alternative perspective may help prevent problems. Furthermore, clients may fail to see their own contributions to their problems by externalizing their issues and blaming others. On the other hand, some clients will take blame themselves while failing to see that others or the situation causes their difficulties. An example is an abused client who states that the abuse is a personal fault rather than being aware that the abuser/perpetrator is the real cause. Discrimination in the form of racism, ableism, ageism, or other forms of oppression may need to be identified for some clients who take too much personal responsibility for their problems.

Confrontation, Step 2: Point Out Issues of Incongruity and Work to Resolve Them

Interviewer and Client Conversation	Process Comments
Counselor: Could I review where we've been so far? I know you have been having some difficulties with your partner that you've detailed over the last two sessions. I also hear that you want to work things out even though you're angry with him. You have a lot of positive history together that you hate to give up. On the other hand, you've found this man on the Internet that you're excited about, and he doesn't live that far away. In the middle of all this, I sense you feel pretty conflicted. Have I got the issues right?	This summary indicates the counselor has been listening. The counselor communicates respect and a nonjudgmental attitude, both verbally and nonverbally. The counselor summarizes the major discrepancies that lead to internal and external conflict and checks out with the client to see if the listening has been accurate.
Client: Yes, I think you've got it. I hear what you're saying; I think I've got to work a little harder on the relationship with my partner, but—wow—I sure would like to meet that guy.	Resolution of conflict and discrepancy best occurs after the situation is fully understood. Through having thoughts and feelings said back, the client starts some movement.

After ten minutes, the client's thoughts and feelings evolve to a new perspective.

Client: (said with conviction) I've got so much time invested in my partner; I've really got to try harder. (The nonverbals again show hesitancy.) How am I going to work this out with my Internet friend?	Even though the conflict is moving and the client is starting to show evidence of new ways of thinking that weren't there in the first two sessions, conflict remains.
Counselor: (solid supportive body language and vocal tone) It looks like you really want to work it out with your partner. You sound and look very sure of yourself. Let's consider what the possibilities are with your Internet friend.	You can confront and help clients face discrepancies, incongruity, and conflict if you are able to listen and be fully supportive.

Labeling the incongruity and saying it back through nonjudgmental confrontation may be enough to resolve a situation. Focus on the elements of incongruity rather than on the person. Confrontation is too often thought of as blaming a person for his or her faults; rather, the issue is intentionally facing the incongruity and helping the client think it through. The following summarizes key dimensions of effective confrontation—supporting while challenging:

▲ Clearly identify the incongruity or conflict in the story or comment. Using reflective listening, summarize it for the client. The simple question, "How do you put these two together?" may lead a client to self-confrontation and resolution.

▲ Draw out the specifics of the conflict or mixed messages using questions and other listening skills. If necessary, share your observations. Aim for facts; avoid being judgmental or evaluative. Address each part of the mixed message, contradiction, or conflict one at a time. If two people are involved, attempt to have the client examine both points of view.

▲ Periodically summarize each dimension of the incongruity. Variations of basic confrontation include "On the one hand . . . but on the other hand . . .," "You say . . . but you do . . .," "I see . . . at one time, and at another time I see . . .," and "Your words say . . . but your actions say. . . ." Follow with a check-out, "How does that sound to you?" When incongruities are pointed out, the client is confronted with facts.

Many clients are unaware of their mixed messages and discrepancies; point these out gently, but firmly. A wide variety of attending and influencing skills may be used to follow up and elaborate on confrontations. Another very different possibility for confrontation is to listen in silence for a short time while the client struggles with internal or external contradiction. This type of confrontation is especially challenging to clients who may ask your opinion—"Don't you agree with me that my partner is wrong?" Most often such questions are answered by throwing the question back to the client (e.g., "Tell me more"). If you say nothing, clients will have to encounter your silence and may more readily find their own answers. But be aware that some could interpret your silence as disapproval.

You will find that many clients are not comfortable with confrontive and challenging approaches. Your personal support can help clients build new behaviors, thoughts, and meanings. Identify strengths and wellness qualities in clients and their relationships. Take time out from confrontation to develop strengths. When clients are aware of their wellness strengths and positive qualities, they may face difficult confrontations more easily.

The antisocial or acting-out client represents a special type of "culture" that is often very challenging to the more gentle atmosphere or culture of interviewing and counseling. When confronting difficult clients, it is important to "center" your body and mind and use a stronger, firmer confronting style. Continue to listen and support, but hold your position when you believe you are on the right track. The antisocial client does not respect apparent weakness in interviewers.

Individual and Multicultural Cautions

Within the wide diversity that is multiculturalism, expect a considerable amount of incongruity and conflict between the individual and the external world. Directly, but with as much support as possible, confront conscious and unconscious sexism, racism, heterosexism, and discrimination of all types. For example, a woman may be depressed, but is this depression "her problem" or is her sadness the result of sexual harassment on the job? A White male client who has not been promoted may be angry, believing that his being passed over for promotion may be the result of what he terms "reverse discrimination." Given the above, your ability to understand and identify the many conflicts and discrepancies related to multiculturalism is essential. Working through these issues is an increasingly important dimension of counseling.

You will find that direct, aggressive confrontations are not necessary if the client contradiction is stated kindly and with a sense of warmth and caring. Direct, blunt confrontations are likely to be culturally inappropriate for traditional Asian, Latina/Latino, and Native American clients. But even here, if good rapport and understanding exist between you and the client, confrontations can be helpful. When issues of oppression need to be confronted, your support will be especially essential. At the same time we should also be aware that silence is a value within much of the Native American, Dene, or Inuit tradition. You may sit with these clients for several minutes as they sort out issues. How comfortable are you with silence?

Confrontation of discrepancies can be highly challenging to any client, but particularly to one who is culturally different from you. The confrontation process may be made acceptable if the helper takes time to establish a solid relationship of trust and rapport before engaging in confrontation. If you have a fragile client or if the relationship is not solid, confrontation skills need to be used with sensitivity, ethics, and care. Each mode of confrontation must be personally authentic and meaningful for the client or it is likely to fail.

Confrontation, Step 3: Evaluating Change

The effectiveness of a confrontation is measured by how the client responds. If you observe closely in the *here and now of the session*, you can rate how effective your interventions have been. You also can assess whether your client has changed as a result of your interviewing and counseling skills. The method of evaluating cognitive/emotional change described here is based on an adaptation of work by Elizabeth Kübler-Ross (1969), who revolutionized our thinking about death and dying.

Kübler-Ross identified five stages of cognitive and emotional change as people faced death and dying (see Box 8-1). Her well-known theory has implications for change in areas ranging from interviewing to addiction and career choice. When people face death, they tend to display one of five reactions ranging from denial to acceptance to transcendence. While the framework has five levels and many people move through them in order, some people stay in one stage and never change, whereas others may "bounce" among the stages. Change is not always as linear and progressive as Kübler-Ross suggests.

Now, let us apply the Kübler-Ross framework to interviewing and counseling and how clients change. The client tells us a story and we, of course, listen. If the client is in the denial stage, the story may be distorted, others blamed unfairly, and the client's part in the story denied. In effect, the client in *denial* (Level 1) does not deal with reality. When the client is confronted effectively, the story becomes a discussion of inconsistencies and incongruity and we see Level 2 *bargaining and partial acceptance*—the story is changing. At *acceptance* (Level 3), the reality of the story is acknowledged and storytelling is more accurate and complete. Moreover, it is possible to move to *new solutions* and *transcendence* (Levels 4 and 5). When changes in thoughts, feelings, and behaviors are

BOX 8-1   National and International Perspectives on Counseling in the Real World

 **Kübler-Ross's Five Stages of Death and Dying Compared
With Five Levels of Change in the Interview**

To help see parallels between death and dying theory and the interviewing process, think about counseling an alcoholic. In counseling, breaking out of firmly rooted denial (Level 1) may take some time, and clearly confrontation of many issues will be important. Many alcoholics go through a stage of bargaining (Level 2) in which they begin to explore what is really going on in their lives. Level 3 represents the first real breakthrough when the alcoholic admits to the problem. But many alcoholics at this stage continue drinking even though they are aware of their alcoholism. True change occurs when the drinking ceases (Level 4). Some alcoholics are able to transcend and make major life changes, including mentoring others, as they work the "steps" of Alcoholics Anonymous (Level 5).

Following are Kübler-Ross's Five Stages of Death and Dying:

Stage 1: Denial. The patient cannot accept and denies the reality that he or she will die. The inevitable is ignored. "It won't happen—not to me!"

The client denies that inconsistency, incongruity, or conflict exists. The story may show considerable confusion and/or key information may not be disclosed.

Stage 2: Partial acceptance of reality: bargaining and anger. "Bargaining" occurs when patients engage in magical thinking. "If I lead a better life, then God will let me live." Another type of partial acceptance is anger when the affected person may be angry at God ("Why me? I've lived a good life") or at the overall unfairness of it all ("It isn't right"). Often anger is a

cover-up for more basic issues, not only in death and dying but in other situations as well.

The client partially recognizes and understands the conflict, but does not understand it fully. The client has moved beyond active denial.

Stage 3: Acceptance and recognition. Dying is acknowledged by the individual and along with this comes a marked shift of emotion. The underlying emotions of sadness, fear, and grief reactions surface. Loss is faced rationally but with appropriate emotions.

The client recognizes the situation as it is and has appropriate emotions, but no significant change occurs.

Stage 4: Generation of a new solution—early transcendence. Death may be reframed as an opportunity to forgive and forget old family arguments or an opportunity to meet God and loved ones in heaven. The patient may decide to donate organs. A new meaning has been given to death that allows both acceptance and some degree of transcendence.

The client generates new thoughts, feelings, and behaviors.

Stage 5: Development of new, larger, and more inclusive constructs, patterns, or behaviors—transcendence. The person may appear to have made a major change in consciousness. Sadness may continue, but the individual becomes peaceful and serene—transcendence.

The client makes major changes in thoughts, feelings, and behaviors. This is coupled with a new sense of being—transcendence of past issues.

integrated into a new story, we see the client move into major new ways of thinking accompanied by action after the session is completed.

Virtually any problem a client presents may be assessed at one of the five levels. If your client starts with you at denial or partial acceptance (Level 1 or 2) and then moves with your help to acceptance and generating new solutions (Level 3 or 4), you have clear evidence of the effectiveness of your interviewing process. The five levels may be seen as a general way to view the change process in interviewing, counseling, and therapy. Each confrontation or other interview intervention in the *here and now* may lead to identifiable changes in client awareness.

Small changes in the interview will result in larger client change over a session or series of sessions. Not only can you measure these changes over time, but you can also contract with the client in a partnership that seeks to resolve conflict, integrate discrepancies, and work through issues and problems. Specifying concrete goals often helps the client deal more effectively with confrontation.

The Client Change Scale (CCS)*

The Client Change Scale is presented below with examples of each of the five levels. The CCS provides you with a systematic way to evaluate the effectiveness of each intervention and to track how clients change in the *here and now* of the interview. If you practice assessing client responses, eventually you will automatically be able to make decisions "on the spot" as you see how the client is responding to you. For example, if the client appears to be in denial of your intervention, you can intentionally shift to another microskill or approach that may be more successful. With confrontation you may find the clearest example of client response levels to your comments; other skills (including both listening and influencing skills) can also be examined for effectiveness via the CCS.

The Client Change Scale can also be used to determine client progress over a full interview or even a long series of sessions. For example, if you are working with a substance abuser, you can expect that it will take some time to help the client move from denial to acceptance to generation of a new solution. A client dealing with the breakup of a significant relationship may start at Level 2 (partial examination) and after an interview or two move to Level 3 (acceptance). With further counseling, the client may be expected to generate new solutions and move on with her or his life.

The following example shows five different reactions to a divorce. Any time clients are working through change they talk about their issues with varying levels of awareness. The client may be in denial one moment, the next talking as if he or she accepts the problem, and then returning to bargaining to avoid change.

> *Level 1. Denial.* The individual may deny or fail to hear that an incongruity or mixed message exists. "I'm not angry about the divorce. These things happen. I do feel sad and hurt, but definitely not angry."
>
> *Level 2. Partial examination.* The individual may work on a part of the discrepancy but fail to consider the other dimensions of the mixed message. "Yes, I hurt and perhaps I should be angry, but I can't really feel it."
>
> *Level 3. Acceptance and recognition, but no change.* The client may engage the confrontation but make no resolution. Until the client can examine incongruity, stuckness, and mixed messages accurately, real change in thoughts, feelings, and behavior is difficult. "I guess I do have mixed

---

*A paper-and-pencil measure of the Client Change Scale was developed by Heesacker and Pritchard and was later replicated by Rigazio-Digilio (cited in Ivey et al., 2005). Factor analytic study of over 500 students and a second study of 1,200 revealed that the five CCS levels are identifiable and measurable.

feelings about it. I certainly hurt about the marriage. I hurt, but now I realize how really angry I am." Coming to terms with anger or some other denied emotion is an important breakthrough and often is a sufficient solution for the client.

Level 4. Generation of a new solution. The client moves beyond recognition of the incongruity or conflict and puts things together in a new and productive way. Needless to say, this usually does not happen immediately. It can take several interviews. "Yes, I've been avoiding my anger, and I think it's getting in my way. If I'm going to move on, I will have to experience anger as part of the total situation."

Level 5. Development of new, larger, and more inclusive constructs, patterns, or behaviors—transcendence. Many clients will never reach this stage. A confrontation is most successful when the client recognizes the discrepancy and generates new thought patterns or behaviors to cope with and resolve the incongruity. "You helped me see that mixed feelings and thoughts are part of every relationship. I've been expecting too much. If I expressed both my hurt and anger more effectively, perhaps I wouldn't be facing a divorce."

When you confront clients, ask them a key question, or provide any intervention they may have a variety of responses. Ideally, they will actively generate new ideas and move forward (Level 4). But they may ignore or deny the fact that you have challenged or confronted them (Level 1). Most often, however, your intervention will be acknowledged and absorbed as part of a larger process of change (Levels 2 and 3).

When clients avoid your confrontation or fail to respond to an interpretation, they are subtly avoiding the full issue (Level 1). As they begin to respond, clients may move to partial acceptance (Level 2). Over time, clients will move toward understanding, generating new solutions, and transcendence (Levels 3, 4, and 5). However, depending on the issue, change may be slow. For some clients, movement to partial acceptance (Level 2) or partial acceptance but no change (Level 3) is a real triumph. *Movement on the scale can occur in one interview or it may take a year or more to help a person move out of denial or partial acceptance.*

▲ **MODULE 8.2**

SUMMARY

- ▲ When confrontation is used clearly and concisely, it encourages clients to look at their situation from a new perspective. Confrontation is an infrequently used skill in a single session, but most interviewers and counselors use it to help clients look at themselves.
- ▲ There are three steps of confrontation, each using different skills: Step 1, identify conflict; Step 2, point out issues of incongruity and work to resolve them; and Step 3, evaluate the change.
- ▲ The Client Change Scale can be applied to any client statement in the interview, or you can use these concepts to evaluate client change over several sessions. The five dimensions are (1) denial; (2) partial examination; (3) acceptance and recognition (but no change); (4) generation of a new solution; and (5) development of new, larger, and more inclusive constructs, patterns, or behaviors—transcendence.
- ▲ Be aware of individual and cultural differences, particularly if you are culturally different from the client.

BOX 8-2 Conflict Resolution and Mediation

You will find that confrontation skills are important in the mediation process. In conflict resolution and mediation—whether between children, adolescents, or adults—the following steps are useful.

Develop rapport and outline the structure of your session. Pay equal, neutral attention to each participant. Lane and McWhirter (1992) suggest four useful rules for children: (a) Agree to solve the problem, (b) no name-calling or put-downs, (c) be honest, and (d) listen; do not interrupt. Agreeing to some variation of these rules with adults is important to obtain commitment to the process of mediation.

Define the problem (concern). Use the basic listening sequence to clearly and *concretely* draw out the point of view of each person involved in the dispute. To avoid emotional outbursts, acknowledgment of feeling rather than reflection of feeling is recommended. Clearly summarize each person's frame of reference and carefully check out your accuracy with each one of them. You may ask each disputant to state the opponent's point of view. Outline and summarize the points of agreement and disagreement, perhaps in written form if the conflict is complex.

Set goals. Use the basic listening sequence to draw out each person's wants and desires for satisfactory problem solution; focus primarily on concrete facts rather than emotions and abstract intangibles. This is the beginning of the negotiation process when problems and concerns may be redefined and clarified.

Summarize the goals for each person, with attention to possible joint goals and points of agreement.

Generate solutions. Negotiation begins in earnest; rely on your listening skills to see whether the parties can generate their own satisfactory solutions. When a level of concreteness and clarity has been achieved (Steps 2 and 3), the parties involved may come close to agreement. If the parties are very conflicted, meet each one separately as you brainstorm alternative solutions. With touchy issues, summarize them in writing. Many of the influencing skills discussed later in this section will be useful in the process of negotiation.

Contract and generalize. Use the basic listening sequence; summarize the agreed-upon solution (or parts of the solution if negotiations are still in progress). Make the solution as concrete as possible and write down touchy main issues to make sure each party understands the agreement. Obtain agreement about subsequent steps. With children, congratulate them on their hard work and ask each child to tell a friend about the resolution.

The Martin Luther King Jr. Center (1989) summarizes six steps for nonviolent change that are closely related to the mediation model above: (1) information gathering, (2) education, (3) personal commitment, (4) negotiations, (5) direct action, and (6) reconciliation. When you work on complex issues of institutional or community change, a review of Dr. King's model may be helpful in thinking through your approach to major challenges.

MODULE 8.3
EXAMPLE INTERVIEW: Balancing Family Responsibilities

KEY CONCEPT QUESTION

▲ How is confrontation integrated into the interview?

Three main points are reviewed simultaneously in this example interview: (1) Listening skills are used to obtain client data, (2) confrontations of client discrepancies are noted, and (3) the effectiveness of the confrontations is considered using the Client Change Scale (CCS). Aim for understanding how confrontation is used in the interview example. You may want to read the segment several times and study it carefully. With more experience and practice, these concepts will be useful and important in your interviewing practice.

The following interview presents a conflict that is common to many working couples—balancing home tasks. Male attitudes and behaviors are changing, but many working women are still burdened with the responsibility for most home tasks. In this example we have both internal and external incongruity. Dominic is struggling internally with the discovery that things have changed and externally with the realization that his wife is behaving differently. Arguments may be particularly intense as two tired people come home from a hard day's work to face needy children and undone housework. Couples may blame each other rather than attributing a major portion of their issues to external causes at work. An exhausted partner or spouse often has little energy left to deal with the concrete issues at home.

Interviewer and Client Conversation	Process Comments
1. *Dominic:* I'm having a terrible time with my wife right now. She's working for the first time and we're having lots of arguments. She isn't fixing meals like she used to or watching the kids. I don't know what to do.	On the CCS, this client response is rated Level 2; he is partially aware of the problem. At the same time, he denies (Level 1) his role in the problem and is attributing the difficulties in the home to husband-wife issues, failing to see how demands at work play into the system.
2. *Ryan:* (holds out one hand to the right) So, on one hand, your wife is working outside the home, but (holds out the left hand) on the other hand you expect her to continue with all the housework, too. You don't like what's going on right now.	Confrontation presented as paraphrase and reflection of feeling. The use of hands with the words helps strengthen and clarify the conflict. Here the counselor shows imbalance or conflict concretely.
3. *Dominic:* You damn betcha she's expected to do what she's always done—I'm not confused about that.	CCS Level 1—denial.
4. *Ryan:* I see. You're not confused; you really don't like what's going on. Could you give me a specific example of what's happening—something that goes on between the two of you when you both get home?	Paraphrase, open question oriented to concreteness.
5. *Dominic:* (sighs, pauses) Yeah, that's right, I don't like what's going on. Like last night, Sara was so tired that she didn't get around to fixing dinner 'til half an hour late. I was hungry and tired myself. We had a big argument. This type of thing has been going on for 3 weeks.	While Dominic is able to identify and talk about the conflict (CCS Level 2), he lacks awareness of how his wife feels. He seems insensitive to the fact that his wife is working and he expects her to do everything she did in the past for him (CCS Level 1).
6. *Ryan:* I hear you, Dominic; you're pretty angry. Let's change focus for a minute. When dealing with conflict, it helps to concentrate on positive things. Could we search for some positive things that have worked for you and Sara in the past?	This summary introduces an incongruity between the difficult present situation and the good things of the past through the positive asset search.

Interviewer and Client Conversation	Process Comments
7. *Dominic:* Yes, I am angry and discouraged. Sara and I were doing pretty well until the baby came. Somehow things just got off kilter. (5-second pause and silence) . . . Well, let me try it your way. We sure had fun times together over the 3 years we've been together. We both like outdoor activity and doing things together. We never seem to have time for that now.	In couples work it is useful to remind them of positive stories from the past. This has been edited for brevity. It is important to explore positives in the relationship in much more depth than presented here.
8. *Ryan:* It's important to remember that you have a good history and have enjoyed each other. I'm wondering if part of the solution isn't finding time just to be together doing fun things. Let's make that part of our discussion later. But for the moment, let's go back to your main issues. Could you give me a specific example of what goes on between you when she gets home?	Paraphrase, suggestion, open question oriented to concreteness. Getting specifics helps clarify the situation. When counseling around couples issues, search for strengths. What brought the couple together and what maintains them now? This helps clients center themselves in positives as they struggle with the difficult negatives in a relationship. Helping couples recapture the good things in their relationship is important. We often recommend a weekly date night for couples.
9. *Dominic:* . . . (pause) Well, lately, I've had a lot of pressure at work. They're downsizing and morale is bad. I worry I'll be next. I try really hard, but when I get home, I just want to sit. Sara's got the same thing. Her new boss just wants more all the time. I guess when she comes home, she's about as exhausted and confused as I am.	It is very common for partners to get angry with each other when external stressors hit one or both individuals in the relationship. One can't argue with the boss or colleagues easily, so the partner is the scapegoat.
10. *Ryan:* I see. You both work all day and come home exhausted. Dominic, do you really think Sara can work that hard and still take care of you like she used to?	Paraphrase, closed question. Ryan's implicit confrontation is now more concrete.
11. *Dominic:* I guess I hadn't thought of it that way before. If Sara is working, she isn't going to be physically able to do what she did. But where does that leave me?	For the first time, Dominic is able to see that Sara can't continue as she has in the past (CCS Level 3). Note that he is still thinking primarily of himself. To move to higher levels on the CCS, Dominic would have to be able to take Sara's perspective and articulate what she likely thinks and feels when she gets home.

Interviewer and Client Conversation	Process Comments
12. *Ryan:* Yes, where does that leave you? Dominic, let me tell you about my experience. My wife started working and I, too, expected her to continue to do the housework, take care of the kids, do the shopping, and fix the meals. She went to work because we needed the money to make a down payment on a small house. Well, what I found was that my wife couldn't work unless I helped around the house. I had to decide which was more important—getting a house or maintaining our traditional roles. I share some of the household work with her. I don't like it, but it seems like it's got to be done. I shop and I pick the kids up at day care, too. How does that sound to you? Do you think you want to continue to expect Sara to do it all?	Self-disclosure followed by a check-out. Ryan is operating like a coach. He is speaking up directly with his ideas, but he is also allowing the client to react to them. Clearly, Ryan is trying to get Dominic's thinking and behavior to move. His last statement contains an important implicit confrontation: "On the one hand, your wife is working and if she continues, she'll need some help; on the other hand, perhaps you don't want her to work—what is your reaction to this?"
13. *Dominic:* Uhhh . . . we need the money. We've missed the last car payment. It was my idea that Sara go to work. But isn't housework "women's work"?	Dominic is now facing up to the contradiction he is posing (CCS Level 3). He has not yet synthesized his desire for his wife to work with the need for his sharing the workload at home, but at least he is moving toward a more open attitude. As he acknowledges his part in the situation and the need for more money, he is beginning to come to a new understanding, or synthesis, of the problem—he is less incongruent and is taking beginning steps toward resolving his discrepancies.

For each developmental task completed in the interviewing process, it often seems that a new problem arises. Just as the counselor is beginning to facilitate client movement, a new obstacle ("women's work") arises. To make the progress shown took half the session. Changing the concept from "women's work" to "work in the home that must be shared if the car payments are to be met" took the rest of the session. Achieving a new and likely more lasting level of male/female cultural differences would require a major transformation in thinking and behavior (CCS Level 5). Major change may require several interviews, group sessions, and time for Dominic, or any other client, to internalize new ideas.

△ **MODULE 8.3**

SUMMARY

▲ Three main points are covered in the example interview: (1) Listening skills are used to obtain client data, (2) confrontations of client discrepancies are noted, and (3) the effectiveness of the confrontations can be assessed using the Client Change Scale.

▲ Effective confrontation helps clarify issues and moves toward problem resolution. Basic listening skills and observation are required to identify and clarify client issues. However, you can see that the interviewer's sharing of experience or other information can be helpful at times.

▲ Major client change is an extended process; it may require several interviews, group sessions, and some time for the client to internalize and act on new ideas.

FOCUSING THE INTERVIEW
Exploring the Story From Multiple Perspectives

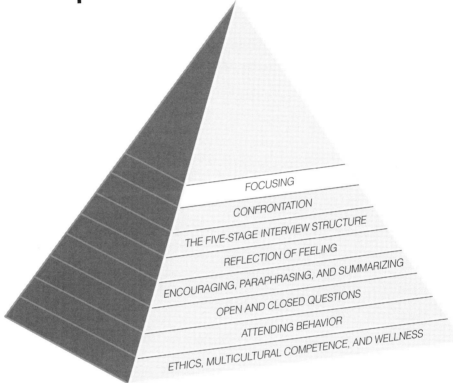

FOCUSING

CONFRONTATION

THE FIVE-STAGE INTERVIEW STRUCTURE

REFLECTION OF FEELING

ENCOURAGING, PARAPHRASING, AND SUMMARIZING

OPEN AND CLOSED QUESTIONS

ATTENDING BEHAVIOR

ETHICS, MULTICULTURAL COMPETENCE, AND WELLNESS

How can the skill of focusing help you and your clients?

CHAPTER
GOALS

Focusing is a skill that enables multiple tellings of the story and will help you and clients think of new possibilities for restorying. Client issues are often complex, and the systematic framework of focusing can help in reframing and reconstructing problems, concerns, issues, and challenges.

Awareness, knowledge, and skills developed through the concepts of this chapter will enable you to

- ▲ Help clients tell their stories and describe their issues from multiple frames of reference, thus expanding their possibilities for restorying and resolving issues.
- ▲ Help clients stay on track when they need to examine themselves or other interpersonal issues in a comprehensive fashion.

145

▲ Enable clients to see themselves as selves-in-relation and persons-in-community through community and family genograms.

▲ Include advocacy, community awareness, and social change as part of your interviewing practice

MODULE 9.1
DEFINING FOCUSING

KEY CONCEPT QUESTIONS

▲ How do you focus an interview?

▲ What are the central dimensions of focusing?

Focusing	*Predicted Result*
Use selective attention and focus the interview on the client, problem/concern, significant others (partner/spouse, family, friends), a mutual "we" focus, the interviewer, or the cultural/environmental context (RESPECT-FUL multicultural background, community, nation).	Clients focus their conversation or story on the dimensions selected by the interviewer. As the interviewer brings in new foci, the story is elaborated from multiple perspectives.

Vanessa walks swiftly into the office and starts talking even before she sits down: "I'm really glad to see you. I need help. My sister and I just had an argument. She won't come home for the holidays and help me with Mom's illness. My last set of exams was a mess and I can't study. I just broke up with the guy I was going with three years. And, now I'm not even sure where I'm going to live next term. And my car wouldn't start this morning. . . ." (She continues with her list of issues and begins repeating stories almost randomly, but always with energy and considerable emotion.)

There are many clients like Vanessa, who have several issues in their lives. We, perhaps like you, often feel overwhelmed when we get 5 or more minutes of problematic stories in which the client rapidly jumps from topic to topic. Sometimes there is an insistence that we do "something" immediately and start solving the issues. When we fall into solving problems for clients they often refuse to listen to us and generate more problems and difficulties.

So, what needs to be done here? Each client is unique and there is no magic answer. But one rule really helps us settle down and start working with the client. *Counseling is for the individual client.* Counseling is most effective when we focus on the client as the core of our interviewing and treatment plan. Our responsibility is to focus on what we can see and work with—specifically, the unique human being in front of us. We can't see the family, we can't see the boyfriend, and we can't study for the client. Most likely, with Vanessa, we would listen to her for no more than 3 to 5 minutes. Just listening to clients talk continuously does neither the client nor you any good. We would likely gently interrupt and say something like:

Vanessa, could we stop for a moment? I really hear *you* loud and clear. There are a lot of things happening right now. One of the best ways to approach these issues is to focus on how *you* are doing and feeling. Once I understand *you* a bit more, we can work on the issues that *you* describe.

I get the sense that *you, Vanessa*, are hurting a lot right now and are confused about what to do next. Could *you* take a deep breath and tell me what *you* are feeling and thinking right now? What are these things doing to *Vanessa*? What's happening with *you*?

In these two paragraphs, we have used the words "Vanessa" and "you" over ten times. The goal here is to help Vanessa focus on herself. Interviewing and counseling are first and foremost for the individual. Once we have a better grasp of the person before us, we can work more effectively toward problem resolution. Another possibility is to help Vanessa focus on one thing at a time. Summarize what you hear about several issues, and then ask her what she would like to start working on first, then suggest exploring other issues later.

Selective attention (Chapter 3) is basic to focusing—clients tend to talk about and focus on topics to which you give your primary attention. Through your attending skills (visuals, vocal tone, verbal following, and body language), you indicate to your client that you are listening. But we all tend to focus on or listen in different ways. It is important to be aware of both your conscious and unconscious patterns of selective attention; clients sometimes follow your lead rather than talk about what they really want to say. If you focus solely on individual issues, clients will talk about themselves and their frame of reference.

A second important area to focus on is the client's problem, issue, or concern. If a client has gone through a breakup of a significant relationship, has study difficulties, has cancer or another serious illness, we need to hear the details. On the other hand, some interviewers get so interested in the problem that they fail to consider how the client thinks, feels, and behaves in relation to the problem or issue. While a problem focus is essential, the client's uniqueness and background cannot be ignored.

"Which issue would you like to focus on first?"

"Sounds like your mother is the most important issue. Have I heard correctly?"

In addition, people live in a broader context of multiple systems. The concept of *self-in-relation* may be helpful. Increasingly, theorists are challenging the idea of a totally autonomous self. The term *being-in-relation* was suggested by the feminist authors Jordan, Hartling, and Walker (2004). The *person-as-community* was stressed from an Afrocentric frame by Obonnaya (1994), who points out that our family and community history live within each of us. The community genogram of this chapter may be useful in helping clients gain new perspectives on themselves and their relationships to others. You will find the community genogram a useful way to understand your client's history and a good place to identify strengths and resources.

Clearly much individual counseling focuses on issues of conflict, incongruity, and discrepancies between the individual and family and friends. In addition, many client problems are caused by and related to issues and events in the broader context (e.g., poor schools, floods, job issues). If you help clients to see themselves and their issues as *persons-in-community*, they can learn new ways of thinking about themselves and use existing support systems more effectively. It is not the individual versus social context; rather, social context enriches our understanding and enhances the uniqueness of each person and client. The following list offers sample comments and questions that allow the interviewer to focus the session in a specific area:

Significant others (partner, spouse, friends, family)

"Vanessa, tell me a bit more about your mother and how she is doing."

"How are your friends helpful to you?"

"What's going on with your sister?"

"You seem to be thinking a lot about the breakup after three years of living together. Let's explore that a bit more now."

"Your grandmother was very helpful to you in the past. What would she say to you?"

Mutual focus and immediacy ("we" statements and talking about what is going on in the session *here and now*)

"Vanessa, you have a lot on your plate, but *we* will work through your issues. Right now I can almost feel your hurt."

"Vanessa, we've been working together for two weeks now. I sense at this moment that you felt angry at what I just said. I'm glad that you can openly express your feelings to me."

Interviewer focus (sharing one's own experiences and reactions)

"I felt really confused and worried when my mother had the same illness. I simply didn't know what to do. Is that close to the way you feel?"

"I can understand your frustration with the car. It happened to me last week."

Cultural/environmental context (unique, personal, RESPECTFUL multicultural background [see Chapter 1] and broader issues such as the impact of the economy)

"Finding a new place to stay is difficult and you think that landlords won't rent to People of Color."

"What are some strengths that you gain from your spiritual orientation?"

"You feel that the college is simply not supporting you at all. Could you tell me a bit more about what they are doing to make it difficult for you?"

As an interviewer, be aware of how you focus an interview and how you can broaden the session so that clients are aware of themselves more fully in relation to others and social systems. You can help them see themselves as persons-in-relation, persons-in-community. In a sense you are like an orchestra conductor, selecting which instruments (ideas) to focus on, thus enabling a better understanding of the whole. Some of us focus exclusively on the client and the problem, failing to recognize the impact and importance of broad contextual issues. Others may fail to give sufficient attention to the client as a person and use the interview as a chance to learn interesting details—almost as a voyeur.

EXERCISE

At this point, we suggest that you develop a community genogram as presented in Box 9-1. Develop a community genogram for yourself using your own style of presentation. This will help you and your clients to see how we are connected to many influences. We are persons-in-relation to others and the social context around us. Think about your own life story and how it has been affected by the many relationships in your community of origin. Usually, the family is a critical part of the community genogram. However, the family genogram can be an useful supplement to the community genogram and bring out additional details of family history (Appendix II).

BOX 9-1   Developing a Community Genogram: Identifying Personal
and Multicultural Strengths

The community genogram is a "free-form" activity in which clients are encouraged to present their community of origin or present community, using their own unique style. Two visual examples of community genograms are presented here. Through the community genogram, we can better grasp the developmental history of our clients and identify client strengths for later problem solving. Clients may construct a genogram by themselves or be assisted by you through questioning and listening to the things that they include.

Step 1: Develop a Visual Representation of the Community

▲ Select the community in which you were primarily raised; the community of origin is where you tend to learn the most about culture. But any other community, past or present, may be used.

▲ Represent yourself or the client with a significant symbol. Use a large poster board or flipchart paper. Place yourself or the client in that community, either at the center or at another appropriate place. Encourage clients to be innovative and represent their communities in a format that appeals to them. This could include maps, constructions, or star diagrams as Janet uses below.

▲ It is important to place family or families, nuclear or extended, on the paper, represented by the symbol that is most relevant for you or the client.

▲ Place important, most influential groups on the community genogram, represented by distinctive visual symbols. School, family, neighborhood, and spiritual groups are most often selected. For teens, the peer group is often particularly important. For adults, work groups and other special groups tend to become more central.

▲ You may wish to suggest relevant aspects of the RESPECTFUL model of Chapter 1. In this way, diversity issues can be included in the genogram.

Step 2: Search for Images and Narratives of Strengths

▲ Post the community genogram on the wall during counseling sessions.

▲ Focus on one single dimension of the community or the family. Emphasize positive stories even if the client wants to start with a negative story. Do not work with the negatives until positive strengths are solidly in mind, unless the client clearly needs to tell you the difficult story.

▲ Help the client share one or more positive stories relating to the community dimension selected. If you are doing your own genogram, you may want to write it down in journal form.

▲ Develop at least two more positive images and stories from different groups within the community. It is often useful to have one positive family image, one spiritual image, and one cultural image so that several areas of wellness and support are included.

(Continued)

BOX 9-1   Developing a Community Genogram: Identifying Personal
and Multicultural Strengths (Continued)

The Community Genogram:
Two Visual Examples

We encourage clients to generate their own visual representations of their "community of origin" and/or their current community support network. The two examples below are only two of many possibilities.

1. *The star:* Janet's world during elementary school tells us a good bit about a difficult time in her life. Nonetheless, note the important support systems.

2. *The map:* The client draws a literal or metaphoric map of the community, in this case a rural setting. Note how this view of the client's background reveals a close extended family and a relatively small experiential world. The absence of friends in the map is interesting. Church is the only outside factor noted.

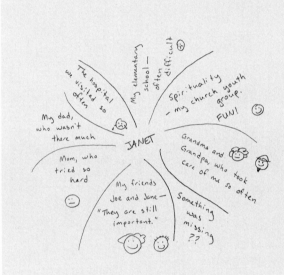

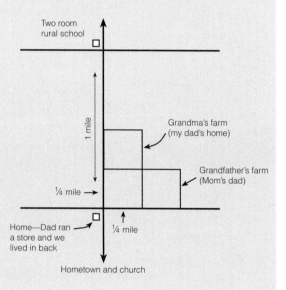

△ **MODULE 9.1**

SUMMARY

▲ Selective attention (Chapter 3) is basic to focusing—clients tend to talk about or focus on topics to which you give your primary attention. Through your attending skills (visuals, vocal tone, verbal following, and body language), you indicate to your client the topics that you consider most important.

▲ The interviewer, through selective attention focuses the interview on the client, problem/concern, important others (partner/spouse, family, friends, organizations such as churches, schools, clubs), or the cultural/environmental context (RESPECTFUL multicultural background, community, nation). In addition, the counselor may focus on himself or herself or what is going on in the *here and now* of the interview.

The community genogram can be a helpful tool in seeing yourself and others as persons-in-relation and persons-in-community. (See Appendix II, The Family Genogram.)

MODULE 9.2

EXAMPLE INTERVIEW: It's All My Fault—Helping Clients Understand Self-in-Relation

KEY CONCEPT QUESTION

▲ How is focusing integrated into the interview?

Carl Rogers's person-centered counseling has had an immense and lasting influence on the way we conduct helping sessions. We can only work with the individual before us and ultimately, it is this unique person who is most important. We live in a culture that focuses on individuality, individual responsibility, and individual achievement, thus the "I" focus. It is only natural that counseling focuses on the immediate person in the *here and now*. At the same time, the issues of self-in-relation and the environmental/cultural/contextual setting in which the person exists also need full attention.

The following interview with Janet focuses first on her individual issue of taking virtually all the responsibility for difficulties in her relationship with Sander. This is the second interview, and during the first session Janet completed a community genogram of the home where she grew up in Eugene, Oregon (see Box 9-1). The community genogram is used to help Janet understand how her history might affect her present behavior, feelings, and thoughts.

Interviewer and Client Conversation	Process Comments
1. *Samantha:* Nice to see you, Janet. How have things been going?	A solid relationship was established during the first session. When Samantha met Janet outside her office, Janet seemed anxious to start the session.
2. *Janet:* Well, I tried your suggestion. I think I understand things a bit better.	Last week, Samantha suggested homework that asked Janet to spend the week listening carefully to Sander and trying to identify what he was really saying. She also advised continuing her own behavioral patterns so that she could note patterns of behavior more easily.
3. *Samantha:* You understand better? Could you tell me more?	Encourage. Focus on problem.
4. *Janet:* Well, I listened more carefully to Sander so I could understand what he really wants from me. He really wants a lot. He wants me to be a better cook, he doesn't like the way I keep house, and the more I listened, the more he wanted. I guess I haven't given him enough attention. I should be doing more and doing it better.	Self-disclosure on observations. Focus on self (the client), others (Sander), and the main theme of relationship.

Interviewer and Client Conversation	Process Comments
5. *Samantha:* Janet, it looks like you feel sad and a little guilty for not doing more. Am I hearing you right?	Reflection of feeling, focus on Janet with secondary focus on the problem.
6. *Janet:* Yes, I do feel sad and guilty; it's my responsibility to keep things together at home. He works so hard.	The key word *responsibility* appears. Janet seems to believe that she is responsible for keeping the relationship together. The acceptance of individual responsibility (and blame) is often characteristic of, but not exclusive to, women of Northern European background.
7. *Samantha:* Sounds like you're punishing yourself, when you're trying so hard and being so responsible. Could you tell me more about how Sander reacts?	Samantha makes an interpretation ("punishing yourself"). The focus is first on Janet and changes to Sander.
8. *Janet:* Yes, I get angry with myself for not doing better. It's hard with work too. But Sander wants the house to run perfectly. I try and try, but I always miss something. Then Sander blows up.	Focus on self and the problem with the close relationship in connection.
9. *Samantha:* I hear you trying very hard. Could you give me a specific example of a time that Sander blew up?	Paragraph and open question. The focus changes from Janet to Sander in a search for concreteness.
10. *Janet:* Last night I made a steak dinner; I try to fix what he wants. He seemed so pleased, but I forgot to buy steak sauce and he blew up. It really shook me up . . . then, when we went to bed, he wanted to make love, but I was so tense that I couldn't. He got angry all over again.	Examples help us understand the specifics of situations. Some clients talk in vague generalities and asking for specifics can make a real difference.
11. *Samantha:* What happened then?	Open question/encourage, focus on problem. Search for more concreteness.
12. *Janet:* He went to sleep. I lay there and shook. As I calmed down, I realized that I need to do a better job and maybe he won't get so angry.	Focus on self and Sander and actions that might be taken on her part to resolve or prevent the difficulties.
13. *Samantha:* Let's see if I understand what you are saying. You are doing every-thing you can to make the relationship work. Sander blows up at little things, and you try harder. And then you feel the problem is your fault. Have I heard you correctly?	Samantha summarizes the situation. She recognizes it as a pattern in Janet's relationship with her husband. No matter how hard she tries, the situation esca-lates and Janet accepts the blame. Focus on Janet, Sander, and the main theme/problem.
14. *Janet:* It is my fault, isn't it?	Self-focus. Note the acceptance of individual responsibility for the difficulties.

Interviewer and Client Conversation	Process Comments
15. *Samantha:* I'm not so sure. We've talked about your problem with Sander. Now let's talk about something that went right for you in the past. As you look at your community genogram, what reminds you of good times, when things were going well?	Focus shifted from interviewer and problem to cultural/environmental context and a search for positive assets and wellness strengths. Strengths and positive behaviors are helpful in understanding present situations.
16. *Janet:* (pause) Well, I loved visiting Grandma and Grandpa. They were friendly and helped me with my problems. Mom was the same way—she kept pointing out that I could do things.	Focus on family.
17. *Samantha:* Could you tell me a story about Grandma and Grandpa or your Mom when they made things better for you?	Open questions focused on positive stories in the family.
18. *Janet:* Well, Mom had to work and carry the family, and I had the most fun with Grandma and Grandpa. One time kids were teasing me at school about my braces. I thought I was funny looking because I was different. They listened to me; they told me that I was beautiful and smart. They taught me to ignore the others, just try harder, and it would all work out. I found that it does— if I try harder, it usually does get better.	We learn about a supportive family. We also hear about a problem-solving style that focuses on ignoring underlying issues and trying harder—exactly what Janet is doing with Sander.
19. *Samantha:* So you learned in your family that ignoring things and trying harder usually helped work things out. Where did your desire to try so hard come from?	We see the emphasis on individual responsibility. Paraphrase with focus on family and client. Linking of past history with present situation.
20. *Janet:* (pauses and looks at community genogram) Dad made impossible demands of Mom. After she talked with the minister of our church, she started standing up for herself. I learned in church that it is important to care for others, but that I can't care for others unless I care for myself.	Focus on community, the family and the church. Janet is beginning to draw on resources from the past. She is becoming aware of being a person-in-community. This helps her to start thinking of herself in new ways.
21. *Samantha:* Connections and relationships are very important to you. There is also need to care for yourself if you are to care for others. Too many women fall into the trap of always caring for others and not caring for themselves. That seems to represent the family lesson of caring. We also need to focus on your Mom starting to care for herself, how that made a difference in your family. I wonder if it would make the same difference for you now?	A brief summary followed by reframing what Janet has said with a new perspective. This is a slight extension of what Janet seemed to be already saying. Reframing and interpretation tend to be best received when they are not too far from the client's present thinking.

Interviewer and Client Conversation	Process Comments
22. *Janet:* I think so. I so appreciate your listening to me. I wonder if I've become too much of a doormat for Sander. But I worry about what he would do if I stood up more for myself. That seems to be my family history. Thank heavens for the church.	Janet focuses on herself as a person in a family within the community. The interviewing session can now move to problem solving and restorying. Her spiritual background may be helpful.
23. *Samantha:* Could you tell me more about what the church and spirituality mean to you?	Open question with focus on the client and the cultural/environmental context in terms of the church.
24. *Janet:* Connections with friends are important, but church was a place where I could quietly meditate and work through issues. I don't seem to give myself time for that any more.	Janet is identifying herself as a self-in-relation and draws on community resources for additional strength. Meditation is a well-known and important strategy that helps build a more positive self.
25. *Samantha:* Meditation and spirituality often give us a foundation for deciding what is best. Let us explore that in more detail.	The focus turns to external sources that may help Janet build on the past to work through current issues.

Samantha helped Janet examine her situation in its broader context. The family and/or community genogram can be helpful in aiding a person who places too much responsibility on herself or himself. This can help both clients and helping professionals see the client as a person-in-relation or a person-in-community. This is a more leading approach, although the professional must continue to listen carefully to what the person has to say. As focus shifts to various dimensions of the larger client story, the client and the counselor begin to understand the multidimensionality of the issue more fully. Janet's problem is not just "Janet's problem." Rather, her issues interact with many aspects of her past and present situation.

Change can be measured in the session, regardless of skills used. At the beginning of this session, Janet took almost total responsibility for the problems she experienced with Sander. After review and discussion of the community genogram, she seems to have moved from a denial (Level 1) on the Client Change Scale (CCS) to acceptance and recognition, but no change (Level 3). She clearly has a new way of thinking and is beginning to see herself as a being-in-relation. But real and lasting change will require new behavior that works successfully in the relationship. Meditation and spirituality, plus the resources of her mother's later life change may help Janet experience further progress in her understanding and future relationship with Sander.

▲ **MODULE 9.2**

SUMMARY

- ▲ The community genogram provided a clear visual picture of the client's background and helped the counselor understand the social context more quickly and fully.
- ▲ Client issues are seldom one-person issues. Focusing on the family background, the church, and spirituality enriched the session and helped the client focus on positive strengths.

BOX 9-2   National and International Perspectives on Counseling

Where to Focus: Individual, Family, or Culture?
WEIJUN ZHANG

Case study: Carlos Reyes, a Latino student majoring in computer science, was referred to counseling by his adviser because of his recent academic difficulties and psychosomatic symptoms. The counselor was able to discern that Carlos's major concern was his increasing dislike of computer science and growing interest in literature. While he was intrigued about changing his major, he felt overwhelmed by the potential consequences for his family, in which he is the oldest of four siblings. He is also the first in his family to ever attend college. Carlos has received some limited financial support from his parents and one of his younger siblings, and the family income is barely above the poverty line. The counseling was at an impasse, for Carlos was reluctant to take any action and instead kept saying, "I don't know how to tell this to my folks. I'm sure they'll be mad at me."

During class discussion of this case, almost everyone argued that Carlos's problem is that he does not give priority to his personal career interests, that he should learn to think about what is good for his own mental health, and that he needs assertiveness training. I did not quite agree with my fellow students, who are all European Americans. I thought they were failing to see a decisive factor in the case: Carlos is Latino!

In traditional Hispanic culture, the extended family, rather than the individual, is the psychosocial unit of cooperation. The family is valued over the individual, and subordination of individual wants to the family needs is assumed. Also, traditional Hispanic families are hierarchical in form; parents are authority figures and children are supposed to be obedient. Given this cultural background, to encourage Carlos to make a major career decision totally by himself was impossible. Any counseling effort that does not focus on the whole family is doomed to fail.

Because it is the financial support from the family that made his college education possible, Carlos may be expected to contribute to the family when he graduates. This reciprocal relationship is a lifelong expectation in Hispanic culture, and the oldest son is especially responsible in this regard. Changing his major in his junior year does not only mean he will be postponing the date when he will be able to help his family financially, but it also means he may not be able to do so at all, for we all understand how hard it is to find a good-paying job in the field of literature. When interdependence is the norm among Hispanic Americans, how can we expect Carlos to focus entirely on his personal interests without giving more weight to his family's pressing economic needs?

If I were Carlos's counselor, rather than focusing immediately on his needs, I would first support him with his family loyalty and then help him understand that there are not just two solutions: either . . . or. . . . Together, we might brainstorm to generate some alternatives, such as having literature as his minor now and as his pastime after he graduates, changing his career when his younger siblings are off on their own, or exploring possibilities that may combine the two. He could, for example, design computer programs to help schoolchildren learn literature. Each of these takes into account family needs as well as those of Carlos.

The professor praised me highly for my "different and sensitive perspective," but I shrugged it off; this is just common sense to most Third World minority people and, probably, many Italian and Jewish Americans as well. (I remember years ago, when I was trying to make major career decisions with my parents; at least ten of my relatives were involved. And these days, I am still obligated to help anyone in my extended family who is in financial need.) It took me almost a year to realize that when I am asked, here in the United States, "How's your family?" I usually need tell how only my wife and child are faring, not my parents, grandparents, and siblings.

If the meaning of family in Hispanic culture is confusing to many counselors, the traditional extended family clan system of Native American Indians, Canadian Dene, or New Zealand Maori can be even more difficult for them to grasp. This family extension can include at times several households and even a whole village. Unless majority group counselors are aware of these differences in family structure, they may cause serious harm through their own ignorance.

MODULE 9.3

INSTRUCTIONAL READING: Multiple Contextual Perspectives on Client Concerns

KEY CONCEPT QUESTIONS

▲ **What is the most important focus dimension?**

▲ **How does the interviewer's context affect how he or she focuses on client topics?**

▲ **How do you help a client focus on different perspectives when working on a difficult issue?**

Although people have much in common with one another, each person we interview or counsel is totally unique. Interviewing and counseling are for the client, and learning about and focusing on that unique human being before you is the most critical and important focus. The person's name and the word *you* are central to every interview. But if we are to fully discover client uniqueness, we need to understand the broader context of the client (friends, family, community). *Contextual interviewing strengthens the "I focus."* Multiple focusing and the family and/or community genograms provide a framework for understanding and action.

We also bring broader understanding and multiple perspectives to the session by our choice of focus on the client's life and social context. Part of what leads us to focus on certain issues is our own social context. Your developmental past is part of that context. You as interviewer can consciously or unconsciously avoid talking about certain subjects with which you are uncomfortable. You may focus on certain issues and dimensions while ignoring others. Becoming aware of your own social context and possible biases will free you to understand the uniqueness of each individual more fully and how her or his context may be similar or different from yours.

We all work with clients who have different values and beliefs from our own. Whether the issue is the role of women, affirmative action, attitudes toward gays or lesbians, spiritual/religious beliefs, or abortion, you are going to counsel clients who think differently from you. Sharing your honest thoughts with a client on very sensitive issues can be dangerous and potentially destructive to the client. Equally, and perhaps more, problematic are the situations when you unconsciously direct the client in a direction that you favor. Seek supervision and consultation if you find yourself in a challenging situation in which your own thoughts get in the way of a successful counseling relationship.

EXERCISE 1

Before you continue with this module take some time to think through your own thoughts on a difficult and challenging issue—abortion. It will help if you take time to write your responses to the *italicized* questions below.

As an interviewer, counselor, or psychotherapist, you will encounter controversial cases and work with clients who have made different decisions than perhaps you would. Abortion is part of what is sometimes called the "culture wars." There are deeply felt beliefs and emotions around this issue. Even the language of "pro-choice" and "pro-life" beliefs can be upsetting to some. *What is your personal position around this challenging issue?*

Review the multiple dimensions of focus. What do your family and those closest to you think about abortion? Your friends? What do your community and church, both past and present, say and think? And how does your understanding of state laws and the extensive national media coverage affect your thinking? *From a more complex, contextual point of view, spend a little time thinking about what has influenced your thinking on this issue; record what you discover.* Our individual thoughts and decisions on critical issues are deeply intertwined in our social context.

As a counselor, it is vital that you understand the situations, thoughts, and feelings of those who take varying positions around abortion or any other controversial issue, whether you agree with them or not. *Can you identify some of the thoughts and feelings of those who have a different position from your own?*

Counseling is not teaching clients how to live or what to believe. It is helping clients make their own decisions. Regardless of your personal position, you may find yourself unconsciously using the interview to further your position. Most would agree that counselors should avoid bias in counseling. You may need to help your client understand more than one position on abortion or recognize and deal with conscious or unconscious sexism, racism, anti-Semitism, anti-Islamism, or other forms of intolerance. The art and mastery of effective counseling merges awareness of and respect for beliefs with unbiased probing in the interest of client self-discovery, autonomy, and growth.

EXERCISE 2

Some school systems and agencies have written policies forbidding any discussion of abortion. Further, if you are working within certain agencies (e.g., a faith-based agency or a pro- or anti-abortion counseling clinic), the agency may have specific policies regarding counseling around abortion. Ethically, clients should be made aware of specific agency beliefs before counseling begins. Again, write your answers to the questions below, but there are no necessarily "right" answers to these difficult issues.

Imagine that a client comes to you who just terminated a fetus. How would you help this client, who clearly needs to tell her story?

Focus on the Individual and on Significant Others

TERESA: I just had an abortion and I feel awful. The medical staff was great and the operation went smoothly. But Cordell won't have anything to do with me, and I can't talk with my parents. The people outside yelling at me as I went in scared me.

What would you say to focus on Teresa as an individual?

What could you say to focus on Cordell?

How would you focus on the noisy and likely disrespectful crowd?

How might you focus on the attitudes and possible supports from her friends?

Choosing an appropriate focus can be most challenging. Too many beginners focus only on the problem. The prompt, "Tell me more about the abortion," may result in drawing out details of the abortion but little may be learned about the client's distinctive personal experience. An extremely important task is drawing out the client's story, "I'd like to hear *your* story" or "What do *you* want to tell me?" There are no final rules on where to focus, but generally, we want to hear the client's unique experience.

Focusing on the individual is usually where to start—review on page 147 where the word *you* was used in the example interviewer comments.

Other key figures (Cordell, the crowd, family, friends) are part of the larger picture. What are their stories? How do they relate to Teresa as a person-in-relation? You can more fully understand her situation when you draw out other stories or viewpoints. It is important to keep all significant others in mind in the process of problem examination and resolution. For a full understanding of the client's experience, all pertinent relationships eventually need to be explored.

Focus on Family and Significant Others

TERESA: My family is quite religious and they have always talked strongly against abortion; it makes me feel all the more guilty. I could never tell them.

How might you focus on the family in response to her statement?

How would you search for others in the family who might be helpful or supportive?

The family is where personal values and ethics are first learned. How does Teresa define "family"? There are many styles of family beyond the nuclear. African American and Hispanic clients may think of the extended family; a lesbian may see her supportive family as the gay community. Issues of single parenthood and alternative family styles continue to make the picture of the family more complex. Developing a community or family genogram may help Teresa locate resources and models that might help her. If her parents are not emotionally available, perhaps an aunt or grandmother might be.

Mutuality Focus

TERESA: I feel like everyone is just judging me. They all seem to be condemning me. I even feel a little frightened of you.

How would you appropriately focus on the relationship between yourself and the client?

What might you say to Teresa that focuses on the "here-and-now" feelings?

A mutual immediate focus often emphasizes the "we" in a *here-and-now* relationship. Working together in an egalitarian relationship can empower clients. Also, helping them recognize the depth of their feelings in the *here and now* can be valuable and powerful. "Right now at this moment, *we* have an issue." "Can *we* work together to help you?" "What are some of your thoughts and feelings about how *we* are doing?" The emphasis is on the relationship between counselor and client. Two people are working on an issue, and the interviewer accepts partial ownership of the problem.

In feminist counseling, the "we" focus may be especially appropriate: *"We* are going to solve this problem." The "we" focus provides a sharing of responsibility, which is often reassuring to the client regardless of her or his background. Many feminist counselors emphasize "we." In some counseling theories and Western cultures, emphasizing the distinction between "you" (client focus) and "me" (interviewer focus) is more common and "we" would be considered inappropriate.

The mutual focus often includes a *here-and-now* dimension and brings immediacy to the session. To focus on the *here and now,* there are several different types of responses. "Teresa, right now you are really hurting and sad about the abortion."

"I sense a lot of unsaid anger right now." There is also the classic, "What are you feeling right now, at this moment?"

Interviewer Focus

TERESA: What do you think about what I did? What should I do?

What would you say? An interviewer focus could be self-disclosure of feelings and thoughts or personal advice about the client or situation, "*I* feel concerned and sad over what happened"; "Right now, *I* really hurt for you, but I know that you have what it takes to get through this"; "*I* want to help"; or "*I*, too, had an abortion . . . *my* experience was. . . ." Opinions vary on the appropriateness of interviewer or counselor involvement, but the value and power of such statements are increasingly being recognized. They must not be overused; keep self-disclosures brief.

How might you share your own thoughts and feelings appropriately?

Would you give advice from your frame of reference? What would it be?

What are the power issues if you share your own thoughts or the agency policies?

Cultural/Environmental/Contextual Focus

Given Teresa's discussion thus far, *what would you say to bring in broader cultural/ environmental/contextual issues?*

Perhaps the most complex focus dimension is the cultural/environmental context. Some topics within these broad areas are listed here, along with possible responses to the client. A key cultural/contextual issue in discussing abortion will often be religion and spiritual orientation. Whether she is conservative, liberal, Christian, Jew, Hindu, Muslim, or a nonbeliever, discussing the values issue from a spiritual perspective may be important to the client.

- ▲ *The crowd:* "You said the crowd scared you. Let's talk about them some more."
- ▲ *Moral/religious issues:* "What can you draw from your spiritual background to help you?"
- ▲ *Legal issues:* "The topic of abortion brings up some legal issues in this state. How have you dealt with them?"
- ▲ *Women's issues:* "A support group for women is just starting. Would you like to attend?"
- ▲ *Economic issues:* "You were saying that you didn't know how to pay for the operation. . . ."
- ▲ *Health issues:* "You seem to be recovering well physically, but how have you been eating and sleeping lately? Do you feel aftereffects?"
- ▲ *Educational/career issues:* "How long were you out of school/work?"
- ▲ *Ethnic/cultural issues:* "What is the meaning of abortion among people in your family/church/neighborhood?"

Any one of these issues, as well as many others, could be important to a client. With some clients all of these areas might need to be explored for satisfactory problem resolution. The counselor or interviewer who is able to conceptualize client issues broadly can introduce many valuable aspects of the problem or situation. Note that much of cultural/environmental/contextual focusing requires sensitive leading and influencing from the interviewer.

▲ **MODULE 9.3**

SUMMARY

- ▲ The major focus dimensions are client, problem or issue, significant others, mutuality focus (often with immediacy), interviewer, and the broader cultural/environmental context.
- ▲ Counseling is for the client and focusing on that client is central to all interviews. Secondarily, we need to focus on the client's problems, issues, and concerns within a broad contextual frame. Too often interviewing focuses just on the client and the problem, thus missing broader understanding.
- ▲ You as an interviewer or counselor also come from a social context and all the focus dimensions apply to you as well. You may consciously or unconsciously focus on certain issues and dimensions while ignoring others.

MODULE 9.4
ADVOCACY AND SOCIAL JUSTICE

KEY CONCEPT QUESTION

▲ What is the interviewer's role in advocacy and social justice?

You are going to face situations when your best counseling efforts are insufficient to help clients resolve their issues and move on with their lives. The social context of homelessness, poverty, racism, sexism, and contextual issues may leave clients in an impossible situation. The problem may be bullying on the playground, an unfair teacher, or an employer who refuses to follow fair employment practices. It is critical that we examine the societal stressors that our clients may face. Traditional approaches to interviewing and counseling may not be enough.

Advocacy is speaking out for your clients; working in the school, community, or larger setting to help clients; and also working for social change. What are you going to do on a daily basis to help improve the systems within which your clients live? Here are some examples when simply talking with clients about their issues may not be enough:

- ▲ As an elementary school counselor, you counsel a child who is being bullied on the playground.
- ▲ You are a high school counselor and work with a tenth grader who is teased and harassed about being gay while the classroom teacher quietly watches and says nothing.
- ▲ As a personnel officer, you discover systematic bias against promotion for women and minorities.
- ▲ Working in a community agency, you have a client who speaks of abuse in the home but fears leaving because she sees no future financial support.
- ▲ You are working with an African American client who has dangerous hypertension. You know that there is solid evidence that racism influences blood pressure.

The elementary counselor can work with school officials to set up policies are around bullying and harassment, actively changing the environment that allowed bullying to occur. The high school counselor faces an especially challenging issue as interview confidentiality may preclude immediate classroom action. If this is not possible, then the counselor can initiate school policies and awareness programs against oppression in the classroom. The passive teacher may become more aware through training you offer to all the teachers. You can help the African American client understand that hypertension is not just "his problem," but rather his blood pressure is partially related to the constant stressors of racism in his environment. You can work to eliminate oppression in your community.

"Whistle-blowers" who name problems that others prefer to avoid can face real difficulty. They will need your support and advice on how to proceed. For example, the company may not want to have its systematic bias exposed. On the other hand, through careful consultation and data gathering, the human relations staff may be able to help managers develop promotion programs that are fairer. Again, the issue of policy becomes important. Counselors can be advocates for policy changes in their work settings.

The counselor in the community agency knows that advocacy is the only possibility when abuse is apparent. For these clients, advocacy in terms of support in getting out of the home, finding new housing, and learning how to set up a restraining order may be far more important than self-examination and understanding.

Counselors who care about their clients also become their advocates when necessary. They are willing to move out of the counseling office and seek social change. You may work with others on a specific cause or issue to facilitate general human development and wellness (e.g., pre-term pregnancy care, child care, fair housing, aid for the homeless, athletic fields for low-income areas). This requires you to speak out, to develop skills with the media, and to learn about legal issues. *Ethical witnessing* moves beyond working with victims of injustice to the deepest level of advocacy (Ishiyama, 2006). Counseling, social work, and human relations are inherently social justice professions, but speaking out for social concerns needs our time and attention.

▲ **MODULE 9.4**
SUMMARY

- ▲ You are going to face situations when your best counseling efforts are insufficient to help your clients resolve their issues and move on with their lives. The social context of poverty, racism, sexism, and many other forms of unfairness may leave your client in an impossible situation.
- ▲ Those who adopt a social justice orientation and ethical witnessing move beyond understanding and take action for their clients.

REFLECTION OF MEANING AND INTERPRETATION/REFRAMING

Helping Clients Restory Their Lives

INFLUENCING SKILLS
AND STRATEGIES

FOCUSING

CONFRONTATION

THE FIVE-STAGE INTERVIEW STRUCTURE

REFLECTION OF FEELING

ENCOURAGING, PARAPHRASING, AND SUMMARIZING

OPEN AND CLOSED QUESTIONS

ATTENDING BEHAVIOR

ETHICS, MULTICULTURAL COMPETENCE, AND WELLNESS

How can the skills of reflection of meaning and interpretation/reframe help you and your clients?

CHAPTER GOALS   Interviewing, counseling, and therapy focus on helping clients change their thoughts, feelings, and behaviors. Underlying this basic triad is the issue of meaning and how to interpret life experience. What is the purpose or significance of it all? What sense does anything make? Two related skills are emphasized in this chapter and both seek to enable the client to think in new and more productive ways.

This chapter is dedicated to the memory of Viktor Frankl. The initial stimulus for the skill of reflection of meaning came from a 2-hour meeting with him in Vienna shortly after we had visited the German concentration camp, Auschwitz, where he had been imprisoned in World War II. He impressed on us the central value of meaning in counseling and therapy—a topic to which most theories give insufficient attention. It was his unusual ability to find positive meaning in the face of impossible trauma that impressed us most. His thoughts also impacted our wellness and positive strengths orientation. His theoretical and practical approach to counseling and therapy deserves far more attention than it receives. We often recommend his gripping, short book, *Man's Search for Meaning* (1959) to our clients who face serious life crises.

Reflection of meaning is concerned with helping clients find deeper meanings underneath thoughts, feelings, and behavior. In turn, finding a deeper meaning leads to new interpretations of life. Interpretation/reframing seeks to provide a new way of understanding these thoughts, feelings, and behaviors and this often also results in perspectives on making meaning. Interpretation often comes from a specific theoretical perspective such as decisional, psychodynamic, or multicultural. Clients generate their own meanings, whereas interpretations/reframes usually come from the interviewer.

Awareness, knowledge, and skills developed through the concepts of this chapter will enable you to

- ▲ Understand the distinction and the relationship of reflection of meaning and interpretation/reframing.
- ▲ Assist clients, through reflection of meaning, to explore their deeper meanings, values, and goals or life mission.
- ▲ Help clients, through interpretation/reframing, find an alternative frame of reference or way of thinking that facilitates personal development.
- ▲ Understand how these skills relate to and are different from other microskills.

MODULE 10.1

DEFINING THE SKILLS OF REFLECTING MEANING AND INTERPRETATION/REFRAMING

KEY CONCEPT QUESTIONS

▲ **How can I demonstrate the skills of eliciting and reflecting meaning and interpreting/reframing?**

▲ **How are these two skills similar and how are they different?**

Reflection of Meaning	Predicted Result
Meanings are close to core experiencing. Encourage clients to explore their own meanings and values in more depth from their own perspective. Questions to elicit meaning are often a vital first step. A reflection of meaning looks very much like a paraphrase but focuses beyond what the client says. Often the words "meaning, values, vision, and goals" appear in the discussion.	The client discusses stories, issues, and concerns in more depth with a special emphasis on deeper meanings, values, and understandings. Clients may be enabled to discern their life goals and vision for the future.
Interpretation/Reframe	*Predicted Result*
Provide the client with a new perspective, frame of reference, or way of thinking about issues. Interpretations/reframes may come from your observations; they may be based on varying theoretical orientations to the helping field; or they may link critical ideas together.	The client may find another perspective or meaning of a story, issue, or problem. The new perspective could have been generated by a theory used by the interviewer, from linking ideas or information, or by simply looking at the situation afresh via focusing.

Both interpretation/reframes and reflection of meaning seek implicit issues and meanings below the surface of client conversation. The formal definition of interpretation is "an explanation of the meaning or significance of something" while meaning is defined as "what a word means" or its purpose and significance (MicrosoftWord, 2001). From those two definitions, you can see the logic of presenting the two skills together as they are closely related.

Eliciting and reflection of meaning is both a skill and a strategy. As a skill, it is fairly straightforward. To elicit meaning, ask the client some variation of the basic question, "What does . . . *mean* to you, your past or future life?" At the same time, effective exploration of meaning becomes a major strategy in which you bring out client stories, past, present, *and future.* You use all the listening, focusing, and confrontation skills to facilitate this self-examination, yet the focus remains on meaning and finding purpose in one's life.

The case of Charlis will serve as a way to illustrate similarities and differences between reflection of meaning and interpretation.

> Charlis, a workaholic 45-year-old middle manager, has a heart attack. After several days of intensive care, she is moved to the floor where you, as the hospital social worker, work with the heart attack aftercare team. Charlis is motivated; she is following physician directives and progressing as rapidly as possible. She listens carefully to diet and exercise suggestions and seems the ideal patient with an excellent prognosis. However, she wants to return to her high-pressure job and continue moving up through the company; you observe some fear and puzzlement about what's happened.

Reflection of Meaning

You recognize that Charlis is reevaluating the meaning of her life. She asks questions that are hard to answer—"Why me?" "What is the meaning of my life? What is God saying to me? Am I on the wrong track? What should I *really* be doing?" You sense that she feels that something is missing in her life, and she also wants to reevaluate where she is going and what she is doing. How might you help Charlis? What thoughts occur to you? What do you see as the key issues that relate to the meaning and purpose of her life?

To elicit meaning, we may ask Charlis some variation of a basic meaning question, "What does the heart attack *mean* to you, your past and future life?" We may also ask Charlis if she would like to examine the meaning of her life through the process of *discernment*, a more systematic approach to meaning and purpose defined in some detail in this chapter. If she wishes, we'd share the specific questions of discernment presented there and ask her which areas she'd like to explore. In addition, we'd ask her to think of questions and issues that are particularly important to her as we work to help her discern the meaning of her life, her work, her goals, and her mission. These questions often bring out emotions, and they certainly bring out meaning in the client's thoughts and cognitions. When clients explore meaning issues, the interview becomes less precise as the client struggles with defining the almost indefinable. As appropriate to the situation, questions such as the following can address the general issue of meaning in more detail:

"What has given you most satisfaction in your job?"

"What's *been missing* for you in your present life?"

"What do you *value* in your life?

"What *sense* do you make of this heart attack and the future?"

"What things in the future will be most *meaningful* to you?"

"What is the *purpose* of your working so hard?"

"You've said that you wonder what God is saying to you with this trial. Could you share some of your thoughts?"

"What gift would you like to leave the world?"

Eliciting meaning often precedes reflection. Reflection of meaning as a skill looks very much like a reflection of feeling or paraphrase, but the key words "meaning," "sense," "deeper understanding," "purpose," "vision," or some related concept will be present explicitly or implicitly. "Charlis, I sense that the heart attack has led you to question some basic understandings in your life. Is that close? If so, tell me more." Eliciting and reflecting meaning is an *opening* for the client to explore issues where there is not a final answer but rather a deeper awareness of the possibilities of life. Both reflecting meaning and interpretation/reframing are designed to help clients look deeper, first by careful listening and then by helping clients examine themselves from a new perspective.

Reflecting meaning involves *client* direction; the interpretation/reframe implies *interviewer* direction. The client provides the new and more comprehensive perspective in reflection of meaning, while an interpretation/reframe supplies the new way of being as suggested by the interviewer or counselor.

Comparing Reflection of Meaning and Interpretation/Reframing

Here are brief examples of how reflecting of meaning and interpretation may work for Charlis as she attempts to understand some underlying issues around her heart attack.

CHARLIS: My job has been so challenging and I really feel that pressure all the time, but I just ignored it. I'm wondering why I didn't figure out what was going on until I got this heart attack. But, I just kept going on, no matter what.

Eliciting and Reflecting of Meaning:

COUNSELOR: I hear you—you just kept going. Could you share what it feels like to *keep going on* and what it *means* to you? (Encourager focusing on the key words "*keep going on*"; open question oriented to meaning)

CHARLIS: I was raised to keep going. My mother always prided herself on doing a good job, even in the worst of times. Grandma did the same thing.

COUNSELOR: Charlis, I hear that keeping going and persistence have been a key family value that remains very important to you. (Reflection of meaning) "Hanging in" is what you are good at. (Positive asset leading to wellness is mentioned) Could we focus now on how that value around persistence and *keeping going on* relates to your rehab? (Open question that seeks to use the wellness dimensions to help her plan for the future)

Interpretation:

COUNSELOR: You could say that you *keep going* until you drop. How does that sound to you? (Mild reframe/interpretation followed by check-out)

CHARLIS: I was raised to keep going. My mother always prided herself on doing a good job, even in the worst of times. Grandma did the same thing.

COUNSELOR: Many of us become who we are because of family history. It sounds as if several generations have taught you to struggle and *keep going on, no matter what.* Do you want to continue that tradition? Or could you use *keeping going* on in a more positive way? (Interpretation/reframe, closed question, open question)

Both reflection of feeling and interpretation ended up in nearly the same place, but Charlis is more in control of the process with reflection of meaning. Whichever approach is used, we are closer to helping Charlis work on the difficult questions of the meaning and direction of her future life. If the client does not respond to reflective strategies, move to the more active interpretation. We need to give clients power and control of the session whenever possible. They can often generate new interpretations/reframe and new ways of thinking about their issues.

Interpretations and reframes vary with theoretical orientation, and the joint term *interpretation/reframe* is used because they both focus on providing a new way of thinking or a new frame of reference for the client, but the word "reframe" is a gentler construct. Keep in mind when you use influencing skills, that interpretive statements are more directive than reflecting meaning. When we use interpretation/reframing we are working primarily from the interviewer's frame of reference. This is neither good nor bad; rather, it is something we need to be aware of when we use influencing skills.

Linking is an important part of interpretation, although it often appears in an effective reflection of meaning as well. In linking, two or more ideas are brought together, providing the client with a new insight. The insight comes primarily from the client in reflection of meaning, but almost all from the interviewer in interpretation/reframing. Consider the following four examples:

Interpretation/reframe 1: Charlis, we are all reflections of our family, and it is clear that family history emphasizing success and hard work has deeply affected you, perhaps even to the point of having a heart attack. (Links family history to the heart attack. A family counselor might use this aproach.)

Interpretation/reframe 2: Charlis, you seem to have a pattern of thinking that goes back a long way—we could call it an "automatic thought." You seem to have a bit of perfectionism there and you keep saying to yourself (self-talk), "Keep going no matter what." (Links the past to the present perfectionism from a cognitive-behavioral perspective.)

Interpretation/reframe 3. It sounds as if you are using hard work as a way to avoid looking at yourself. The avoidance is similar the way you avoid dealing what you think you need to change in the future to keep yourself healthier. (Combines confrontation with linking with what is occurring in the interview series. This is close to a person-centered approach.)

Interpretation/reframe 4. The heart attack almost sounds like unconscious self-punishment, as if you wanted it to happen to give you time off from the job and a chance to reassess your life. (Linking interpretation from a psychodynamic perspective.)

▲ MODULE 10.1
SUMMARY

- ▲ A reflection of meaning looks very much like a paraphrase but focuses beyond what the client says. Often the words "meaning, values, and goals" will appear in the discussion. Clients are encouraged to explore their own meanings in more depth from their own perspective. Questioning and eliciting meaning are often vital as first steps.
- ▲ Interpretations/reframes provide the client with a new perspective, frame of reference, or way of thinking about issues. They may come from observations of the counselor, they may be based on varying theoretical orientations to the helping field, or they may link critical ideas together.
- ▲ The two skills are similar in helping clients generate a new and potentially more helpful way of looking at things. Reflection of meaning focuses on the client's worldview and seeks to understand what motivates the client; it provides more clarity on values and deeper life meanings. An interpretation results from interviewer observation and seeks new and more useful ways of thinking.

MODULE 10.2

EXAMPLE INTERVIEW: Travis Explores the Meaning of a Recent Divorce

KEY CONCEPT QUESTION

▲ How is reflection of meaning integrated into the interview?

In the following session, Travis is reflecting on his recent divorce. When relationships end, the thoughts, feelings, and underlying meaning of the other person and the time together often remain an unsolved mystery. Moreover, some clients are likely to repeat the same mistakes in their relationships when they meet a new person.

However, both the interpretation/reframe and reflection of meaning are central skills in helping clients take a new perspective on themselves and their world. Terrell, the interviewer, seeks to help Travis think about the word *relationship* and its meaning. Note that Travis stresses the importance of connectedness with intimacy and caring. The issue of self-in-relation to others will play itself out very differently among individuals in varying cultural contexts. Many clients will focus on their need for independence.

Interviewer and Client Conversation	Process Comments
1. *Terrell:* So, Travis, you're thinking about the divorce again . . .	Encourager/restatement.
2. *Travis:* Yeah, that divorce has really thrown me for a loop. I really cared a lot about Ashley and . . . ah . . . we got along well together. But there was something missing.	
3. *Terrell:* Uh-huh . . . something missing?	Encouragers appear to be closely related to meaning. Clients often supply the meaning of their key words if you repeat them back exactly.

Interviewer and Client Conversation	Process Comments
4. *Travis:* Uh-huh, we just never really shared something very basic. The relationship didn't have enough depth to go anywhere. We liked each other, we amused one another, but beyond that . . . I don't know . . .	Travis elaborates on the meaning of a closer, more significant relationship than he had with Ashley.
5. *Terrell:* You amused each other, but you wanted more depth. What sense do you make of it?	Paraphrase using Travis's key words followed by a question to elicit meaning.
6. *Travis:* Well, in a way, it seems like the relationship was shallow. When we got married, there just wasn't enough depth for a meaningful relationship. The sex was good, but after awhile, I even got bored with that. We just didn't talk much. I needed more . . .	Note that Travis's personal constructs for discussing his past relationship center on the word *shallow* and the contrast *meaningful.* This polarity is probably one of Travis's significant meanings around which he organizes much of his experience.
7. *Terrell:* Mm-hmmm . . . you seem to be talking in terms of shallow versus meaningful relationships. What does a meaningful relationship feel like to you?	Reflection of meaning followed by a question designed to elicit further exploration of meaning.
8. *Travis:* Well, I guess . . . ah . . . that's a good question. I guess for me, there has to be some real, you know, some real caring beyond just on a daily basis. It has to be something that goes right to the soul. You know, you're really connected to your partner in a very powerful way.	Connection appears to be a central dimension of meaning. We often believe that connectedness is a female construct, but many men also see it as central.
9. *Terrell:* So, connections, soul, deeper aspects strike you as really important.	Reflection of meaning. Note that this reflection is also very close to a paraphrase, and Terrell uses Travis's main words. The distinction centers on issues of meaning. A reflection of meaning could be described as a special type of paraphrase.
10. *Travis:* That's right. There has to be some reason for me to really want to stay married, and I think with her . . . ah . . . those connections and that depth were missing. We liked each other, you know, but when one of us was gone, it just didn't seem to matter whether we were here or there.	
11. *Terrell:* So there are some really good feelings about a meaningful relationship even when the other person is not there. You didn't value each other than much.	Reflection of meaning plus some reflection of feeling. Note that Terrell has added the word *values* to the discussion. In reflection of meaning it is likely that the counselor or interviewer will add words such as *meaning, understanding, sense,* and *value.* Such words lead the client to make sense of experience from the client's own frame of reference.

Interviewer and Client Conversation	Process Comments
12. *Travis:* Uh-huh.	
13. *Terrell:* Ah . . . could you fantasize how you might play out those thoughts, feelings, and meanings in another relationship?	Open question oriented to meaning.
14. *Travis:* Well, I guess it's important for me to have some independence from a person, but when we were apart, we'd still be thinking of one another. Depth and a soul mate is what I want.	Travis's meaning and desire for a relationship are now being more fully explored.
15. *Terrell:* Um-hum.	
16. *Travis:* In other words, I don't want a relationship where we always tag-along together. The opposite of that is where you don't care enough whether you are together or not. That isn't intimate enough. I really want intimacy in a marriage. My fantasy is to have a very independent partner I care about and who cares about me. We can both be individuals but still have bonding and connectedness.	Connectedness is an important meaning issue for Travis. With other clients, independence and autonomy may be the issue. With still others, the meaning in a relationship may be a balance of the two.
17. *Terrell:* Let's see if I can put together what you're saying. The key words seem to be independence with intimacy and caring. It's these concepts that can produce bonding and connectedness, as you say, whether you are together or not.	This reflection of meaning becomes almost a summarization of meaning. Note that the key words and constructs have come from the client in response to questions about meaning and value.

Further counseling would aim to bring behavior or action into accord with thoughts. Other past or current relationships could be explored further to see how well the client's behaviors or actions illustrate or do not illustrate expressed meaning.

▲ MODULE 10.2
SUMMARY

- ▲ The counselor used listening skills and key word encouragers to focus on meaning issues.
- ▲ Open questions oriented to values and to meaning are often effective in eliciting client talk about meaning issues.
- ▲ A reflection of meaning looks very much like a paraphrase except that the focus is on implicit deeper issues, often not expressed fully in the surface language or behavior of the client.

MODULE 10.3

INSTRUCTIONAL READING 1: The Specific Skills of Eliciting and Reflection of Meaning

KEY CONCEPT QUESTIONS

▲ **What are more detailed skills of eliciting and reflecting meaning?**

▲ **How does the process of discernment help clients?**

▲ **What key multicultural issues concern eliciting and reflecting meaning?**

Meaning issues often become prominent after a person has experienced a serious illness (AIDS, cancer, heart attack, loss of sight), encountered a life-changing experience (death of a significant other, divorce, loss of a job), or gone through serious trauma (war, rape, abuse, suicide of a child). Issues of meaning are also prominent among older clients who face major changes in their lives. These situations cannot be changed; they are a permanent part of the life experience.

BOX 10-1   National and International Perspectives on Counseling

What Can You Gain From Counseling Persons With AIDS and Serious Health Issues?
WEIJUN ZHANG

A good friend of mine had just started working with Persons with AIDS. When I asked him, "What does this mean to you?" he started to grumble: "It's being around people with serious illness who could die at any time. It also means that few are cured, despite my best efforts." What a bleak picture he painted. No wonder some counselors are reluctant to work with AIDS clients or those facing truly serious health issues. Can something as miserable and difficult as AIDS be meaningful? How can one work as a counselor in a kidney dialysis unit? What about working in a Hospice where all are expected to die within a reasonably short time? Certainly, there is much to learn and profit from in this type of work. What my friend was missing is that there are precious rewards available.

Years ago, I happened on an article outlining the positive aspects of working with clients who face extremely difficult futures or death.

1. We can help clients appreciate each moment. Working with people who have no choice but to live in the present can change our perspective. It can help us find a deeper meaning in life and learn to watch the world in wonder and appreciation as if this were our last day.

2. It is possible to learn something from each patient or client if we are willing to listen and be with his or her experience. Having direct contact with clients who face unthinkable pain and suffering but who still strive to live fully can help us understand the great strength that is the human spirit. This courage in the face of adversity can be very contagious.

3. Doing AIDS work or counseling the seriously ill will enable us to witness a lot of truly unconditional love and help us to become bigger-hearted, more loving, and caring persons.

I have always liked doing work with the seriously ill because of the selfless giving needed on the part of the counselor. But I have learned that it can mean a tremendous taking, learning, and satisfaction for those who help others most in need. Though this taking should never be our primary motive in doing AIDS or related work, it is certainly rewarding to see the light when we deal with the darkness associated with major life challenges. This positive insight I wish to share with my good friends.

Reflecting meaning can also help clients work through issues of daily life. In the sample interview Travis gained understanding of himself as he reflected on the meaning of divorce. Everyday issues and many typical concerns can be resolved if we turn to serious examination of meaning, values, and life purpose. Religion and spiritual life provide a value base and can be a continuing source of strength and clarity.

Eliciting Client Meaning

Understanding the client is the essential first step. Consider storytelling as a useful way to discover the background of a client's meaning making. If a major life event is critical, illustrative stories can form the basis for exploration of meaning. Clients do not often volunteer meaning issues, even though these may be central to the clients' concerns. Critical life events such as illness, loss of a parent or loved one, accident, or divorce often force people to encounter deeper meaning issues. If spiritual issues come to the fore, draw out one or two concrete example stories of the client's religious heritage. Through the basic listening sequence and careful attending, you may observe the behaviors, thoughts, and feelings that express client meaning.

Fukuyama (1990, p. 9) outlined some useful questions for eliciting stories and client meaning systems. Adapted for this chapter, they include the following:

"When in your life did you have existential or meaning questions? How have you resolved these issues thus far?"

"What significant life events have shaped your beliefs about life?"

"What are your earliest childhood memories as you first identified your ethnic-cultural background? Your spirituality?"

"What are your earliest memories of church, synagogue, mosque, a higher power, of discovering your parents' vital life values?"

"Where are you now in your life journey? Your spiritual journey?"

Reflecting Client Meanings

Say back to clients their exact key meaning and value words. Reflect their own unique meaning system, not yours. Implicit meanings will become clear through your careful listening and questions designed to elicit meaning issues from the client. Using the client's key words is preferable, but occasionally you may supply the needed meaning word yourself. When you do so, carefully check that the word(s) you use feel right to the client. Simply change "You feel . . ." to "You mean. . . ." A reflection of meaning is structured similarly to a paraphrase or reflection of feeling. "You value . . . ," "You care . . . ," "Your reasons are . . . ," or "Your intention was. . . ." Distinguishing among a reflection of meaning, a paraphrase, and a reflection of feeling can be difficult. Often the skilled counselor will blend the three skills together. For practice, however, it is useful to separate out meaning responses and develop an understanding of their import and power in the interview. Noting the key words that relate to meaning (*meaning, value, reasons, intent, cause,* and the like) will help distinguish reflection of meaning from other skills.

Reflection of meaning becomes more complicated when meanings or values conflict. Here concepts of confrontation (Chapter 8) may be useful. Conflicting values, either explicit or implicit, may underlie mixed and confused feelings expressed by the client. For instance, a client may feel forced to choose between loyalty to family and loyalty to spouse. Underlying love for both may be complicated by a value of dependence fostered by the family and the independence represented by the spouse. When clients make important decisions, sorting out key meaning issues may be crucial.

For example, a young person may be experiencing a value conflict over career choice. Spiritual meanings may conflict with the work setting. The facts may be paraphrased accurately and the feelings about each choice duly noted, yet the underlying *meaning* of the choice may be most important. The counselor can ask, "What does each choice mean for you? What sense do you make of each?" The client's answers provide the opportunity for the counselor to reflect back the meaning, eventually leading to a decision that involves not only facts and feelings but also values and meaning. And, as in confrontation, you can evaluate client change in meaning systems using the Client Change Scale, Chapter 8.

Discernment: Identifying Life Mission and Goals

> Listen. Listen, with intention, with love, with the "ear of the heart." Listen not only cerebrally with the intellect, but with the whole of feelings, our emotions, imaginations, and ourselves. (de Waal, 1997)

Discernment is "sifting through our interior and exterior experiences to determine their origin" (Farnham, Gill, McLean, & Ward, 1991). The word *discernment* comes from the Latin *discernere*, which means "to separate," "to determine," "to sort out." In a spiritual or religious sense, discernment means identifying when the spirit is at work in a situation—the spirit of God or some other spirit. The discernment process is important for all clients, regardless of their spiritual or religious orientation or lack thereof. Discernment has broad applications to interviewing and counseling; it describes what we do when we work with clients at deeper levels of meaning. Discernment is also a process whereby clients can focus on envisioning their future as a journey into meaning. (See Box 10-2.)

"There is but one truly serious problem, and that is . . . judging whether or not life is worth living" (Camus, 1955, p. 3). Viktor Frankl (1978), talks about the "unheard cry for meaning." Frankl claimed that 85% of people who successfully committed suicide saw life as meaningless, and he blamed an excessive focus on self. He said that people have a need for transcendence and living beyond one's self.

BOX 10-2   Questions Leading Toward Discernment of Life's Purpose and Meaning

You may find it helpful to share this list with the client before you begin the discernment process and identify together the most helpful questions to explore. Add topics and questions that occur to you and the client. Discernment is a very personal exploration of meaning. The more the client participates, the more useful it is likely to be. Questions that focus on the *here and now* and intuition may facilitate deeper discovery.

Following is a systematic approach to discernment. First, you or your client may wish to begin by thinking quietly about what might give life purpose, meaning, and vision.

Here-and-now body experience and imaging can serve as a physical foundation for intuition and discernment.

▲ Relax, explore your body, find a positive feeling of strength to serve as an anchor for your search. Build on that feeling and see where it goes.

▲ Sit quietly and allow an image (visual, auditory, kinesthetic) to build.

▲ What is your gut feeling? What are your instincts? Get in touch with your body.

▲ Discerning one's mission cannot be found solely through the intellect. What feelings and thoughts occur to you at this moment?

BOX 10-2   (Continued)

▲ Can you recall feelings and thoughts from your childhood that might lead to a sense of direction now?

▲ What is your felt body sense of spirituality, mission, and life goal?

Concrete questions leading to telling stories can be helpful.

▲ Tell me a story about that image above. Or a story about any of the *her- and-now* experiences listed there.

▲ Can you tell me a story that relates to your goals/vision/mission?

▲ Can you name the feelings you have in relation to your desires?

▲ What have you done in the past or are doing presently that feels especially satisfying and close to your mission?

▲ What are some blocks and impediments to your mission? What holds you back?

▲ Can you tell about spiritual stories that have influenced you?

For self-reflective exploration, the following are often useful.

▲ Let's go back to that original image and/or the story that goes with it. As you reflect on that experience or story, what occurs for you?

▲ Looking back on your life, what have been some of the major satisfactions? Dissatisfactions?

▲ What have you done right?

▲ What have been the peak moments and experiences of your life?

▲ What might you change if you were to face that situation again?

▲ Do you have a sense of obligation that impels you toward this vision?

▲ Most of us have multiple emotions as we face major challenges such as this? What are some of these feelings and what impact are they having on you?

▲ Are you motivated by love/zeal/a sense of morality?

▲ What are your life goals?

▲ What do you see as your mission in life?

▲ What does spirituality mean to you?

The following questions place the client in larger systems and relationships—the self-in-relation. They may

also bring multicultural issues into the discussion of meaning.

▲ Place your previously presented experiences and images in broader context. How have various systems (family, friends, community, culture, spirituality, and significant others) related to these experiences? Think of yourself as a self-in-relation, a person-in-community.

▲ *Family.* What do you learn from your parents, grandparents, and siblings that might be helpful in your discernment process? Are they models for you that you might want to follow, or even oppose? If you now have your own family, what do you learn from them and what is the implication of your discernment for them?

▲ *Friends.* What do you learn from friends? How important are relationships to you? Recall important developmental experiences you have had with peer groups. What do you learn from them?

▲ *Community.* What people have influenced you and perhaps serve as role models? What group activities in your community may have influenced you? What would you like to do to improve your community? What important school experiences do you recall?

▲ *Cultural groupings.* What is the place of your ethnicity/race in discernment? Gender? Sexual orientation? Physical ability? Language? Socioeconomic background? Age? Life experience with trauma?

▲ *Significant other(s).* Who is your significant other? What does he or she mean to you? How does this person relate to the discernment process? What occurs to you as the gifts of relationship? The challenges?

▲ *Spiritual.* How might you want to serve? How committed are you? What is your relationship to spirituality and religion? What does your holy book say to you about this process?

Discernment questions from Ivey, A., Ivey, M., Myers, J., & Sweeney, T. (2005). *Developmental counseling and therapy: Promoting wellness over the lifespan.* Boston: Lahaska/Houghton Mifflin. Reprinted by permission.

The vision quest, often associated with the Native American Indian, Dene, and Australian Aboriginal traditions, is oriented to helping youth and others find purpose and meaning in their lives. These individuals often undertake a serious outdoor experience to find or envision their central life goals. Meditation is used in some cultures to help members find meaning and direction.

Visioning and finding meaning may often be facilitated if issues are explored with a guide, counselor, or interviewer. This can be a spiritual or religious quest for some clients, but the discernment process will be useful for all. (Review Ivey, Ivey, Myers, and Sweeney, 2005, for additional information.) In Box 10-2, the specific discernment questions lead to further examination of goals, values, and meaning. Share the list of questions and encourage the client to participate with you in deciding which questions and issues are most important.

Multicultural Issues and Reflection of Meaning

For practical multicultural interviewing and counseling, recall the concept of focus. When helping clients make meaning, focus exploration of meaning not just on the individual but also on the broader life context. In much of Western society, we tend to assume that the individual is the person who makes meaning. But in many other cultures—for example, the traditional Muslim world—the individual will make meaning in accord with the extended family, the neighborhood, and religion. Individuals do not make meaning by themselves; *they make meaning in a multicultural context*. In truth, Western society also draws meaning from family and culture. However, individualism rather than collectivism is generally the focus.

Cultural, ethnic, religious, and gender groups all have systems of meaning that give an individual a sense of coherence and connection with others. Muslims draw on the teachings of the Qur'an. Similarly, Jewish, Buddhist, Christian, and other religious groups will draw on their writings, scriptures, and traditions. African Americans may draw on the meaning strengths of Malcolm X, Martin Luther King, Jr., or on support they receive from Black churches as they deal with difficult situations. Women, who are often more relational than men, may make meaning out of relationships whereas men may focus more on issues of personal autonomy and tasks. Witness the conversations in a mixed social group. Often we find women on one side of the room talking about relationships. Men will generally be talking about sports, politics, and their accomplishments.

Viktor Frankl, a German concentration camp survivor, could not change his life situation, but he was able draw on important strengths of his Jewish tradition to change the meaning he made of it. The Jewish tradition of serving others facilitated his survival and enabled him to help fellow sufferers. When times were particularly bad, prisoners had been whipped and were not being given food, Frankl (1959, 131–133) counseled his entire barracks, helping them reframe their terrors and difficulties, pointing out that they were developing strengths for the future.

> I quoted from Nietzsche, "That which does not kill me, makes me stronger." I spoke to the future. I said that . . . the future must seem hopeless. I agreed that each of us could guess . . . how small were chances for survival. . . . I estimated my chances at about one in twenty. But I also told them that, in spite of this, I had no intention of losing hope and giving up. . . . I also mentioned the past; all its joys and how its light shone even in

the present darkness. . . . Then I spoke of the many opportunities of giving life a meaning. I told my comrades . . . that human life, under any circumstances has meaning. . . . I said that someone looks down on each of us in difficult hours—a friend, a wife, somebody alive or dead, or a God—and He would not expect us to disappoint him. . . . I saw the miserable figures of my friends limping toward me to thank me with tears in their eyes.

You may counsel clients who have experienced some form of religious bias or persecution. As religion plays such an important part in many people's lives, members of dominant religions in a region or a nation may have different experiences from those who follow minority religions. For example, Schlosser (2003) talks of Christian privilege in North America where people of Jewish and other faiths may feel uncomfortable, even unwelcome, during Christian holidays. Anti-Semitism, anti-Islamism, anti-liberal Christianity, and anti-evangelical Christianity are all possible results when clients experience spiritual and/or religious intolerance. We also recall that when Christians and other religious groups find themselves in countries where they are a minority, they can suffer serious religious persecution, to the point of death.

▲ **MODULE 10.3**
SUMMARY

- ▲ Eliciting meaning is accomplished through carefully listening to the client for meaning words. Questions related to values, meaning, life goals, and ultimate causal issues bring out client meanings. "What meaning does that have to you?" "What sense do you make of that?"

- ▲ A reflection of meaning looks much like a paraphrase or reflection of feeling except that the key words related to meaning receive special attention. "Your goals (e.g., spirituality/family/life) mean much to you as you plan your next step."

- ▲ Discernment is a form of listening that goes beyond our usual descriptions and could be termed "listening with the heart." Both you and the client seriously search for deeper life goals and direction. Specific discernment questions are in Box 10-2.

- ▲ Multicultural and family issues and stories may be key in helping clients discover personal meaning. Eliciting meaning and focusing reflection on contextual issues beyond the individual will enhance and broaden one's understanding of life's deeper concerns.

MODULE 10.4
INSTRUCTIONAL READING 2: The Skills of Interpretation/Reframing

KEY CONCEPT QUESTIONS

▲ **What are more detailed skills of interpretation/reframing?**

▲ **How does interpretation/reframing relate to other microskills?**

▲ **How is interpretation/reframing used differently among varying theoretical approaches to counseling?**

▲ **What are some multicultural issues within interpretation/reframing?**

When you use the microskill of interpretation/reframing, you are helping the client to restory or look at the problem or concern from a new, more useful perspective. This new way of thinking is central to the restorying and action process. In the microskills hierarchy, the words *interpretation* and *reframe* are used interchangeably. Interpretation reveals new perspective and new ways of thinking beneath what a client says or does. The reframe provides another frame of reference for considering problems or issues. And eventually the client's story may be reconsidered and restoried.

An interpretation/reframe generally comes from the helper rather than the client and often is presented through a specific theoretical perspective. Reflection of meaning can inspire clients to find new meanings, new ways of looking at their situation, thus enabling them to reframe/interpret their situations on their own with minimal guidance from the interviewer.

The basic skill of interpretation may be defined as follows:

▲ The counselor listens to the client story, issue, or problem and learns how the client makes sense of, thinks about, or interprets the story or issue.

▲ The counselor, drawing from personal experience or a theoretical perspective, provides an alternative meaning or interpretation of the narrative. This may include *linking* together information or ideas discussed earlier that closely relate to each other. Linking is particularly important as it integrates ideas and feelings for clients and frees them to develop new approaches to their issues.

▲ (Example based on personal experience) "You feel coming out as gay led you to lose your job, and you blame yourself for not keeping quiet. Maybe you just really needed to become who you are. You seem more confident and sure of yourself. It will take time, but I see you growing through this difficult situation." Here self-blame has been reinterpreted or reframed as a positive step in the long run.

▲ (Example based on psychoanalytic theory with multicultural awareness) "It sounds like the guy who fired you is insecure about anyone who is different from him. He sounds as if he is projecting his own insecurities on you, rather than looking at his own heterosexism or homophobia."

Consider another example interpretation developed from the logic of the interviewer. Allen, the client, was going through a divorce and was very angry—a common reaction for those engaged in a major breakup, particularly when finances are involved. He was telling his attorney, at some length, about what he wanted and why. Attorneys use a form of interviewing involving many questions, and it sometimes involves informal counseling. After listening for a while to Allen's issues, the attorney got out from behind the desk and stood over Allen saying: "Allen, that's your story. But I can tell you that you won't get what you want. Your wife has a story as well and what will happen is something between what you both feel you need and deserve. For your own and your children's sake, think about that." This was a rather rough and confrontive reframing of Allen's story. It also changed the focus from Allen and his problems to his wife and children. Fortunately, he heard this powerful reframe, and resolution of differences in the divorce finally began.

This story has several implications. First, even with the most effective listening, clients may still hold on to unworkable stories, ineffective thinking, and self-defeating behaviors. Clearly, they need a new perspective. Respect clients' frame of reference before interpreting or reframing their words and life in new ways. In effect, *listen before you provide your interpretation or reframe.* There will always be some clients who will need the strong, confrontive interpretation that Allen got, but recall that the attorney first listened attentively to Allen.

The value of an interpretation or reframe depends on the client's reaction to it and how he or she changes thoughts, feelings, or behaviors. Think of the Client Change

Scale (CCS)—how does the client react to each interpretation? If the client denies or ignores the interpretation, you obviously are working with denial (Level 1 on the CCS). If the client explores the interpretation/reframe and makes some gain, you have moved that client to bargaining and partial understanding (Level 2 on the CCS). Interchangeable responses and acceptance of the interpretation (Level 3) will often be an important part of the gradual growth toward a new understanding of self and situation. If the client develops useful new ways of thinking and behaving (Level 4 on CCS), movement is clearly occurring. Transcendence (Level 5) will appear only with major breakthroughs that change the direction of interviewing, counseling, and psychotherapy. But let us recall that movement from denial (Level 1) to partial consideration of issues (Level 2) may be a major breakthrough, beginning client improvement.

The potential power of the effective interpretation/reframe can be seen in the divorce example above. Allen was in denial about what he could "win" in the divorce and refused even to bargain. But confronted by the attorney towering over him, he moved almost immediately from denial (Level 1) to a new understanding (Level 3) by accepting the attorney's reframe. The real test of change would be whether *he does change his behavior as a result of his new insights.* New solutions (Level 4) are seldom reached without behavior change. Transcendence (Level 5) is rarely found in complex cases of divorce!

Interpretation/Reframe and Other Microskills

Focusing, like reflection of meaning and interpretation/reframing, is another influencing skill that greatly facilitates the generation of new client perspectives. In the story of Allen and his attorney, the focus on the wife and children was key to the successful reframe. As another example, you may work with a male or female client who feels that he or she has been subjected to gender discrimination or sexual harassment. If you just focus on the individual, the client may blame himself or herself for the problem. By focusing on gender or other multicultural issues, you are expanding the client's perspectives, and the client may generate a new perspective, meaning, or way of solving the problem on her or his own.

Interpretation may be contrasted with the paraphrase, reflection of feeling, focusing, and reflection of meaning. In those skills the interviewer remains in the client's *own* frame of reference. In interpretation the frame of reference comes from the counselor's personal and/or theoretical constructs. The following are examples of interpretation (reframing) paired with other skills.

CLIENT 1:   (with a record of absenteeism) I'm in trouble because I missed so many days of work.

COUNSELOR: You're really troubled and worried. (reflection of feeling)

You've been missing a lot of work and you know your boss doesn't like it. (paraphrase/restatement)

Could you tell me what missing work means to you? (eliciting meaning . . . then the client responds followed by this interviewer statement) I hear that you have tended to avoid conflict of any kind for years and this relates to your avoiding work in recent months. (eliciting and reflecting meaning)

As I listen to you, I sense you're angry that your friend got the promotion and you didn't. How do you react to that? (Interpretation/reframe—note that the interview goes "beyond the data" and provides a new frame of reference for viewing the situation.

The check-out "How do you react to that?" enables the client to deal with the interpretation in a more open fashion.)

CLIENT 2: (with agitation) My wife and I had another fight over sex last night. We went to a sexy movie and I was really turned on. I tried to make love and she rejected me again.

COUNSELOR: You're upset and angry. (reflection of feeling)

You had a fight after the "turn-on" movie and were rejected again. (paraphrase/ restatement)

As I've listened to you over the past two sessions, I hear your deep caring for your wife, and when she rejects you, it means you fear losing her. (reflection of meaning)

Sounds like you didn't take it as slowly and easily as we talked about last week and she felt forced once again. Am I close? (interpretation #1 with check-out)

Your anger with her seems parallel to the anger you used to feel toward your first wife. I wonder what sense you make of that? (interpretation #2 with check-out)

The feelings of rejection really bother you. Those sad and angry feelings sound like the dream last week. Does that make sense? (linking interpretation #3 with check-out)

In each of these interpretations, the interviewer or counselor adds something beyond what the client has said. Any number of interpretive responses may be made to any client statement, and they may vary according to the theory and personal experience of the counselor.

Interpretation has traditionally been viewed as a mystical activity in which the interviewer reaches into the depths of the client's personality to provide new insights. However, if we consider interpretation to be merely a new frame of reference, the concept becomes less formidable. Viewed in this light, the depth of a given interpretation refers to the magnitude of the discrepancy between the frame of reference from which the client is operating and the frame of reference supplied by the interviewer.

Interpretations are best given by first attending carefully to the client and listening to the story or concern, providing the interpretation, then checking out the client's reactions to the new frame of reference ("How does that idea come across to you?"). If an interpretation is unsuccessful, the interviewer can use data obtained from the check-out to develop another, more meaningful response, most often a return to listening skills.

Theories of Counseling and Interpretation/Reframing

Theoretical interpretations can be extremely valuable as they provide the interviewer with a tested conceptual framework for thinking about the client. Each theory is itself a story—a story told about what is happening in interviewing, counseling, and therapy and what the story means. Integrative theories find that each theoretical story has some value. Most likely, as you generate your own natural style you will develop your own integrative theory, drawing from those approaches that make most sense to you.

Below are several examples of how counselors with different theoretical orientations might interpret the same information. A dream that Charlis had is described and you will see how counselors with different theories might interpret it. Before the actual interpretation, you will see a brief theoretical paragraph that provides a background for the theory-oriented intepretation that follows.

Imagine that you have worked with Charlis over a longer period, and she came to you upset over a troubling dream. This dream recurred frequently in her childhood, and after the heart attack, it returned with a vengeance and to wake Charlis, sweating, in the middle of the night. Charlis tells you her dream story.

CHARLIS: I dreamed that I was walking along the cliffs with the sea raging below. I felt terribly frightened. There was a path that I could have taken away from the cliffs, but I just felt so undecided about what to do. The dream just went on and on. I woke up in a cold sweat—and I've had that dream almost every night since I last saw you.

Decisional Theory. A major issue in interviewing for all clients is making appropriate decisions and understanding alternatives for action. Decisions need to be made with awareness of cultural/environmental context. Interpretation/reframing helps clients find new ways of thinking about their decisions. Linking ideas together is particularly important.

COUNSELOR: Charlis, you're facing new challenges since the heart attack and have many key decisions to make, including what you want to do with the rest of you life. You feel almost as if you might fall off the cliff if things don't straighten out soon. The whole situation is frightening and making decisions can make it worse. On the other hand, we have already identified several strengths that will enable you to make the important decisions you have to make. (Interpretation links the dream to new and vital decisions related to the heart attack and then draws on strengths and wellness.)

Person-Centered. Clients are ultimately self-actualizing and our goal is to help them find the story that builds on their strengths and helps them find deeper meanings and purpose. Reflection of meaning helps clients find alternative ways of viewing the situation while interpretation/reframing are not used. Linking can occur through effective summarization.

COUNSELOR: Charlis, that dream seems to mean something important to you. I hear your terrible fright and I notice the rage of the sea. And you've had the dream many nights and now you wonder what it means. (Reflection of meaning and reflection of feelings. Interpretations would be very rare in this theory.)

Brief Counseling. Brief methods seek to help clients find quick ways to reach their central goals. The interview itself is conceived first as a goal-setting process and then methods are found to reach goals through time-efficient methods. Interpretation/reframing will be rare except for links of key ideas.

COUNSELOR: You're facing new challenges since the heart attack and have some important decisions to make. Goal setting is important. Which path do you want to take to get well? (Mild interpretation with a move to goal setting.)

Cognitive-Behavioral Theory. The emphasis is on sequences of behavior and thinking and what happens to the client, internally and externally, as a result. Often interpretation/reframing is useful in understanding what is going on in the client's mind and/or linking the client to how the environment affects cognition and behavior.

COUNSELOR: The dream seems very close to what you face now. You have told me that you feel rage toward what happened to you and now you are wondering which direction to go in. Our next task is to work on some stress management strategies to help you find behaviors to cope with these challenges. Later, let's look at how this might relate to what's going on with your parents. (Here we see the counselor active in linking the dream with present issues.)

Psychodynamic Theory. Individuals are dependent on unconscious forces. Interpretation/reframing are used to help link ideas and enable the client to understand how the unconscious past and long-term, deeply seated thoughts, feelings, and behaviors frame the *here and now* of daily client experiencing. Freudian, Adlerian, Gestalt, Jungian, and several other psychodynamic theories each tell different stories.

COUNSELOR: You feel rage at your parents and you can't tell them how you really feel. It frightens you. And now you find the people around you force you to keep quiet about your feelings, but the prospect of challenging them is terrifying. This links back to earlier stories you mentioned about not being able to depend on your parents. (Emphasis on how the past affects the present.)

Multicultural Counseling and Therapy (MCT). Everyone is always situated in a cultural/environmental context and we need to help clients interpret and reframe their issues, concerns, and problems in relation to their multicultural background (see the RESPECTFUL model). MCT is an integrative theory and uses all of the methods above, as appropriate, to help clients understand themselves and how the cultural/environmental context affects them personally.

COUNSELOR: You felt frightened—I hear that. From what you've told me, sexual harassment was part of the stressors you faced before the heart attack. The cliff could be the hassles you had at the office and returning to the job clearly is frightening at this point. I also hear a woman who has the courage to get out on those cliffs and face the challenges. We will have to work together to help you find some support here to cope with the challenges. (Feminist frame of reference and issues are interpreted in a multicultural context.)

All of the above provide the client with a new, alternative way to consider the situation. In short, interpretation renames or redefines "reality" from a new point of view. Sometimes just a new way of looking at an issue is enough to produce change. Which is the correct interpretation? Depending on the situation and context, any of these interpretations could be helpful or harmful. The first two responses deal with here-and-now reality, whereas psychodynamic interpretation deals with the past. The feminist interpretation links the heart attack with sexual harassment on the job.

▲ MODULE 10.4
SUMMARY

▲ First, be sure that you have heard the client's story or concerns, and then draw from personal experience or a theoretical perspective to provide the client a new way of thinking and talking about issues.

▲ The effectiveness of an interpretation can be measured on the Client Change Scale. The new perspective is useful if the client moves in a positive direction.

▲ Focusing and multicultural counseling and therapy are the most certain ways to bring multicultural issues into the interview. A woman, a gay or lesbian, or a Person of Color may be depressed over what is considered a personal failure. By helping the client see the cultural/environmental context of the issue, a new perspective will appear, providing a totally new and more workable meaning.

▲ Each interviewing and counseling theory provides us with a new and different story about the interview. Drawing from theory for interpretation/reframing provides a more systematic frame for considering the client. However, logic and your personal experience and observations may be as effective as a theoretically oriented reframe.

SELF-DISCLOSURE AND FEEDBACK
Bringing Immediacy
Into the Interview

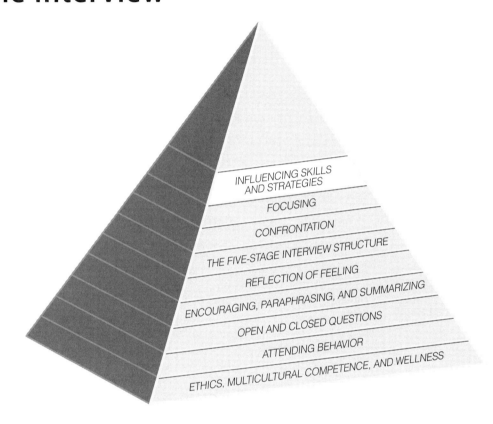

INFLUENCING SKILLS AND STRATEGIES

FOCUSING

CONFRONTATION

THE FIVE-STAGE INTERVIEW STRUCTURE

REFLECTION OF FEELING

ENCOURAGING, PARAPHRASING, AND SUMMARIZING

OPEN AND CLOSED QUESTIONS

ATTENDING BEHAVIOR

ETHICS, MULTICULTURAL COMPETENCE, AND WELLNESS

How can the skills of self-disclosure and feedback help you and your clients?

CHAPTER GOALS

This chapter first reviews some key issues about interpersonal influence in the interview. Then two closely related influencing skills, most often used in humanistic/existential and person-centered theories, are reviewed. When an interviewer effectively self-discloses or provides feedback, the *here-and-now* atmosphere of the interview becomes more immediate, personal, and real.

181

Awareness, knowledge, and skills developed through the concepts of this chapter will enable you to

- ▲ Better understand how listening skills and influencing skills facilitate client change and growth.
- ▲ *Use appropriate self-disclosure,* which builds a sense of equality and encourages client trust and openness. Disclosure may be about immediate *here-and-now* feelings, history of the interviewer, or thoughts and feelings that the counselor may have.
- ▲ *Offer accurate feedback* on how clients are experienced by the interviewer in the *here and now* of the session; how clients are progressing on issues; how others view the clients; and thoughts, feelings, and behaviors observed by the interviewer.

MODULE 11.1

INTERPERSONAL INFLUENCE, LISTENING SKILLS, AND INFLUENCING STRATEGIES—INTERVIEW EXAMPLE

KEY CONCEPT QUESTIONS

▲ **How do listening skills relate to influencing skills and strategies?**

▲ **What is the "1-2-3" pattern of interpersonal influence?**

▲ **How should we disclose to the client that we are using influencing skills?**

Influencing is part of all interviewing and counseling, and even a person-centered approach using only attending skills still influences what occurs in the session. Through selective attention and the topics you choose consciously or unconsciously to emphasize (or ignore) you influence what the client says. *You cannot **not** influence what happens in the interview.* Confrontation, focusing, reflection of meaning, and interpretation/reframing have been identified as strategies of interpersonal influence with which you may impact the client more immediately than through just listening alone.

Ethical practice demands respect for the client and awareness of the power relationship inherent in the interview. Interviewers and counselors, by their position, have perceived power. Use your power with awareness of client needs and encourage client participation in the session. As you move to the direct action associated with the influencing skills, do not forget the foundation of listening and empathic understanding. Carefully developed listening skills of paraphrasing, reflecting feelings, and summarizing are sometimes lost when one masters the influencing skills and strategies. Step back and remember that counseling and interviewing are for the client, not for you. Effective use of influencing skills enables full client participation in the session.

The degree of interpersonal influence desired in the interview varies from theory to theory. The word *influence* can be upsetting to a humanistic or person-centered counselor. By way of contrast, the many proponents of cognitive-behavioral theory aim to influence directly as much client change as possible. But all theories agree that client involvement in the change process remains central.

Disclosure of what is going to happen in the session is an important part of structuring the five-stage interview. This same egalitarian disclosure is helpful when you use a specific new skill or strategy. By way of comparison, think of the effective dentist, nurse, or physician and how each one tells you ahead of time what to expect and whether it might be painful. Our clients deserve the same respect. Disclosure tends to build comfort and trust even when the next step of the interview may not be comfortable. For example, if you have focused on listening and then decide to use influencing strategies such as interpretation/reframing, self-disclosure, or feedback, or you want now to provide specific directions for the session, spend a moment acquainting the client with the change in style and the potential benefits. The general rule is to avoid surprises, although occasionally it is the very surprise that helps a client discover important new ideas.

The "1-2-3" strategic model for using influencing skills is vital to maintaining client participation in the session. Keep listening skills as your most prominent style, even though you may be using a very directive intervention.

1. Listen to clients and be sure that you understand where they are coming from and whether they know what to expect from you.
2. Select a relevant influencing strategy, keep it brief, and time it appropriately to meet client needs.
3. Observe client response to your intervention. The check-out may be useful ("How do you respond to what I just suggested?"). The client will be giving you immediate feedback on the effectiveness of your use of influencing skills. If the client ignores your lead or takes your comment in an inappropriate direction, return to listening and either try again or move to a completely different intervention.

The effectiveness of your intervention can be readily assessed using the Client Change Scale (CCS, Chapter 8). It takes some practice, but eventually, you will be able to assess client reactions to your leads in the *here and now* of the session. Being intentional demands that you be flexible and ready to move with the client.

The Case of Alisia: How Listening Skills Can Influence Clients

The client, Alisia, comes in with the complaint that she can't express herself and people "run all over" her. The first interview began with a short rapport phase, and permission was obtained to record the session. The following transcript is an edited version of Alisia's first two interviews and listening skills were used almost exclusively. This is a modified *person-centered approach* in that questions are used more frequently than is typical of that theory. Effective listening skills and selective attending empower Alisia and enable her to see herself more as a self-in-relation, a person-in-community. Each of the influencing strategies presented in this and the next chapter will be applied to her issues.

The counselor spent time on Alisia's strengths and wellness assets. As part of the wellness search, the counselor encouraged Alisia to discuss several women heroes on whom Alisia would like to model herself. By the end of the interview, Alisia was still at Level 3 on the CCS but understood her issues *and her strengths and resources.*

Interviewer and Client Conversation	Process Comments
1. *Counselor:* Alisia, could you tell me what you'd like to talk about today?	The counselor personalizes the interview by using the client's name and the word *you* twice in the opening question.
2. *Alisia:* I simply can't express myself. I've tried many times and I can't get people to listen to me. Whether it is the boss, my partner, or the man at the garage, they all seem to run over me.	Alisia immediately identified her central issue. She appears to start the interview with acceptance and recognition of her problems (Level 3 on the Client Change Scale-CCS). You will find that some clients take several interviews before the problem is defined this clearly. But Alisia likely needs further understanding of this issue before change can be expected.
3. *Counselor:* Run over you?	Encourager focused on last few words.
4. *Alisia:* Yeah, I keep finding that I'm so accommodating that I'm always trying to get along. I was taught that I should please others. People like me for going along with them, but I never get what I want. I'm discouraged and disgusted with myself.	Alisia's body language is agitated and her vocal tone moves to a higher pitch, which often indicates insecurity.
5. *Counselor:* Sounds as if you are really frustrated and disgusted about your inability to express yourself.	Reflection of feeling. Do you think the counselor should have changed the feeling word "discouraged" to "frustrated"?
6. *Alisia:* Right, it just goes on and on . . . I never seem to change.	Resignation in her vocal tone, almost a sound of defeat.
7. *Counselor:* Could you give me a specific example of the last time you had these feelings of discouragement? What happened? What did you say? What did they do?	Open question searching for concreteness. If you look for one specific example, you will often obtain a much clearer understanding of client style and the depth of the problem.
8. *Alisia:* Well, I was at the garage. I had called in for an early morning appointment; I had to go to a meeting at 10:00. They said come in at 8:00 and so I was there on time. When I checked at 9:30, they hadn't even started yet. The service manager just smiled and said, "Sorry, lady, we couldn't get to it." He's one of those guys who really like to demean women. But I just looked down and didn't say anything—even though I really wanted to scream. I made another appointment, but my car still has that screwy, strange sound.	As Alisia shares the concrete example, she starts speaking in a more angry tone of voice and clenches her fist. Note that her lack of assertiveness shows here in a situation where she is not fully comfortable—the garage. But she is also able to point out that the service manager was likely being unfair to other women as well. She shows awareness of cultural/contextual issues and starts to get in touch with underlying anger. This is further evidence of her functioning at the levels of acceptance and recognition, but no change on the CCS.

Interviewer and Client Conversation	Process Comments
9. *Counselor:* And after all this the car still isn't right. As I see you now, Alisia, you also seem to be getting angry. What's happening with you as you talk to me about this?	Paraphrase, reflection of feeling, open question oriented to the *here and now*.
10. *Alisia:* Angry! Men!! I hurt too, deep inside. And I'm confused. (tears, but her eyes are flashing with determination) Everywhere I turn, it's there.	Listening skills also influence clients. Through sharing her story, Alisia becomes more aware of how she feels. The counselor was surprised at this explosion.
11. *Counselor:* I hear your anger and frustration. You're really angry and upset. You're tired of taking things as they are. The situation at the garage is just one instance of a pattern—something that repeats in various forms again and again. Have I heard you correctly?	Summarization with an emphasis on repeating patterns. Not all clients can see that they exhibit similar behaviors in different situations. A more concrete and less verbal client likely would be unable to realize that the situations are parallel.
12. *Alisia:* Yes, it's a pattern. The same day as the problem at the garage, my boss started leering at me again. I'm sick and tired of it. I used to think it was my fault, but now I'm wondering if men are the problem. The garage hassles me, the boss hassles me, and my partner does the same thing when he doesn't listen to me.	Notice how Alisia builds on the garage awareness to look at herself in other situations. Through effective use of listening skills, Alisia is starting to consider changes. This really is an expansion of acceptance/awareness (Level 3 on the Client Change Scale).

Listening has brought to Alisia a greater and clearer awareness of her issues. The second interview continues much the same as the first session, but near the end of the session, we hear the following:

Interviewer and Client Conversation	Process Comments
Counselor: So, Alisia, we've been talking for nearly an hour now. How do you put together all we've talked about? Have we missed something today?	The counselor could have summarized the session for Alisia, but uses the two questions as a way to involve the client in evaluation and planning for the future. The questioning process makes this version of person-centered counseling more active and influencing in style.
Alisia: I realize that much of what's been happening to me is a result of societal sexism. I learned in my family to do what "a good girl" should do and try to let the negative go and just be pleasant. But I'm not a girl; I'm a woman. I'm going to file harassment charges against my boss. And if we're going to stay together, I think I need to go with my partner for couples counseling. There! I feel better about myself right now.	She starts to see the need for behavioral change. Clients are not always so clear. This and the counselor statement above have been shortened from several client–counselor exchanges.

Interviewer and Client Conversation	Process Comments
Counselor: You said a mouthful there, Alisia. That is a lot of things to do. *Let's pick one or two of these possibilities and contract for what you might do next week as a start.*	By suggesting contracting for change in behavior, the counselor has decided to move toward an active influencing approach and has presented a directive to the client. But even this directive includes Alisia in the planning of what is to happen.

Alisia is generating a new solution (Level 4 of the CCS) but still has some distance to go if her behavior is to change. Cognitively and emotionally, she is starting to touch on Level 4, but behavioral change will also be necessary to cement her newer thoughts and feelings. Drawing out her story carefully through the person-centered approach of these first two sessions provides a foundation of more active influencing later in this chapter.

△ **MODULE 11.1**

SUMMARY

▲ Listening skills are integral to effective use of influencing skills. We need to remember that listening skills can be as or more influential than influencing skills. Help clients set their own direction as much as possible.

▲ The "1-2-3" pattern applies to all influencing skills: (1) Listen to the client's story, (2) use an appropriate influencing skill, and (3) note client response. Use the Client Change Scale (CCS) to assess the effectiveness of your lead. Listen again and be ready to flex intentionally in response to the client.

▲ Structure the interview and disclose what is happening when you use a new strategy with the client. This helps avoid surprising the client and builds client comfort and trust.

▲ The case of Alisia again demonstrates that listening skills influence client growth and development. Listening also sets the stage for effective use of influencing skills.

MODULE 11.2
DEFINING SELF-DISCLOSURE

KEY CONCEPT QUESTIONS

▲ **How do we define the strategy of self-disclosure?**

▲ **When is it appropriate to use this skill? When not?**

Self-Disclosure	Predicted Result
As the interviewer, share your own related past personal life experience, *here-and-now* observations or feelings toward the client, or opinions about the future. Self-disclosure often starts with an "I" statement. *Here-and-now* feelings toward the client can be powerful and should be used carefully.	The client is encouraged to self-disclose in more depth and may develop a more egalitarian interviewing relationship with the interviewer. The client may feel more comfortable in the relationship and find a new solution relating to the counselor's self-disclosure.

Should you share your own personal observations, experiences, and ideas with the client? Self-disclosure can encourage client talk, create additional trust between counselor and client, and establish a more equal relationship in the interview. However, self-disclosure by the counselor or interviewer has been a highly controversial topic. Not everyone agrees that this is a wise strategy to include among the counselor's techniques. Many theorists argue against counselors sharing themselves openly, preferring a more distant, objective persona. They express valid concerns about the counselor's monopolizing the interview or abusing the client's rights by encouraging openness too early. Self-disclosure can become therapy for the interviewer with too much talk not really relating to the client.

However, humanistically oriented and feminist counselors have demonstrated the value of appropriate self-disclosure. Multicultural theory considers self-disclosure early in the interview as key to trust building in the long run, particularly if your multicultural background is substantially different from that of your client. Research reveals that clients of counselors who self-disclose like their counselors more and report lower levels of symptom distress (Barrett & Berman, 2001).

You cannot expect to have experienced all that your clients bring to you. When a male works with a woman, for example, it may be useful to say, "Men don't always understand women's issues. The things you are talking about clearly relate to gender experience. I'll do my best, but if I miss something, let me know." If you are White or African American working with a person of the other race, frank disclosure that you recognize the differences in cultures at the initiation of the interview can be helpful in developing trust. "I'm Black, you're White" (or "I'm White, you're an African American"). "Do you have any questions for me or issues you'd like to raise?" The above suggestions and statements are generalizations. Imagine that you are a heterosexual Christian Asian counselor working with a conservative Christian Latina struggling with lesbian issues. Your background is very different and truly empathizing with the client may be a challenge. How would you self-disclose?

When you are multiculturally different from your client, self-disclosure requires more forethought, and it is vital that you are personally comfortable with difference. Open discussion and some self-disclosure on your part may be essential. The frank disclosure of differences can be helpful in establishing rapport. Many alcoholics are dubious about the ability of nonalcoholics to understand what is occurring for them. A client suffering from cancer or a heart attack may feel that no one can really understand if that person has not experienced this particular illness. On the other hand, if you have had a difficult life experience with alcohol, sharing your story briefly can be very helpful. It often helps to say to the client, "Please feel free to ask me questions about myself if you wish." Just remember to keep your responses brief! Be sure that what you do or do not do is authentic to your own knowledge and comfort level, but be sure that the self-disclosure is reasonable and comfortable for the client.

Here are four dimensions of self-disclosure:

1. *Listen.* Follow the "1-2-3" pattern from Module 11.1—attend to the client's story, assess the appropriateness of your self-disclosure and share it briefly, and return focus to the client, while noting how he or she receives the self-disclosure
2. *Use "I" statements.* Interviewer self-disclosure almost always involves "I" statements or self-reference using the pronouns *I, me,* and *my*—or *the self-reference may be implied.*

BOX 11-1 National and International Perspectives on Counseling

When Is Self-Disclosure Appropriate?
WEIJUN ZHANG

My good friend Carol, a European American, has had lots of experience counseling minority clients. She once told me that one of the first questions she asks her minority clients is "Do you have any questions to ask me?" which often results in a lot of self-disclosure on her part. She would answer questions not only about her attitudes toward racism, sexism, religion, and so forth, but also about her physical health and family problems. During the initial interview, as much as half of the time available could be spent on her self-disclosure.

"But is so much self-disclosure appropriate?" said a fellow student in class after I mentioned Carol's experience.

"Absolutely," I replied. We know that many minority clients come to counseling with suspicion. They tend to regard the counselor as a secret agent of society and doubt whether the counselor can really help them. Some even fear that the information they disclose might be used against them. Some questions they often have in mind about counselors are, "Where are you coming from?" "What makes you different from those racists I have encountered?" and "Do you really understand what it means to be a minority person in this society?" If you think about how widespread racism is, you might consider these questions legitimate and healthy. And unless these questions are properly answered, which requires a considerable amount of counselor self-disclosure, it is hard to expect most minority clients to trust and open up willingly.

Some cultural values held by minority clients necessitate self-disclosure from the counselor, too.

Asians, for example, have a long tradition of not telling personal and family matters to "strangers" or "outsiders" in order to avoid "losing face." Thus, relative to European Americans, we tend to reveal much less of ourselves in public, especially our inner experience. A mainstream counselor may well regard openness in disclosing as a criterion for judging a person's mental health, treating those who do not display this quality as "guarded," "passive," or "paranoid." Nonetheless, traditional Asians believe that the more self-disclosure you make to a stranger, the less mature and wise you are. I have learned that many Hispanics and Native Americans feel the same way, too.

Because counseling cannot proceed without some revelation of intimate details of a client's life, what can we do about these clients who are not accustomed to self-disclosure? I have found that the most effective way is not to preach or to ask, but to model. Self-disclosure begets self-disclosure. We can't expect our minority clients to do well what we are not doing ourselves in the counseling relationship, can we?

According to the guidance found in most counseling textbooks here, excessive self-disclosure by the counselor is considered unprofessional; but if we are truly aware of the different orientation of minority clientele, it seems that some unorthodox approaches are needed.

The classmate who first questioned the practice asked with a smile, "Why are you so eloquent on this topic?" I said, "Perhaps it is because I have learned this not just from textbooks, but mainly from my own experience as both a counselor and a minority person."

3. *Share and describe briefly your thoughts, feelings, or behaviors.* "I can imagine how much pain you feel." "I feel happy to hear you talk of that wonderful experience—it was a real change!" "My experience of divorce was hurtful." "I think your friends are taking advantage of you." "I also grew up in an alcoholic family and understand some of the confusion you feel."
4. *Appropriate immediacy and tense.* The most powerful self-disclosures are usually made in the *here and now*, the present tense. ("Right now I feel _____." "I am hurting for you at this moment—I care.") However, variations in tense are used to strengthen or soften the power of a self-disclosure.

Making self-disclosures relevant to the client is a complex task involving the following issues, among others.

Genuineness in Self-Disclosure. To demonstrate genuineness, the counselor must truly and honestly have the feelings, thoughts, or experiences that are shared. Second, self-disclosure must be genuine and appropriate in relation to the client. For example, a client may have performance anxiety about a part in a school play or a presentation to a small class. The counselor may genuinely feel anxiety about giving a lecture before 100 people. The feelings may be the same or at least similar, but true genuineness demands a synchronicity with the client's world. The counselor's experience, in this case, may be too distant from that of the client.

Tense. Consider the following:

ALISIA:	I am feeling really angry about the way I'm treated by men in power positions.
COUNSELOR:	(present tense) You're coming across really angry right now. I like that you finally are in touch with your feelings.
COUNSELOR:	(past tense) I've had the same difficulty expressing feelings in the past. I recall when I would just sit there and take it.
COUNSELOR:	(future tense) Awareness of emotions can help us all be more in touch with ourselves in the future. I know that keeping in touch with feelings will continue to aid me.

Be Careful When Clients Say, "What Would You Do If You Were in My Place?" Clients will sometimes ask you directly for opinions and advice on what you think they should do. "What do you think I should major in?" "If you were me, would you leave this relationship?" "Would you have an abortion?" Effective self-disclosure and advice can potentially be helpful, *but* it is not the first thing you need to do. Your task is to help the client make her or his own decisions. The right solution for you may not be the right solution for the client, and involving yourself too early can foster dependency and lead the client in the wrong way. Note the following exchange.

ALISIA:	How do you think I ought to present the idea of couples counseling to Chris?
COUNSELOR:	I'm not in your position and I've not heard too much about Chris yet. First, could we explore your relationship in more detail?
COUNSELOR:	(If you feel forced to share your thoughts when you prefer not to, keep your comments brief and ask the client for her reflections.) Alisia, my own thought would be to share with Chris how you are hurting. But I'm not you. Chris may not hear that. Does that relate to you at all?
COUNSELOR:	(after drawing out more information on the relationship.) From what I've heard, it sounds wise to bring up the idea of counseling when Chris is in a good mood. I think it is important to bring it up directly and I admire the way you are thinking ahead. How does that sound?

▲ **MODULE 11.2**

SUMMARY

- ▲ Self-disclosures are basically "I" statements made by the interviewer to share her or his own personal experience, thoughts, or feelings. *Here-and-now* self-disclosures tend to be the most powerful.
- ▲ The self-disclosure needs to be relevant to the client's worldview. It needs to be brief, genuine and authentic, and timed appropriately to client needs. The 1-2-3 pattern is particularly important when using self-disclosure.

▲ When clients ask you what you would do in their place, your task is to help them make their own decisions. Involving yourself too early can foster dependency and potentially mislead clients. It is important to discuss multicultural differences openly and with respect.

MODULE 11.3
DEFINING FEEDBACK

KEY CONCEPT QUESTION

▲ How do we define feedback and identify some important considerations of using feedback?

Feedback	Predicted Result
Present the client with clear information on how the interviewer believes the client is thinking, feeling, or behaving and how significant others may view them or their performance.	Clients may improve or change their thoughts, feelings, and behaviors based on the interviewer's feedback.

To see ourselves as others see us,

To hear how others hear us,

And to be touched as we touch others . . .

These are the goals of effective feedback.

Knowing how others see us is a powerful dimension in human change, and it is most helpful if the client solicits feedback. Feedback is an important influencing strategy if you have developed good rapport and enough experience with the client to know that he or she trusts you. These feedback guidelines are critical in counseling and interviewing:

1. *The client receiving feedback should be in charge.* Listen first and use the 1-2-3 pattern to determine whether the client is ready for feedback. Feedback is more successful if the client solicits it. (Listen—provide feedback—check-out.)
2. *Feedback should focus on strengths and/or something the client can do something about.* It is more effective to give feedback on positive qualities and build on strengths. Corrective feedback focuses on places in which the client can improve thinking, feeling, and behaving. Corrective feedback needs to be about something the client can change or a situation the client needs to recognize and accept as something that can't be changed.
3. *Feedback should be concrete and specific.* "You had two recent arguments with Chris that upset both of you. In each case, I hear you giving in almost immediately. You seem to have a pattern of giving up, even before you have a chance to give your own thoughts. How do you react to that?"
4. *Feedback should be relatively nonjudgmental and interactive.* Stick to the facts and specifics. Facts are friendly; judgments may or may not be. Demonstrate your nonjudgmental attitude through your vocal qualities and body language.

"I do see you trying very hard. You have a real desire to accept the way Chris is and learn to live with what you can't change. How does that sound?"—not "You give in too easily, I wish you'd try harder" or the all-too-common "That was a *good* job."

5. *Feedback should be lean and precise.* Don't overwhelm the client; keep corrective feedback brief. Most of us can hear only so much and can change only one thing at a time. Select one or two things for feedback and save the rest for later.

6. *Check out how your feedback was received.* Involve clients in feedback through the check-out. Their response indicates whether you were heard and how useful your feedback was. "How do you react to that?" "Does that sound close?" "What does that feedback mean to you?"

Positive feedback has been described as the "the breakfast of champions." Your positive, concrete feedback helps clients restory their problems and concerns. Whenever possible, find things right about your client. Even when you have to provide challenging feedback, try to include positive assets of the client. Help clients discover their wellness strengths, positive assets, and useful resources.

Corrective feedback is a delicate balance between negative feedback and positive suggestions for the future. When clients need to seriously examine themselves, corrective feedback may need to focus on things that clients are doing wrong or behavior that may hurt them in the future. Management settings, correctional institutions, and schools and universities often require the interviewer to provide corrective feedback in the form of reprimands and certain types of punishments. When you must give negative corrective feedback, keep your vocal tone and body language nonjudgmental and stick to the facts, even though the issues may be painful. *Praise and supportive statements* ("You can do it and I'll be there to help") convey your positive thoughts about the client, even when you have to give troubling feedback.

COUNSELOR: Alisia, I admire your ability to hang in with Chris and accept things as they are, but you really are giving away too much control. You need stronger boundaries. Times are changing and it is OK for you to be assertive and own your own space. You have strength and ability. We can work on helping you become your own person. How does that feedback sound to you?

Feedback when the client avoids certain topics. You may have a client who suddenly switches topic or gives you only a brief vague response. Many clients have sensitive issues or topics that they don't want to explore. If the interview is just for one to three sessions, it is usually best to accept that behavior. But sometimes, the issue really needs to be faced. Then, you need to meet the client and use confrontation skills as part of the feedback. Some examples:

> We've talked around the issue of dealing with Chris, but you never say whether you really want to stay together. On one hand, I hear you wanting to resolve issues, but on the other hand, you avoid expressing what you feel about the relationship and what you want.

> On one hand, Alisia, you really do seem to want to become more assertive, but then when we start to talk seriously about how you might actually change, you avoid the issues and turn away.

> Just now, I saw it again. We were starting to deal with real issues and you changed the topic. What's going on?

Here are some feedback examples with our client, Alisia:

Vague, judgmental, negative feedback	Alisia, I really don't think the way you are dealing with people who hassle you is effective. You come across as a weak person.
Concrete, nonjudgmental, positive feedback	Alisia, you have potential; I sense that you tried very hard to stand up for your rights in the garage. Now, you seem more assertive than you used to be. May I suggest some specific things that might be helpful the next time you face that situation?
Corrective feedback	Your effort was in the right direction. You can do even more if we set up an assertiveness training session for you. As we do this, I can offer more suggestions to help you change behavior. (See Chapter 14 for an example cognitive-behavioral assertiveness training session.)

▲ **MODULE 11.3**

SUMMARY

▲ Use the 1-2-3 pattern to ensure appropriateness of feedback. The client receiving feedback should be in charge. Focus on strengths, be concrete and specific, be nonjudgmental, keep feedback lean and precise, and check out with the client how the feedback was received. Involve the client as much as possible.

▲ Positive feedback is "the breakfast of champions." Use this skill relatively frequently and it will balance more challenging necessary corrective feedback.

▲ Corrective feedback will be necessary at times and needs to focus on things that the client can actually change; seek to avoid criticism. Be specific and clear and, where possible, supplement with client strengths that support the change.

LOGICAL CONSEQUENCES, INFORMATION/ADVICE, AND DIRECTIVES

Helping Clients Move to Action

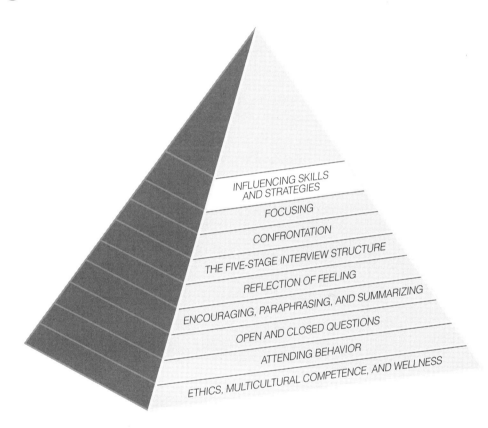

INFLUENCING SKILLS AND STRATEGIES

FOCUSING

CONFRONTATION

THE FIVE-STAGE INTERVIEW STRUCTURE

REFLECTION OF FEELING

ENCOURAGING, PARAPHRASING, AND SUMMARIZING

OPEN AND CLOSED QUESTIONS

ATTENDING BEHAVIOR

ETHICS, MULTICULTURAL COMPETENCE, AND WELLNESS

How can these three influencing strategies help you and your clients?

CHAPTER GOALS — Help clients examine new possibilities for behavioral, thought, and feeling changes by providing them with information or advice, helping them see the logical consequences of future actions, and directly telling them what to do in the interview or through homework assignments.

193

Awareness, knowledge, and skills developed through the concepts of this chapter will enable you to

- ▲ Help clients examine the *logical consequences* of alternatives and the implications of various actions for the future.
- ▲ Provide information and advice to the client in an appropriate and timely manner.
- ▲ Direct the client to try systematic change strategies such as relaxation and guided imagery and engage in specific homework activities between interviews.

MODULE 12.1
DEFINING LOGICAL CONSEQUENCES

KEY CONCEPT QUESTIONS

▲ **How do we define the skill of logical consequences?**

▲ **What are some implications of this skill, particularly in discipline situations?**

▲ **How does focusing increase the value of logical consequences?**

Logical Consequences	*Predicted Result*
Explore specific alternatives and the logical positive and negative concrete consequence of each possibility with the client. "If you do this . . . , then. . . ."	Clients may change thoughts, feelings, and behaviors through better anticipation of the consequences of their actions. Through exploring the positives and negatives of each possibility, the client is more involved in the process of decision making.

This strategy of logical consequences is particularly important in making decisions and is used among many theoretical approaches to the interview. It is most often a gentle strategy used to help people sort through issues when a decision needs to be made. It may be used to rank alternatives when a more complex decision is faced. In interviewing, the task is to assist clients in foreseeing consequences as they sort through alternatives for action—"If you do . . . , then . . . will possibly result."

The strategy of logical consequences is most often used in Adlerian counseling (Sweeny, 1998) and decisional counseling (Chapters 7 and 13). The task of the interviewer is to help individuals explore alternatives, consider consequences of alternatives, and facilitate decision making among the possibilities. For example, an individual may come to the interview aware only of the fact that changing jobs offers more pay, but also may be fearful of the effects of moving to a new city. Through systematic questioning and discussion, the interviewer can help the client clarify the factors involved in the decision. Potential *negative consequences* could include leaving a smoothly functioning and friendly work group, disrupting long-term friendships, moving children to a new school, and other factors that might cause problems. *Positive consequences* might be a pay raise and the opportunity for further advancement, a better school system, and money for a new home.

The interviewer or counselor may need to help clients become aware of the potential negative consequences of actions, even punishment. Some examples include a client thinking of dropping out of school, a pregnant client who has not stopped smoking, a boss, coworker, or friend whom the client wants to "tell off." It is equally important to help clients anticipate the positive consequences, results, and rewards of specific behaviors. Finishing school will result in a better job, the non-smoking pregnant woman's baby is likely to be healthier, and a better alternative for handling difficult people may be simply to keep one's mouth shut for the moment. It is best when your clients can generate the likely consequences of any given action through your listening skills, questioning, and confrontation.

It does not happen as fast as the example below, but this is the general pattern of introducing logical consequences.

COUNSELOR: What is likely to happen if you continue smoking while pregnant?

CLIENT: I know that it isn't good, but I can't stop and I really don't want to.

COUNSELOR: Again, what are the possible negative consequences of continuing to smoke?

CLIENT: (pause) I've been told that the baby could be harmed.

COUNSELOR: Right, is that something you want? What is the benefit of stopping smoking for the baby?

CLIENT: No, I don't want to do harm. I'd be so guilty. But how can I stop smoking?

COUNSELOR: Let's explore that. There are several ways, none of them easy. But let us consider . . .

For disciplinary issues or in situations when the client has been required to come to the session, it is important to note that even more power rests with the interviewer. The school, agency, or court may ask the interviewer to recommend actions that the legal system could take. The gentle logical consequence skill becomes more powerful. Warnings are a form of logical consequences and may center on *anticipation of punishment;* if used effectively and coupled with clients' rapport and listening, warnings may reduce dangerous risk taking and produce desired behavior. In disciplinary situations, clients need to think about the fact that they will have happier lives in the long run if they select more positive alternatives for their lives. A disciplinary school official, an attorney, or a correctional officer often needs to help the client see clearly what might be ahead. But people who hold power over others need to *follow through with the consequences* they warned about earlier, or their power to influence will be lost. The "if, then" language pattern is especially useful to summarize the situation: "If we don't make the counseling sessions work, you know what the judge will do."

It is the rare human behavior that does not have its costs and benefits. By involving the client in examining the pluses and minuses of alternatives, the decision is given to the client or at least shared more openly. Consider the following suggestions for using the strategy of logical consequences.

1. Through listening skills, make sure you understand the situation and the way your client understands it. After drawing out the situation, either you or the client can summarize what is happening.
2. Use questions and brainstorming to help the client generate alternatives for resolving issues. Where necessary, provide additional alternatives for consideration.
3. Work with the client and outline both the positive and negative consequences of any potential decision or action. In important cases, ask the client to generate a possible future story of what might happen if a particular choice is made. For example, "Imagine yourself two years from now. Now what would your life be like if you choose the alternative we just discussed?"

4. As appropriate to the situation, provide clients with a summary of positive and negative consequences in a *nonjudgmental* manner, or ask them to make the summary. With many people this step is not needed; they will have made their own judgments and decisions already.
5. Encourage client decision making as much as possible. In disciplinary situations, you may have to enforce appropriate consequences if the needed decision is not made.

The following exchange with Alisia demonstrates one possible use of logical consequences. In this case, the decision is between keeping things as they are or introducing a new behavior and style.

Interviewer and Client Conversation	Process Comments
1. *Counselor*: Alisia, we know that you would like to be more assertive and speak up more for yourself. What are the likely positive consequences if you can do this?	The counselor paraphrases and then asks Alisia to identify positive consequences of change.
2. *Alisia*: Well, I've learned that if I don't speak up to the garage service manager, nothing is going to happen. I suppose that I have nothing to lose by trying to be stronger. I guess the positive result would simply be something different.	Alisia responds well and notes that she has "nothing to lose" by trying something different.
3. *Counselor*: "Something different," sounds like you'd feel better about yourself and maybe even get the car fixed.	Encourager and paraphrase. The counselor suggests another potential positive consequence of change.
4. *Alisia*: That would be nice, but it is a little scary.	Change is not easy.
5. *Counselor*: I hear that. What are the negative consequences of continuing your past behavior?	Open question with a strong influencing dimension. Balancing the decision with negative consequences of not changing.
6. *Alisia*: Not good. I'll continue to be too passive and will be "run over."	
7. *Counselor*: So the consequences of trying a change may make something happen for the good and you have nothing to lose. On the other hand, the consequences of staying as you are, as you say, are "not good."	Summary of the positive and negative consequences of taking or not taking an action. Decisional counseling, Adlerian, and many other forms of cognitive counseling all use the logical consequences strategy.
8. *Alisia*: Right, well let's try something new. I've decided I'm ready for a change.	

Alisia also said that she wanted to take a stronger role with her partner. As she explored the negative consequences of speaking more forcefully, she realized the first negative consequence was that her partner might leave her. The financial challenge and the likely need to find a new and much less expensive apartment emerged as additional negative consequences. Alisia also feared being alone, as she had had other bad experiences with loss. These are common fears that women experience around separation and unfortunately often result in women returning to abusive mates. On the more positive side, Alisia realized how good it would feel to speak up for herself, and she wasn't at all sure that her partner actually would leave. She was not worried about abuse. She would feel better about herself if she could speak up for herself. As she balanced the positives and negatives, she decided it was time for her to speak up and see what happened. She and the counselor agreed to explore this issue in more detail in subsequent interviews.

The decisional balance sheet. When clients have important decisions with several possibilities, it helps to write down the alternatives and the pluses and minuses of each. For example, in choosing a college or a job change, list the several possibilities and what the client likes and dislikes about each one so they can be seen clearly. If there is one especially important issue, mark it with two "+" or "−" signs (Mann, 2001).

Combine focusing with logical consequences and help the client see issues in a broader context. What are the logical consequences for others if Alisia changes her style—the service manager, her partner, and others within the cultural/environmental context? The counselor could use varying focus dimensions to broaden Alisia's understanding. Here are some examples of focusing to help individuals see themselves as beings-in-relation, persons-in-community.

Interviewer and Client Conversation	Process Comments
9. *Counselor:* Alisia, what are the implications for the service manager if you become more assertive?	Focus on others—service manager, in particular.
10. *Alisia:* Hummm. Well, I imagine he would do one of three things. First, he might ignore me and continue as he had before, but I wouldn't allow that, as I want him to deal with me. Second, I bet he'll do a better job and perhaps he will respect other women as well. The third possibility is that he will talk back to me rudely. But, if so, I'm going to talk to the manager of the garage. I'm fed up.	Here Alisia is looking at the logical consequences for the service manager if she becomes more assertive.
11. *Counselor:* And what are the consequences for your partner if you say that you want counseling because you want more equality in the relationship?	Focus on significant others, the partner. Open question.
12. *Alisia:* I think Chris will be put off; he is not very verbal and fears counseling. But I also know that he would like us to get along better.	Alisia can make a better decision if she anticipates what her decisions mean for others.
13. *Counselor:* So, Chris might accept it. It does sound as if you want to be a stronger woman. Your grandmother was a powerful role model. You did say that talking back to your service manager might be a strike for women in general.	Focus on Chris, then on family, and finally, cultural/environmental context, namely the role of women in society.

Interviewer and Client Conversation	Process Comments
14. *Alisia:* One thing that I'm learning here is that every woman has a responsibility to speak up. I need to be part of that.	We are seeing cognitive and emotional change to generating new solutions. But she has to implement her thoughts and feelings in behavior to reach this level fully.
15. *Counselor:* It makes me feel good to hear you say that you see your responsibility for others. That may help you "hang in" when the going gets tough as you change your style.	Focus on the interviewer with a self-disclosure followed by pointing out the logical consequences for women in general as Alisia changes her style.
16. *Alisia:* I'm ready to start. What next?	

▲ MODULE 12.1

SUMMARY

- ▲ The steps of logical consequences are (1) listen to clients and clarify issues, (2) generate alternatives with them to resolve their issues, (3) carefully sort out the positive and negative consequences of each alternative, (4) summarize the alternatives using a nonjudgmental and positive stance, and (5) encourage client decision making.
- ▲ "If, then" language can be helpful in clarifying key decisions. "If you do . . . , then the likely result is. . . ." Writing down the pluses and minuses of each alternative leads to better decision making. If clients make a "wrong" decision with negative consequences, they will at least have more awareness that this was their decision.
- ▲ In disciplinary situations, maintain a nonjudgmental attitude, and continue to encourage client decision making. Also, in some disciplinary situations, you may have to recommend unfortunate consequences for the client.
- ▲ Combine focusing with logical consequences to help clients make decisions with much more awareness of their impact on others and the cultural/environmental context.

MODULE 12.2
DEFINING INFORMATION AND ADVICE

KEY CONCEPT QUESTIONS

▲ What are the strategies of information and advice?

▲ What are guidelines for implementing these strategies effectively?

Information and Advice	Predicted Result
Share specific information with the client— e.g., career information, choice of major, where to go for community assistance and services. Offer advice or opinions on how to resolve issues and provide useful suggestions for personal change.	If given sparingly and effectively, the client will use information and ideas to act in new, more positive ways.

Giving the client information, offering advice and your opinions, or making suggestions can be an important part of interviewing and counseling. However, be aware that advice giving is fraught with danger; unless the advice is actively sought, it is very difficult for even the best of advice to be heard. For example, try offering teens suggestions on how they should dress, drive, and or handle alcohol. It is immensely difficult to help a person stop smoking. Children resist suggestions. Adults are told to lose or gain weight, get more exercise, and eat more fruits and vegetables, but we have real difficulty in listening to or following advice that may be critical to our physical well-being.

When listening to counselor advice, the client needs to be in charge and actually want the information, perhaps even more so than when receiving feedback. Career and college counseling must provide students with career and college admissions information and here the teen may actually listen. Students facing critical life decisions frequently want to know your opinions and advice. A family member caring for an older parent often desperately wants advice on how to handle this extremely challenging part of life.

If you want to advise a client to take relaxation training or a meditation program to help develop a more relaxed lifestyle, listen to the client's story and wait for a timely and appropriate opportunity to share information. Provide the client with clear information on the potential value and health gains that would result. More challenging is the student who is not doing well in school or the office worker who shows up late for work. Both know that change would be wise and what your advice is likely to be. It is all the more important to hear their stories and points of view before attempting any advice. Pointing out logical consequences is likely to be more helpful than giving advice.

This strategy is clear and the issue is getting information across and motivating clients. It is especially important to use the 1-2-3 pattern (listen—advice—check-out) from Module 11.1 when you offer information, give advice, share your opinion, or provide suggestions. Change your approach when you see clients roll their eyes, slump back in the chair, or look at the ceiling. However, some clients will look to you for important information and, as you build trust with clients, they are anxious to hear your advice. Provide advice sparingly and only when the client is likely to need and accept it. Successful advice giving on the part of the interviewer can be addicting, so be very careful not to offer too much too soon.

Following are examples of giving advice and sharing information with Alisia:

CAREER INFORMATION: Alisia, it is clear that you have not allowed yourself to stretch and move ahead with the job you have now. I'd like you to explore some alternatives. I'm going to show you our career library, and we can explore other career possibilities for the future. One of the issues we need to look at is related job opportunities. You are now in computer science, but you're not using all your talents. This chart shows a projected 25% increase in computer career opportunities coming in the next decade. How does this sound?

ADVICE/ OPINION: You asked for my advice about Chris. It's not my place to tell you what to do. But I do think it is time for you to sit down with him and have a serious talk. I've got some ideas for you that might help you express your thoughts and feelings in a way that Chris might actually hear you. Would you like to do this?

ADVICE/
SUGGESTION:

One route toward handling difficult situations is to engage in attending behavior—listening carefully to the person whom you find difficult. We know that you tend to give in too easily, but if you listen and observe someone carefully, you may find new ways to understand that person and act more effectively. I'll teach you some of the basics of effective listening. Later, we can work on developing a cognitive-behavioral program of assertiveness training to help you speak up. Would you like to try this?

▲ **MODULE 12.2**

SUMMARY

▲ All influencing skills are concerned with imparting information to the client. The task is to be clear, specific, and relevant to the client's world.

▲ Provide specific data, judiciously, for clients that will help them in decision making; you may follow up with logical consequences. Counselor advice may be taken too seriously so use it sparingly. Use the 1-2-3 pattern of listening when providing information or advice and check out with the client how you were received.

MODULE 12.3
DEFINING DIRECTIVES

KEY CONCEPT QUESTIONS

▲ **How do we define directives?**

▲ **What are some example directives?**

Directives	Predicted Result
Direct clients to follow specific actions. Directives are important in broader strategies such as assertiveness or social skills training or specific exercises such as imagery, thought stopping, journaling, or relaxation training. They are often important when assigning homework for the client.	Clients will make positive progress when they listen to and follow the directives and engage in new, more positive thinking, feeling, or behaving.

Directives are useful in developing a new story or thinking in new ways, and they are especially effective in helping a client move to behavioral action. A positive new story may be sufficient for some clients, but many will profit from directive strategies outlining specific behaviors and actions. Directive strategies are drawn from various counseling theories that direct the client to follow a specific sequence of events designed to produce a likely result.

Effective directives require an expansion of the 1-2-3 pattern.

1. *Involve your client as co-participant in the directive strategy.* Rather than simply tell the client what to do, be sure that you have carefully heard the story, issues, and problems. Usually directives come later in the interview or, more often, in future sessions. Inform the client what you are going to do and the likely result. Some practitioners like to use surprises (e.g., Gestalt theory) and these can be useful in some situations. But as a general rule, we urge *working with,* rather than *working on,* your client.

2. *Use appropriate visual, vocal tone, verbal following, and body language.* When you use influencing skills, your attending behaviors need to be flexible in response to the needs of the client. Usually, a more forward and active behavioral style is needed. For example, when challenging an acting-out teen or an outgoing client, you may need a stronger persona with even clearer verbal and nonverbal behavior. With a quieter, more tentative client, appropriate attending may require being still and tentative yourself as you share new ways of thinking about issues. Directives given softly can be very effective.

3. *Be clear and concrete in your verbal expression and time the directive to meet client needs.* Directives need to be authoritative and clear but also stated in such a way that they are in tune with the needs of the client. Compare the following:

VAGUE: Go out and arrange for a test.

CONCRETE: After you leave today, contact the testing office to take the Strong-Campbell Interest Blank. Complete it today, and they will have the results for us to discuss during our meeting next week.

VAGUE: Relax.

CONCRETE: Sit quietly . . . feel the back of the chair on your shoulders . . . tighten your right hand . . . hold it tight . . . now let it relax slowly . . .

These examples illustrate the importance of indicating clearly to your client what you want to happen. Know what you are going to say and say it clearly and explicitly.

4. *Check out whether your directive was heard and understood.* Just because you think you are clear doesn't mean the client understands what you said. Explicitly or implicitly check to make sure your directive is understood. This is particularly important when a more complex directive has been given. For example, "Could you repeat back to me what I just asked you to do?" or "I suggested three things for you to do for homework this coming week. Would you summarize them to me to make sure I've been clear?" The CCS can be used to determine whether the client actually changed thoughts, feelings, or behaviors as a result of your directive.

The counselor prepares Alisia ahead of time before giving a directive:

COUNSELOR: Alisia, I've heard your story about how frustrated you feel with that service manager. I'd like to use imagery to understand the situation a bit more fully. This will require you to relax, sit back, and allow yourself to recall the situation. It often helps to visualize the specifics of the situation, what was said, and so on—almost like a movie. As we start, I'd like you to remember just one particular scene that first occurs to you. Is all this OK with you? Any questions? (Note the concreteness: the counselor has involved Alisia by providing an explanation and has checked out with her to see whether proceeding with the strategy is satisfactory to her.)

Test the following directive strategies with a friend or classmate and then have them try the same approach with you. If you practice the details of directives, you will have a better idea of their potential and how to pace or time the strategy. All of the following are well-known and effective strategies but must be in full attunement with client needs and wishes. Additional directive strategies may be found in Box 12-1.

BOX 12-1   Example Directive Strategies Used by Counselors of Different Theoretical Orientations

These example directive strategies are presented in very brief form. With further study and some imagination and practice—and client participation in the process—you can successfully use many of them. For more detailed presentations of these and other strategies in highly concrete form, see Ivey, D'Andrea, Ivey, and Simek-Morgan's *Theories of Counseling and Psychotherapy: A Multicultural Perspective* (2007).

Specific suggestions/ instructions for action	"I suggest you try . . ."
	"Alisia, the next time you go to the garage, I'd like you to stand at the counter, make direct eye contact, and clearly and firmly tell the manager that you have a meeting at 10:00 and you need prompt service—now! If he says there will be a delay, get him to make a firm time commitment. Then follow up 15 minutes later."
	Detail and concreteness are very important when providing a directive.
Spiritual images	"You say you gain strength from your spirituality and religion. Could you tell me about an image that comes to your mind related to a spiritual strength?" (Listen to the story and the feelings that go with it.) "Now, close your eyes and visualize (that symbol, person, experience) and allow it to enfold you completely. Just relax, focus on that image, and note what occurs in your body."
	In recent years the counseling and interviewing field has recognized the strengths and power in spirituality and religion. Many clients benefit from spiritual imagery and often find peace in their inner body and strength to move on. Forgiveness of the transgressions and omissions of others can come from spiritual imagery or your client may find new strengths to deal with a difficult illness or serious loss. A spiritual orientation even helps some clients recover from operations or serious illness.
Role-play enactment	"Now return to that situation and let's play it out."
	"Let's role-play it again, only change the one behavior we agreed to."
	Role-playing is an especially effective technique to make the abstract concrete. It makes the client behavior clear and specific. This is one of the most basic techniques used in assertiveness training, which you will see in Chapter 14.
Positive reframing combined with a directive	"We've identified the problem and how it feels. Now feel that wellness strength in your body. Do it fully, magnify it, and take it to the problem."
	Taking real positives to attack problems through the body can be effective. If the strength is not able to meet and counteract the negative, add another resource—or just have the strength approach one part of the negative at a time.
Relaxation	"Close your eyes and focus on the moment."
	"Tighten your forearm, very tight, now let it go." (Directions for relaxation continue throughout the body parts, ending with full body relaxation.)
	Alisia may be tight and tense; once she is able to relax and be in control of her body, she will be better able to cope with stressful daily encounters. Relaxation training helps all clients loosen tight muscles and cope better with the constant stress that many of us must deal with.
Journaling	"Alisia, you like to write and think about things. How would it be if you started a journal of your work with me? You might want to reflect on each interview and its impact and how what we discuss relates to what you see happening in your life daily. You can share this with me or not as you choose."
	Keeping a journal is helpful to many clients. This helps them reflect on the interview and its impact on them during the week.

Guided Imagery Focusing on a Relaxing Scene. This is a popular technique to help clients relax and discover ways to reduce tension. All of us have past positive experiences that are important for us—maybe a lakeside or mountain scene, or a snowy setting, or a quiet, special place. The image can become a positive resource to use when we feel challenged or tense. For example, Alisia likely feels real tension in her body when she encounters conflict. If she learns to notice her internal body tension, then she can immediately and briefly focus on a relaxing scene, take a deep breath, and deal with the challenging situation more effectively. When giving a guided imagery directive, time your presentation to your observations of the client.

> Close your eyes and relax. (pause) Notice your breathing and the general feelings in your body. Focus on that place where you felt safe, comfortable, and relaxed. Allow yourself to enter that scene. What are you seeing? . . . Hearing? . . . Feeling? . . . Allow yourself to enjoy that scene in full relaxation. Notice the good feelings in your body. Enjoy it now for a moment before coming back to this room. Now, as you come back, notice your breathing (pause) and as you open your eyes, notice the room, the colors, and your surroundings. How was this experience for you?

Positive Images of Strength. Images of people who have meant a lot to us serve as examples of strength and give us the courage to meet difficult issues. The community genogram is a good place to find people who represent positive strengths and resources. Use the guided imagery exercise above and help the client focus on a person who was helpful in the past or who can serve as a model for the future. As you go through this exercise, add one dimension—ask the client to note where the feelings inspired by the image are located in her or his own body. Some note warm feelings in their stomach, others observe feelings of strength in their upper chest or arms; most of us can identify where the positive image is located in our body. This physical strength from others can be a resource to help us cope with current problems and concerns.

As you begin your work with interviewing and counseling, it is very important that you work only with positive images. Negative imaging is potentially useful in psychotherapy and imagery can be used to go over difficult situations from past history, but negative imagery has been found to develop false memories. Exploration of negative images is highly inappropriate unless the interviewer is fully qualified and the time and situation are appropriate for the client. Wait until you are qualified or have appropriate supervision to use imagery of past problems.

Encourage Physical Exercise and Nutrition. A sound body is fundamental to mental health. Moving the body increases blood flow and an exercise routine has been found to help reduce stress and depression. Proper eating habits and a regime of stretching and meditation make a difference in the lives of your clients. Teaching clients how to nourish their bodies is becoming a standard part of counseling. We love and work more effectively if we are comfortable in our bodies.

COUNSELOR: Alisia, you seem stressed much of the time. What's happening with exercise in your life?

ALISIA: I simply don't have time and when I think of it, I realize that I have some errands to run or someone calls me on the cell phone.

COUNSELOR: Evidence is clear that tension can be relieved by exercise. I'd like you to consider the possibility. What types of exercise have you enjoyed in the past?

ALISIA: Well, I used to run and I did feel more "up" when I got out. But since I've moved to the city, I just don't seem to find time any more.

COUNSELOR: As part of dealing with Chris and your various stressors, I think it is very important that we start some sort of exercise routine. You'll feel better and will be able to deal more effectively with those challenges if you take care of yourself. What do you think?

ALISIA: Well . . . I should consider it. I did feel better when I did run. (pause) But, how?

COUNSELOR: Let's work on it. Tell me more about your schedule. (the session continues)

It is obvious that we can't tell Alisia what to do. For example, "You should start exercising and running daily" simply won't work and will build client resentment. Helping clients change their behavior involves a more subtle use of directives in which the client is a full co-participant in the process. Regardless of what directive you want to provide on any topic, the client has to "buy in" and be central in the choice of action.

Thought-Stopping. This strategy has consistently been found to be one of the most effective interventions a counselor or therapist can use. If you take the time to learn and practice thought-stopping on yourself, you gain a valuable tool to increase your own self-esteem and effectiveness and you will see its potential for clients. Thought-stopping is useful for all kinds of client problems: perfectionism, excessive culture-based guilt or shame, shyness, and mild depression. This is one of our favorite strategies and we have found it very helpful to us over the years when we get into negative thinking about ourselves. Almost everyone engages in internalized negative self-talk. Self-talk is stressful thoughts you say to yourself, perhaps several times a day. For example:

"Why did I do that?"

"I'm always too shy."

"I always foul up."

"I should have done better."

"Life is so discouraging for me."

"Nobody will listen to me."

Other negative thoughts include guilty feelings, procrastination where you "over-think" the situation, fear that things will only get worse, anger that others "never get it right," repetitively thinking about past failures, or always needing the approval of others. Negative self-talk erodes self-esteem and increases self-doubt over time.

The following is the basic process for learning and using thought-stopping:

Step 1. Learn the basic process. Relax, close your eyes, and imagine a situation in which you make the negative self-statement. Take time and let the situation evolve. When the thought comes, observe what happens and how you feel after the negative self-talk. Then tell yourself silently "STOP." If you are alone, say it loudly and firmly.

Step 2. Transfer thought-stopping to your daily life. Place a rubber band around your wrist and every time during the day that you find yourself thinking negatively, snap the rubber band and say "STOP!" This simple step almost sounds silly, but it works.

BOX 12-2 National and International Perspectives on Counseling

Can We Be "Nonjudgmental" About Crime?
WEIJUN ZHANG

Tom, age 14, comes for help because he is scared. Several of his friends were involved in a house break-in over the weekend. Although he didn't go into the house, he was outside waiting for his friends to come out. Everyone in town is talking about the vandalism and Tom is afraid he'll be implicated.

After reading this case in a class, the professor asked us to decide which theoretical approach was most suitable for using with Tom. Some students suggested person-centered, with a focus on listening to his story, while others preferred to use Gestalt to deal with his present feelings. We then role-played some of these ideas in class. Much to my surprise, my classmates were so good at being "nonjudgmental" that their focus was all on the boy's feelings and cognition; there wasn't the slightest hint that anyone gave any thought to the vandalism, or that being silent about vandalism might be immoral.

There was no attention to the logical consequences of his action and little attempt to provide him with ideas for building a more successful future. Listening skills, of course, are of vital importance, but to me, this is a situation in which some judgment may be helpful. I'll admit that we need to use a respectful nonjudgmental vocal tone and attitude, but judgment of right and wrong remains an issue.

I suppose a 14-year-old boy can't be expected to have very mature judgment. But given this, what effect would counseling sessions such as those we role-played have had on him? Apart from having his anxiety reduced, he might very likely have learned a moral lesson from the counselor's being nonjudgmental, namely, that there might be nothing right or wrong about break-ins, that it might be all right to not report a crime, and that one's mental health could be totally separated from social responsibility.

I am not suggesting here that counselors should act like the police in dealing with the boy. I do believe, however, that the counselor should let him know clearly that she or he personally does not approve of such law-violating actions, even though confidentiality would nevertheless be strictly observed. The point here is when counselors believe they should remain "value free" on an issue, they should also take ethical responsibility to see that such a youngster does not get any confusing or incorrect impressions about their nonjudgmental approach.

If I were Tom's counselor, I would not feel comfortable until my duty as a responsible adult was also fulfilled in the counseling process. I would try to raise the boy's community consciousness by asking him questions like these: How would you feel if you were the victim of the break-in? What impact has this break-in had on the whole community? What difference can it make if you report the crime voluntarily? I believe that many non-European Americans, because of their strong sense of community, would agree with my orientation.

A classmate criticized me for being too judgmental, and he is probably right. After all, it is impossible to remain completely nonjudgmental about such matters. Your questions, your paraphrases, your reflection of feelings and meaning, and especially what you choose to focus on, will all reflect your judgment and have a profound impact on the youngster. The distinction I am trying to make is that by trying to be completely "nonjudgmental" with the boy, my fellow students were conveying to the boy that an individual's feelings and concerns could take precedence over a community's interests, while I suggest that we should take the good of the community into full account when we work to promote the mental health of an individual.

Step 3. Add positive imaging. Once you have developed some understanding of how often you use negative self-talk and after you say "STOP" or snap the rubber band, substitute a more positive statement about yourself immediately. You may use positive imagery or think about an example when you had a positive experience or a brief, broader statement emphasizing general strengths.

"I can do lots of things right."

"I am lovable and capable."

"I sometimes mess up—no one's perfect."

"I did the best I could."

Homework. The fifth stage of the interview is concerned with generalizing thoughts, feelings, and behaviors to the "real world" outside of the session. Working with the client to *do something different or new* during the coming week can be invaluable.

Homework assignments can include thought-stopping, using positive imaging or meditation daily, playing basketball with friends, starting a program of walking or running, or keeping a diary of foods eaten. Another type of homework may be to have the client write down the negative or faulty thought each time it occurs during the day. A couple with difficulties may be asked to observe and count the number of arguments they have. They record the before, during, and after aspects of the argument to discuss with the counselor. No change is expected as the client is simply expected to observe and record what is going on. With some clients, just observing themselves leads them to change their behavior! The client can also record what happened just before the thought and what happened afterward. Such records can be valuable in changing faulty thinking patterns. There are endless ways to involve clients in homework following the interview.

▲ **MODULE 12.3**
SUMMARY

- ▲ Directive strategies are used to tell the client what to do in a timely, individually and culturally appropriate manner. Directives may range from telling the client to seek career information to using complex theoretical strategies.
- ▲ Used sparingly, directives can be critical in leading to client change and growth, measured on the Client Change Scale (CCS).
- ▲ Homework is a useful strategy to help clients generalize what they have learned in the interview to their daily life in the "real world."

SKILL INTEGRATION, TREATMENT PLANNING, AND USING THEORY WITH MICROSKILLS

SECTION

What is your style of interviewing and counseling? This section provides a framework to help you integrate the many skills and concepts of this book.

Chapter 13 presents decisional counseling, a systematic approach to helping clients make critical life decisions. As all clients are constantly making decisions and choices, understanding and mastery of decisional counseling will help you work with many other theories of interviewing and counseling. A complete decisional counseling interview transcript shows you how to plan for an interview, make case notes, and develop treatment plans. The final exercise in this chapter is the most important. You are asked to make an audio or video recording of a full interview and develop your own transcript. Classify the skills and strategies you use and compare and contrast this session with the first interview you recorded, as recommended in Chapter 1. A careful analysis of your behavior in the session will aid in identifying your natural style and its special qualities.

Chapter 14 provides information on three very different orientations to interviewing and counseling—person-centered, cognitive-behavioral assertiveness training, and brief counseling. The microskills approach can help you understand and become more competent in multiple theoretical approaches. We anticipate that you will find all three approaches useful in your eventual practice, but you may find that you personally favor one method over another. Each can be helpful as you think through your own favored approach to helping clients. However, be aware some of your clients may prefer a different approach from the one you favor, so be prepared to intentionally flex your theoretical choice as well as skills and strategies.

Chapter 15 provides you with the opportunity to review your work with microskills, interview structure, and various orientations to the interview. You will be asked to think about your own natural style of interviewing and plan for the future.

The following objectives of this section provide you with a comprehensive overview of the interviewing and counseling process. You can use your knowledge and skills to build your own culturally intentional, culturally appropriate interviewing style. Careful study of these concepts enables you to

1. Analyze and integrate the concepts of intentional interviewing and counseling.
2. Examine and analyze your own behavior and thinking in the interview and discuss your specific impact on clients.
3. Review your helping style and your sensitivity to the multiple issues of diversity within and beyond the RESPECTFUL model.
4. Define your ideas and intentions about the theory and methods you believe to be most important in counseling and interviewing.
5. Conduct a beginning full interview using four alternative theoretical/practical structures:

   ▲ *Decisional counseling.* The five stages of the interview may be constructed within a problem-solving framework. Decisions underlie most issues and skills and will be useful with many types of clients. Even if you prefer another theory, you will find that integrating a brief use of decisional ideas is helpful.

   ▲ *Person-centered counseling.* If you have completed a full interview using only the basic listening sequence (Chapter 7), you have made a useful beginning in the understanding and practice of this theoretical orientation. Chapter 14 adds skills of reflection of meaning, focusing, and feedback to broaden this framework and place it more in tune with Carl Rogers's original thinking.

   ▲ *Cognitive-behavioral assertiveness training.* Many of your clients will benefit from this strategy, regardless of your personal theoretical orientation. It is a useful supplement to help overly passive or overly aggressive clients achieve their own personal goals.

   ▲ *Brief counseling.* This is a short-term problem-solving approach to human change. In a time of accountability, you may find this model useful in aiding clients to move to action. Questioning is the central microskill, differing from person-centered counseling, where it is rarely used.

DECISIONAL COUNSELING, SKILL INTEGRATION, AND DEVELOPING TREATMENT PLANS

SKILL INTEGRATION

INFLUENCING SKILLS AND STRATEGIES

FOCUSING

CONFRONTATION

THE FIVE-STAGE INTERVIEW STRUCTURE

REFLECTION OF FEELING

ENCOURAGING, PARAPHRASING, AND SUMMARIZING

OPEN AND CLOSED QUESTIONS

ATTENDING BEHAVIOR

ETHICS, MULTICULTURAL COMPETENCE, AND WELLNESS

How can your skill integration help you and your clients?

CHAPTER GOALS

You and your clients will greatly benefit from a naturally flowing interview and treatment plan using a smooth integration of the skills, strategies, and concepts of intentional interviewing and counseling.

Awareness, knowledge, and skills developed through the concepts of this chapter will enable you to

- ▲ Understand the basics of decisional counseling and use it as a model in helping clients make decisions that help them clarify their thinking, emotions, and behavior. Also, effective decisional counseling leads to generalization from the interview to changes in daily life.
- ▲ Develop long-term treatment plans for a client and keep systematic interview records.
- ▲ Integrate the skills, strategies, and concepts of intentional interviewing with your understanding of other theoretical models of the helping process.

MODULE 13.1
DEFINING DECISIONAL COUNSELING

KEY CONCEPT QUESTIONS

▲ **How does Benjamin Franklin's decision-making model relate to interviewing and counseling today?**

▲ **What is trait and factor counseling and where did it originate?**

▲ **What is decisional counseling and how does it relate to the microskills five-stage interviewing framework?**

Decisional counseling may be described as a practical model that recognizes decision making and the microskills as a foundation for most—perhaps all—systems of counseling. Another term for decisional counseling is problem-solving counseling. Many see Benjamin Franklin as the originator of systematic decision making. He suggested three stages of problem solving: (1) Identify the problem clearly, (2) generate alternative answers, and (3) decide what to do. Although Franklin's framework does not speak to the relationship between counselor and client nor to ensuring that clients actually generalize new ideas and decisions to their daily lives, these three stages are basic to all problem solving and decisional models.

Decision making is a lifelong issue. Clients are always solving problems and making decisions. Young adults must choose a college or career or decide to continue a relationship, get married, or have a child. Later they will make decisions about how to succeed in a work setting, deal with difficult colleagues, and plan finances for their children's education and their own retirement. They will find that decisions don't end with retirement as the first question faced by many retirees is "What shall I do with all this time?" Finally, difficult decisions around health issues, wills, and plans for their own funeral often require counseling.

Regardless of theoretical approach, the essential issue is this: *How can we help clients work through issues and come up with new answers?* All theories of counseling—behavioral, person-centered, or even psychoanalytic—deal with problem solving and decisions. The cognitive-behavioral counselor helps clients make their decisions more effectively through cognitive control and behavioral action. The person-centered counselor enables clients to make decisions for themselves through self-examination and self-reflection. The brief counselor helps clients make positive decisions during a short series of sessions. Even those in psychoanalytic therapy make decisions about the meaning of dreams and unconscious behavior.

The Trait-and-Factor Legacy of Decisional Counseling

Decisional counseling examines the many *traits and factors* underlying any single issue or problem when making a decision. Trait-and-factor theory has a long history in the counseling field, dating back to the development of the Boston Vocational Bureau by Frank Parsons in 1908. Parsons pointed out that in making a vocational decision the client needs to (a) consider personal traits, abilities, skills, and interests; (b) examine the environmental factors (opportunities, job availability, location, etc.); and (c) develop "true reasoning on the relations of these two groups of facts"(Parsons, 1909/1967, p. Over time trait-and-factor theory has researched the many dimensions that underl "true reasoning" and decision making; however, it came to be seen as limited, and new decisional and problem-solving models emerged (Brammer & MacDonald, 2002; D'Zurilla, 1999; Egan, 2002; Ivey & Ivey, 2007; Mann, 2001). All of these newer models are modern reformulations of Benjamin Franklin's original model and Parson's trait-and-factor theory.

Decisional Counseling and the Five Stages of the Interview

Benjamin Franklin's original ideas and trait-and-factor theory are basic to the microskill five-stage interview and all problem-solving systems. The five stages of the interview are based on a decisional model.

1. Initiate the session—develop rapport and structuring ("Hello; this is what might happen in this session"). This step is not often stressed as a separate element, but it is an important part of any problem-solving approach.
2. Gather data—draw out stories, concerns, problems, or issues ("What's your concern? What are your strengths or wellness resources?"). Benjamin Franklin outlined problem definition, and trait-and-factor theorists consider personal traits, abilities, skills, and interests. The trait-and-factor approach gave special attention to the environment while the five stages give attention to the cultural/environmental context.
3. Set goals mutually—establish outcomes ("What do you want to happen?"). In many problem-solving approaches, this is considered part of defining the problem. Goal setting is often the first issue addressed in brief counseling and the five-stage microskills model considers it essential. *If you don't know where you are going, you may end up somewhere else!*
4. Explore and create alternatives—confront client incongruities and conflict, restory ("What are we going to do about it?"). Problem-solving models often use brainstorming to find alternatives and the historically important trait and factor theory employed "true reasoning" to discover the relationship of the person to the environment.
5. Conclude—generalize and act on new stories ("Will you do it?"). Most problem-solving models, including many modern approaches as well as Franklin and trait-and-factor theory, give insufficient attention to taking ideas and behaviors into the "real world."

The basic model of decision making in the five-stage interview is often sufficient in itself to produce significant change. Those who practice decisional counseling will often use a variety of other theories, approaches, and strategies. The following chapter presents brief counseling, a very effective and closely allied approach. Cognitive-behavioral assertiveness training is often useful in helping clients generalize important decisions to their daily lives (see Table 13-1).

Some Additional Strategies of Decisional Counseling

Decisional counseling has its own strategies for change. While the five-stage structure is central, the following will be useful additions to your work.

▲ **TABLE 13-1** Estimated Time Spent in Stages/Dimensions Given Different Theoretical/Practical Orientations

Stage/ Dimension	Decisional Counseling	Person-Centered Theory	Cognitive-Behavioral Assertiveness Training	Brief Counseling
1. Initiate the session— develop rapport and structuring	Medium	Some; rapport stressed throughout (also true of other theories as well)	Some	Goal setting occurs early in the interview and is part of rapport/ structuring
2. Gather data—draw out stories, concerns, prob-lems, or issues	Medium	Great	Great	Medium
3. Set goals mutually— establish outcomes	Medium	Little emphasis on goals	Medium	Great, a central issue
4. Explore and create alterna-tives—confront client incon-gruities and conflict, restory	Medium	Medium	Medium	Medium— Dimensions 4 and 5 combined
5. Conclude— generalize and act on new stories	Great	Little	Medium	See above

Creative Brainstorming. While decisions start with logic, generating possible alternatives for action is a creative act. Encourage clients to "loosen up" and let any thought come to their mind. You can help through your own creativity, but focus on helping the clients generate their own solutions.

Logical Consequences. This is a particularly important strategy to use in decisional counseling. Once several alternatives for problem solution have been brainstormed, it is helpful to review each one and anticipate the possible positive and negative results of each decision.

The Balance Sheet. The balance sheet is an extension of logical consequences, but here each alternative is written down and rated with a "+" or "−" (Mann, 2001). As a specific example, motivational interviewing, a substance abuse treatment method closely allied to microskills, uses the balance sheet to help abusers look at issues around drinking or using drugs. It lists the positives—what drinking does for them, and then lists the negatives. Adding focus concepts to the balance sheets helps alcoholics see the broader implications of their drinking on the lives of others. All this is done on a sheet of paper worked on jointly by the helper and the client.

Emotional Balancing. Special attention is given to future pacing and how the client would feel given each possible decision. Emotional awareness is fundamental to substantial change. While decision making is a cognitive activity, real satisfaction comes with pleasing feelings about the result. With this activity, emotions are stressed throughout the logical consequences strategy or the balance sheet. For example, "What do you feel and enjoy about drinking; "What does cocaine do for you?" and "Imagine yourself not drinking; how would you feel about yourself?" "What would your family feel?" Use both *here-and-now* emotions and those of the past and anticipated future. Look forward to the longer-term benefits that will come with change.

Future Imaging. The directive of guided imagery can be used to help clients imagine alternative futures that might occur from varying decisions. Clients relax and close their eyes and then think through a possible future day if they make a particular decision. When debriefing clients after this experience, help them focus on feelings and search for an emotionally satisfying decision. Mann (2001) suggests the *Future Diary* in which clients write journals of what a day would be like if they made certain decisions.

MODULE 13.1

SUMMARY

- Benjamin Franklin's basic decision-making model is (1) clearly identify the problem, (2) generate alternatives, and (3) decide what to do.
- All counseling theories can be organized using the five-stage interviewing model, even though the content and practice of each theory may vary extensively.
- Trait-and-factor counseling originated with Frank Parsons in the Boston Vocational Bureau in 1908. His decisional model involved (1) considering personal traits, abilities, skills, and interests; (2) examining the environmental factors (opportunities, job availability, location, etc.); and (3) developing "true reasoning on the relations of these two groups of facts."
- The microskills five-stage interview is basic to the process of creative decision making. Decisional counseling helps clients make a wide array of decisions from simple ones in daily life to complex problems.
- Five example strategies that may be helpful in decisional counseling include *creative brainstorming, logical consequences, the balance sheet, emotional balancing, and future imaging.*

MODULE 13.2
PLANNING THE FIRST INTERVIEW

KEY CONCEPT QUESTIONS

▲ **How can a plan be developed for the first interview?**

▲ **What if the interview does not proceed as planned?**

The decisional counseling interview presented for study is a role-play conducted by Allen and Mary Ivey, based on Mary's real-life career planning. Mary role-plays a 36-year-old

BOX 13-1   First Interview Treatment Plan

Before the first interview, study the client file; anticipate important issues and how you might handle them. This plan shows Allen's assessment of his forthcoming interview with Mary.

Stage/Dimension Key Questions	Counselor Preparation
Initiate the session—develop rapport/structuring *What structure do you have for this interview? Do you plan to use a specific theory? What special issues do you anticipate with regard to rapport development?*	Mary appears to be a verbal and active person. I note she likes swimming and physical activity. I like to run and that may be a common bond to discuss. I'll be open about structure but keep the five stages in mind. It seems she may be unhappy in her current job and want to look into another career choice. Another personal issue is her divorce. I'll need to listen to her stories and use mainly questions and reflective listening skills, and follow a decision-making model.
Gather data—draw out stories, concerns, problems, or issues *What are anticipated problems? Strengths? How do you plan to define the issues with the client? Will you emphasize behavior, thoughts, feelings, meanings?*	I'll use Mary's wellness strengths early and focus on finding out what she *can* do. I'll use the basic listening sequence to bring out issues from her point of view and learn about her thoughts about her job and her thoughts about the future. I'll be interested in her personal life as well. How are things going since the divorce? What is it like to be a woman in a changing world? Mary may well bring up several issues. I'll summarize them toward the end of this phase, and we may have to list them and set priorities if there are too many issues. Mainly, however, I expect an interview on career choice.
Set goals mutually—establish outcomes *What is the ideal outcome? How will you elicit the client's idealized self or world?*	I'll ask her what her fantasies and ideas are for an ideal resolution and follow up with the basic listening sequence. I'll end by confronting and summarizing the real and the ideal. As for outcome, I'd like to see Mary define her own direction from a range of alternatives.
Explore and create alternatives—confront client incongruities and conflict, restory *What theories would you probably use here? What specific incongruities have you noted or do you anticipate in the client? How will you generate alternatives?*	Working from the decisional model, I hope to begin this stage by summarizing her positive strengths and wellness assets. I'd like to see several new alternative possibilities considered. Counseling and business are indicated in her pre-interview form as two good possibilities. Are there other possibilities? The main incongruity will probably be between where she is and where she wants to go. I expect to ask her questions and develop some concrete alternatives even in the first session. . . . I hope she will act on some of them following our first session. I think career testing may be useful.
Conclude—generalize and act on new stories *What specific plans do you have for transfer of training? What will enable you, the interviewer, to feel that the interview was worthwhile?*	I'll feel satisfied if we have generated some new possibilities and can do some exploration of career alternatives after the first session. We can plan from there. I'd like it if we could generate at least one thing Mary can do for homework before our second session.

divorced client, with two children. She stated in her information file, completed before counseling, "I find myself bored and stymied in my present job as a physical education teacher. I think it is time to look at something new. Possibly I should think about business. Sometimes I find myself a bit depressed by it all." This initial interview illustrates that career counseling is closely related to personal counseling. The personal issues arise along with the career issues further into the session. Additionally, gender is an important multicultural issue that needs to be considered. Within this transcript and the process notes, Allen analyzes his behavior in the session, and Mary reviews and analyzes his comments. It is this type of analysis that we will ask you to do as a self-study project.

Given the five-stage interview structure, it is possible to develop an advance plan for the session. You are less likely to help the client effectively without an appropriate advance plan. You should not impose your views or concepts on the client; rather, you think through ahead of time likely approaches that will help the client achieve whatever goal he or she may have. Equally important, just because you have a plan, don't expect things to always work out as you anticipate. Clients will bring up issues that cause you to rethink where to go next, and you may even need to scrap your plan entirely. As always, intentionality, the ability to be open to alternatives and flex with the *here and now*, is critical.

Allen developed the session plan from his study of a client file consisting of a pre-interview questionnaire (see Box 13-1). Mary stated in her intake form, "I'd like to do something new with my career. I'm ready for something new—but, what?" Note that the interview plan is oriented to help the client develop her own unique career plan and to facilitate the discussion of personal issues as well. The plan is structured to help the client achieve her objectives and make her own decisions, but remains flexible enough to adapt as the interview progresses and new issues are brought up.

▲ **MODULE 13.2**
_____
SUMMARY

▲ Systematically plan for an initial interview using the five-stage structure of the interview.

▲ It is important to be intentionally flexible and ready to change your plan if events in the session suggest that another approach is needed. The five stages provide a useful checklist to ensure covering all points even if the interview does not go as expected.

MODULE 13.3
A FULL INTERVIEW TRANSCRIPT: I'd Like to Find a New Career

KEY CONCEPT QUESTIONS

▲ **How are microskills and the five-stage interview actually implemented in a real interview?**

▲ **How do we analyze the specific use of skills and their effectiveness in the session?**

▲ **How might others have responded to the same client?**

Skill Integration	Predicted Result
Integrate the microskills into a well-formed interview and generalize the skills to situations beyond the training session or classroom.	Developing interviewers and counselors will integrate skills as part of their natural style. Each of us will vary in our choices, but increasingly we will know what we are doing, how to flex when what we are doing is ineffective, and what to expect in the interview as a result of our efforts.

In Table 13-2, the counselor and client verbatim transcript of a career decision interview is supplemented by a skill-and-focus analysis of the session. The microskill five stages are demonstrated within the session. The *Process Comments* column analyzes the effectiveness of skills throughout the interview, and special attention is given to the effect of confrontations ("C") on the client's developmental change.

As you read this interview, evaluate and assess Allen's interviewing style. What responses make sense to you? Are his interventions appropriate, and what might you do differently? While it is important to define your own natural style, it is also important to look at your style and how others view it. You will find some responses and strategies are less effective than others. We all make errors; it is our ability to learn from them and change that enables us to become more effective.

Our use of listening skills influences what a client says next and the general direction of the interview. Allen, the interviewer, constructed the session addressing primarily career counseling and focused on pertinent, important decisions. However, a person-centered counselor might have responded rather quickly to personal issues with a greater emphasis on reflection of feeling and reflection of meaning (see page 261). A cognitive-behaviorally oriented interviewer might be more directive (see page 266). A brief solution-focused counselor would focus much sooner on client goals and use many more questions (see page 273). The systematic decisional microskills counseling model underlies most, perhaps all, theories of helping and provide a good foundation for mastering other theories, including your own unique approach to the helping fields.

▲ **MODULE 13.3**

SUMMARY

▲ The microskills can be integrated into a well-formed interview that prepares the interviewer to focus on clients' presenting issues but still allows room to flex to meet emerging needs. Counselors with varying theoretical orientations will approach the case in different ways.

▲ A person-centered counselor might focus more on Mary and her feelings, thoughts, and meanings around herself.

▲ A cognitive-behavioral counselor would be more interested in specific behavioral descriptions and aim for change in actions.

▲ The interview transcript provides a systematic analysis through process comments, behavioral counts of microskill usage, examines the five-stage structure of the interview, and evaluates client movement on the Client Change Scale.

▲ **TABLE 13-2** The Allen and Mary Five-Stage Decisional Interview

This five-column format may be a suitable structure for you to use to prepare your own interview analyses.				
Skill Classifications				
Listening & Influencing	*Focus*	*C**	*Counselor and Client Conversation*	*Process Comments*
STAGE/DIMENSION 1: Initiate the session—develop rapport and structuring				
Open question	Client		1. *Allen:* Hi, Mary. How are you today?	
	Client, interviewer		2. *Mary:* Ah . . . just fine. . . . How are you?	As Mary walked in, Allen saw her hesitate and sensed some awkwardness on her part. Note that she opens with two speech hesitations.
Information, paraphrase	Interviewer, client		3. *Allen:* Good, just fine. Nice to see you. . . . Hey, I noted in your file that you've done a lot of swimming.	
	Client, main theme		4. *Mary:* Oh, yeah, (smiling) . . . I like swimming; I enjoy swimming a lot.	Consequently, Allen decides to take a little time to develop rapport and put Mary at ease in the interview. Note that he focused on a positive aspect of Mary's past. It is often useful to build on the client's strengths even this early in the session.
Information, closed question	Main theme, interviewer, client		5. *Allen:* With this hot weather, I've been getting out. Have you been able to?	The distinction between providing information and a self-disclosure is illustrated at *Allen 5* and *Mary 6*. Allen comments that he's been getting out, whereas Mary gives information and personal feelings.
	Client		6. *Mary:* Yes, I enjoy the exercise. It's good relaxation.	

(Continued)

*This column will record the presence of a confrontation.

▲ **TABLE 13-2** The Allen and Mary Five-Stage Decisional Interview (Continued)

Skill Classifications				
Listening & Influencing	*Focus*	*C*	*Counselor and Client Conversation*	*Process Comments*
Paraphrase, reflection of feeling	Client		7. *Allen:* I also saw you won quite a few awards along the way. (*Mary:* Um-hmm.) . . . You must feel awfully good about that.	Mary's nonverbal behavior is now more relaxed. Client and counselor now have more body language symmetry.
	Client		8. *Mary:* I do. I do feel very good about that. It's been lots of fun.	
Information, closed question	Main theme		9. *Allen:* Before we begin, I'd like to ask if I can tape-record this talk. I'll need your written permission, too. Do you mind?	Obtaining permission to tape-record interviews is essential. If the request is presented in a comfortable, easy way, most clients are glad to give permission. At times it may be useful to give the tapes to clients to take home and listen to again.
Client			10. *Mary:* No, that's okay with me. (signs form permitting use of tape for *Intentional Interviewing and Counseling*)	
Information giving, self-disclosure	Client, interviewer		11. *Allen:* As we start, Mary, there are some important things to discuss. We'll have about an hour today and then we can plan for the future together. Today, I'd like to get to know you and I'll try to focus mainly on listening to your concerns. At the same	Allen provides some additional structure for the session so that Mary knows what she might expect. He introduces gender differences and provides an opportunity for Mary to react and ask questions. Note "*we* can plan." This leads to a more mutual interview.

▲ **TABLE 13-2** (Continued)

Skill Classifications				
Listening & Influencing	Focus	C	Counselor and Client Conversation	Process Comments
			time, from your file, I know that some of your issues relate to women's issues. Obviously, I'm a man, and I think it is important to bring this up so that you will be more likely to feel free to let me know if I seem to be "off-target" or misunderstand something. Feel free to ask me any questions you'd like around this or other matters.	
	Client, interviewer		12. *Mary:* I feel comfortable with you already. But, a couple questions. One is that I'm interested in the counseling field as a possibility—and the other is around the issue of living with divorce and being a single parent. What can you say about those?	Mary gives the OK, but then asks two questions. She leans forward when she asks them. This question is a surprise to the interviewer and should be noted as divorce and relationship issues may show themselves to be important later in the session.
Self-disclosure, open question	Interviewer, client		13. *Allen:* Well, first I'm divorced and have one child living with me while the other is in college. Of course, I'd be glad to talk	Keep self-disclosures brief and return the focus to the client. But be comfortable and open in that process.

(Continued)

▲ **TABLE 13-2** The Allen and Mary Five-Stage Decisional Interview (Continued)

Skill Classifications				
Listening & Influencing	*Focus*	*C*	*Counselor and Client Conversation*	*Process Comments*
			about the counseling career and share some of my thoughts. What thoughts occur to you around divorce and counseling?	
	Client, main theme		14. *Mary:* That helps. Going through my divorce was the worst thing of my life. My children are so important to me. Perhaps your experience with divorce will help you understand where I am coming from. Let's get started and look at what my career should be.	Mary smiles, sits back, and appears to have the information she was wondering about.
STAGE/DIMENSION 2: Gather data—draw out stories, concerns, problems, issues				
Open question	Client		15. *Allen:* Could you tell me, Mary, what you'd like to talk about today?	In this series of leads you'll find that Allen uses the basic listening sequence of open question, encourager, paraphrase, reflection of feeling, and summary, in order. Many interviewers in different settings will use the sequence or a variation to define the client's problem.

▲ **TABLE 13-2** (Continued)

Skill Classifications				
Listening & Influencing	*Focus*	*C*	*Counselor and Client Conversation*	*Process Comments*
	Client, problem/ concern, others		16. *Mary:* Well . . . ah . . . I guess there's a lot that I'd like to talk about. You know, I went through . . . ah . . . a difficult divorce and it was hard on the kids and myself and . . . ah . . . we've done pretty well. We've pulled together. The kids are doing better in school and I'm doing better. I've . . . ah . . . got a new friend. (breaks eye contact) But, you know, I've been teaching for 13 years and really feel kind of bored with it. It's the same old thing over and over every day; you know . . . parts of it are okay, but lots of it I'm bored with.	As many clients do, Mary starts the session with a "laundry list" of issues. Though the last thing in a laundry list is often what a client wants to talk about, the eye-contact break at mention of her "new friend" raises an issue that should be watched for in the interview. As the session moves along, it becomes apparent that more than the career issue needs to be looked at. Mary discusses a "pattern" of boredom. This is indicative of an abstract client who is able to reflect on herself and see patterns of behavior.
Encourage	Client		17. *Allen:* You say you're *bored* with it?	The key word *bored* is emphasized.
	Client, problem/ concern		18. *Mary:* Well, I'm bored, I guess . . . teaching field hockey and . . . ah . . . basketball and softball, certain of those team sports. There are certain	Note that Mary elaborates in more detail on the word *bored*. Allen used verbal underlining and gave emphasis to that word, and Mary did as most

(Continued)

▲ **TABLE 13-2** The Allen and Mary Five-Stage Decisional Interview (Continued)

Skill Classifications				
Listening & Influencing	Focus	C	Counselor and Client Conversation	Process Comments
			things I like about it, though. You know, I like the dance, and you know, I like swimming—I like that. Ah . . . but . . . you know . . . I get tired of the same thing all the time. I guess I'd like to do some different things with my life.	clients would: She elaborated on the meaning of the key word to her. Many times short encouragers and restatements have the effect of encouraging client exploration of meaning and elaboration on a topic. "I'd like to do some different things" is a more positive "I" statement.
Paraphrase	Client		19. *Allen:* So, Mary, if I hear you correctly, sounds like change and variety are important instead of doing the same thing all the time.	Note that this paraphrase has some dimensions of an interpretation in that Mary did not use the words *change* and *variety*. These words are the opposite of boredom and doing "the same things all the time." This paraphrase takes a small risk and is slightly additive to Mary's understanding. It is an example of the positive asset search, in that it would have been possible to hear only the negative "bored." Working on the positive suggests what *can* be done. Note her response.

▲ **TABLE 13-2** (Continued)

Skill Classifications				
Listening & Influencing	Focus	C	Counselor and Client Conversation	Process Comments
	Client, family, problem/ concern		20. *Mary:* Yeah . . . I'd like to be able to do something different. But, you know, ah . . . teaching's a very secure field, and I have tenure. You know, I'm the sole support of my two daughters, but I think, I don't know what else I can do exactly. Do you see what I'm saying?	Mary, being heard, is able to move to a deeper discussion of her issues. Note that Mary tends to be abstract and discusses patterns and generalizations. If she were primarily concrete, she would give many more linear details and tell specific stories about her issues. She continues for most of the interview in this mode of expression. She has equated "something different" with a lack of security. As the interview progresses, you will note that she associates change with risk. It is these basic meaning constructs, already apparent in the interview that lie under many of her issues.
Reflection of feeling, followed by check-out	Client, problem	C	21. *Allen:* Looks like the security of teaching makes you feel good, but it's the boredom you associate with that security that makes you feel uncomfortable. Is that correct?	This reflection of feeling contains elements of a confrontation as well, in that the good feelings of security are contrasted with the boredom associated with teaching.

(Continued)

▲ **TABLE 13-2** The Allen and Mary Five-Stage Decisional Interview (Continued)

Skill Classifications				
Listening & Influencing	*Focus*	*C*	*Counselor and Client Conversation*	*Process Comments*
	Client, problem/ concern		22. *Mary:* Yeah, you know, it's that security. I feel good being . . . you know . . . having a steady income and I have a place to be, but it's boring at the same time. You know, ah . . . I wish I knew how to go about doing something else.	Note that Mary often responds with a "Yeah" to the reflections and paraphrases before going on. Here she is wrestling with the confrontation of *Allen 21.* She adds new data, as well, in the last sentence. On the CCS, this would be acceptance and recognition (Level 3).
Summary, check-out	Client, family, problem/ concern	C	23. *Allen:* So, Mary, let me see if I can summarize what I've heard. Ah . . . it's been tough since the divorce, but you've gotten things together. You mentioned the kids are doing pretty well. You talked about a new relationship. *I heard you mention that.* (Mary: Yeah.) But the issue that you'd like to talk about now is . . . this feeling of boredom (*Mary:* Ummm . . .) on the job, and yet you like the security of it. But maybe you'd like to try something new. Is that the essence of it?	This summarization concludes the first attempt at problem definition in this brief interview. Allen uses Mary's own words for the main things and attempts to distill what has been said. The positive asset search has been used briefly ("You've gotten things together . . . kids . . . doing well"). See other leads that emphasize client strength. Mary sits forward and nods with approval throughout this summary. The confrontation of the old job with "maybe you'd like to try

▲ **TABLE 13-2** (Continued)

Skill Classifications				
Listening & Influencing	Focus	C	Counselor and Client Conversation	Process Comments
				something new" concludes the summary. Note the check-out at the end of the summary to encourage Mary to react. Nonetheless, he missed the new friend as part of his summary.
	Client, problem		24. *Mary:* That's right. That's it.	Mary again responds at Level 3 on the CCS, acceptance and recognition.
STAGE/DIMENSION 3: Set goals mutually—establish outcomes				
Open question	Main theme		25. *Allen:* I think it might be helpful if you could specifically define what some things are that might represent a more ideal situation.	In Stage 3 find where the client wants to go in a more ideal situation. You'll note that the basic listening sequence is present in this stage, but it does not follow in order, as in the preceding stage.
	Client, problem, others		26. *Mary:* Ummm. I'm not sure. There are some things I like about my job. I certainly like interacting with the other professional people on the staff. I enjoy working with the kids. I enjoy talking with the kids. That's kind of fun.	Mary associates interacting with people as a positive aspect of her job. When she says "enjoy working with kids," her tone changes, suggesting that she doesn't enjoy it that much. But the spontaneous tone returns when she mentions "talking with them"

(Continued)

▲ **TABLE 13-2** The Allen and Mary Five-Stage Decisional Interview (Continued)

Skill Classifications				
Listening & Influencing	Focus	C	Counselor and Client Conversation	Process Comments
			You know, it's the stuff I have to teach I'm bored with. I have done some teaching of human sexuality and drug education.	and talks about teaching subjects other than team sports.
Paraphrase, open question	Client, main theme		27. *Allen:* So, would it be correct to say that some of the teaching, where you have worked with kids on content of interest to you, has been fun? What else have you enjoyed about your job?	The search here is for positive assets and things that Mary enjoys. Note the "what else?"
	Client, family, problem		28. *Mary:* Well, I must say I enjoy having the same summer vacations the kids have. That's a plus in the teaching field. (pause)	
Encourage			29. *Allen:* Yeah . . .	Mary found only one plus in the job. Allen probes for more data via an encourager. This type of encourager can't be classified in terms of focus.
	Client, others		30. *Mary:* You see, I like being able to . . . Oh, I know, one time I was able	Mary brings out new data that support her earlier comment that she

▲ **TABLE 13-2** (Continued)

Skill Classifications				
Listening & Influencing	Focus	C	Counselor and Client Conversation	Process Comments
			to do teaching of our own teachers and that was really . . . I really felt good being able to share some of my ideas with some people on the staff. I felt that was kind of neat, being able to teach other adults.	liked to teach when the content was of interest to her. The "I" statements here are more positive and the adjective descriptors indicate more self-assurance.
Closed question	Client, others		31. *Allen:* Do you involve yourself very much in coun- seling the students you have?	A closed question with a change of topic to explore other areas.
	Client, others		32. *Mary:* Well, the kids . . . you know, teaching them is a nice, comfortable environment, and kids stop in before class and after class and they talk about their boyfriends and the movies; I find I like that part . . . about their concerns.	Mary responds to the word *counseling* again with discus- sion of interactions with people. It seems important to Mary that she have contact with others.
Summary, closed question	Client, problem, others		33. *Allen:* So, as we've been review- ing your current job, it's the training, the drug education, some of the teach- ing you've done with kids on topics other than phys. ed. (*Mary:* That's right.) And getting out and doing	This summary attempts to bring out the main strands of the posi- tive aspects of Mary's job. In an ongoing interview, a closed question on a relevant topic can be as facilitating as an open question.

(Continued)

▲ **TABLE 13-2** The Allen and Mary Five-Stage Decisional Interview (Continued)

Skill Classifications				
Listening & Influencing	*Focus*	*C*	*Counselor and Client Conversation*	*Process Comments*
			training and other stuff with teachers . . . ah, sharing some of your expertise there. And the counseling relationships. (*Mary:* Ummm.) Out of those things, are there fields you've thought of transferring to?	Note, however, that the interviewer still directs the flow with the closed question.
	Client, problem/ concern		34. *Mary:* Well, a lot of people in physical education go into counseling. That seems like a natural second thing. Ah . . . of course, that would require some more going to school. Umm . . . I've also thought about doing some management training for a business. Sometimes I think about moving into business . . . entirely away from education. Or even working in a college as opposed to working here in the high school. I've thought about those things, too. But I'm just not sure which one seems best for me.	Mary talks with only moderate enthusiasm about counseling. In discussing training and business, she appears more involved. Mary appears to have assets and abilities, makes many positive "I" statements, is aware of key incongruities in her life, and seems to be internally directed. She is clearly an abstract, formal-operational client. For career success, she also needs to become more concrete and action-oriented.

▲ **TABLE 13-2** (Continued)

Skill Classifications				
Listening & Influencing	*Focus*	*C*	*Counselor and Client Conversation*	*Process Comments*
Paraphrase, closed question	Client, problem/ concern		35. *Allen:* So the counseling field, the training field. You've thought about staying in schools and perhaps in management as well. (*Mary:* Um-hm, um-hm.) Anything else that occurs to you?	This brief paraphrase distills Mary's ideas in her own words.
	Problem/ concern		36. *Mary:* No, I think that seems about it.	
Summary, open question, eliciting meaning	Client, problem/ concern	C	37. *Allen:* Before we go further, you've talked about teaching and the security it offers. But at the same time you talk about *boredom.* You talk with excitement about business and training. How do you put this together? What does it *mean* to you?	This summary includes confrontation and catches both content and feeling. The question at the end is directed toward issues of meaning. The word *boredom* was underlined with extra vocal emphasis.
	Client, others		38. *Mary:* Uhhh . . . Ah . . . If I stay in the same place, it's just more of the same. I see older teachers, and I don't want to be like them. Oh, a few have fun; most seem just *tired* to me. I don't want to end up like that.	Mary elaborates on the meaning and underlying structure of *why* she might want to avoid the occasional boredom of her job. When she talks about "ending up like that," we see deeper meanings.

(Continued)

▲ **TABLE 13-2** The Allen and Mary Five-Stage Decisional Interview (Continued)

Skill Classifications				
Listening & Influencing	Focus	C	Counselor and Client Conversation	Process Comments
				On the CCS, the client may again be rated at acceptance and recognition (Level 3). Though considerable depth of understanding and clarity is being developed, no large change has occurred. You will find that developmental movement often is slow and arduous. Nonetheless, each confrontation moves to more complete understanding.
Encourage/ restatement	Client		39. *Allen:* You don't want to end up with that.	The key words are repeated.
	Client		40. *Mary:* Yeah, I want to do something new, more exciting. Yet my life has been so confused in the past, and it is just settling down. I'm not sure I want to risk it.	Mary moves on to talk about what she wants, and a new element— risk—is introduced. Risk may be considered Mary's opposing construct to security.
Reflection of feeling	Client		41. *Allen:* So, Mary, risk frightens you?	This reflection of feeling is tentative and said in a questioning tone. This provides an implied check-out and gives Mary room to accept it or suggest

▲ **TABLE 13-2** (Continued)

Skill Classifications				
Listening & Influencing	*Focus*	*C*	*Counselor and Client Conversation*	*Process Comments*
				changes to clarify the feeling.
	Client, problem/concern		42. *Mary:* Well, not really, but it does seem scary to give up all this security and stability just when I've started putting it together. It just feels strange. Yet I do want something new so that life doesn't seem so routine . . . and . . . ah . . . I think maybe I have more talent and ability than I used to think I did.	Mary responds as might be predicted with a deeper exploration of feelings of fear of change. At the same time, she draws on her personal strengths to cope with all this.
Reflection of meaning, check-out	Client, problem/concern	C	43. *Allen:* So you've felt the meaning in this possible job change as an opportunity to use your *talent* and take risks in something new. This may be contrasted with the feelings of stability and certainty where you are now. But *now* means you may end up tired and burned-out like some co-workers you have observed. Am I reaching the sense of things? How does that sound?	This reflection of meaning also confronts underlying issues that impinge on Mary's decision. It contains elements of the positive asset search or positive regard as Allen verbally stresses the word *talent*.

(Continued)

▲ **TABLE 13-2** The Allen and Mary Five-Stage Decisional Interview (Continued)

Skill Classifications				
Listening & Influencing	Focus	C	Counselor and Client Conversation	Process Comments
	Client, problem/ concern		44. *Mary:* Exactly! But I hadn't touched on it that way before. I do want stability and security, but not at the price of bore- dom and feeling down as I have lately. Maybe I do have what it takes to risk more.	Mary is reinterpret- ing her situation from a more positive frame of reference. Allen could have said the same thing via an interpretation, but reflection of meaning lets Mary come up with her own definition. This reinterpreta- tion of Mary's meaning represents generation of a new solution (CCS Level 4). She has a new frame of reference with which to look at herself. But this newly integrated frame is *not* prob- lem resolution; it is a *step* toward a new way of think- ing and acting. Allen decides to move to Stage 4 of the interview. It would be possi- ble to explore problem definition and detail the goals more pre- cisely, but we can take up these matters in later interviews.

▲ **TABLE 13-2** (Continued)

Listening & Influencing	Focus	C	Counselor and Client Conversation	Process Comments
Skill Classifications				
STAGE/DIMENSION 4: Working—Explore and create alternatives, confront client incongruities and conflict, restory				
Feedback	Client		45. *Allen:* Mary, from listening to you, I get the sense that you do have considerable ability. Specifically, you can be together in a warm, involved way with those you work with. You can describe what is important to you. You come across to me as a thoughtful, able, sensitive person. (pause)	Allen combines feedback on positive assets with some self-disclosure here and uses this lead as a transition to explore alternative actions. The emphasis here is on the positive side of Mary's experience. Allen's vocal tone communicates warmth, and he leans toward Mary in a genuine manner.
			46. *Mary:* Ummm . . .	During the feedback, Mary at first shows signs of surprise. She sits up, then relaxes a bit, smiles, and sits back in her chair as if to absorb what Allen is saying more completely. There are elements of praise in Allen's comment.
Directive, paraphrase, open question	Client, main theme		47. *Allen:* Other job ideas may develop as we talk . . . ah . . . I think it might be appropriate at this point to explore some alternatives you've talked about. (*Mary:* Um-hm.) The first thing you talked about was you	Allen starts exploring alternatives a little more concretely and in depth. The systematic problem-solving model—define the problem, generate alternatives, and set priorities for solutions—is in his mind throughout

(Continued)

▲ **TABLE 13-2** The Allen and Mary Five-Stage Decisional Interview (Continued)

Skill Classifications

Listening & Influencing	Focus	C	Counselor and Client Conversation	Process Comments
			liked teaching drug education and sexuality. What else have you taught kids?	this section. He begins with a mild directive. "What else?" keeps the discussion open.
	Client, problem/ concern		48. *Mary:* Let's see . . . The general areas I liked were human sexuality, drug education, family life, and those kinds of things. Ah . . . sometimes communication skills.	
Closed question	Problem/ concern		49. *Allen:* Have you attended workshops on any of these topics?	Closed questions oriented toward concreteness can be helpful in determining specific background important in decision making.
	Client, problem/ concern, others		50. *Mary*: I've attended a few. I've enjoyed them . . . I really did. You know, I've gone to the university and taken workshops in values clarification and communication skills. I liked the people I met.	Note that virtually all counselor and client comments have focused on the client and the problem. It is important to consider the client in each of your responses; too heavy an emphasis on the problem may cause you to miss the unique person before you. At the same time, a broader focus might expand

▲ **TABLE 13-2** (Continued)

Skill Classifications				
Listening & Influencing	Focus	C	Counselor and Client Conversation	Process Comments
				the issue and provide more understanding. Social work, for example, might emphasize the family and social context.
Reflection of feeling, information, check-out	Client, problem/ concern		51. *Allen:* Sounds like you've really enjoyed these sessions. One of the important roles in counseling, education, and business is training—for example, psychological education through teaching others skills of living and communication. How does that type of work sound to you?	Allen briefly reflects her positive feelings, and then shares a short piece of occupational information. This is followed by a check-out returning the focus to Mary.
	Client, problem/ concern		52. *Mary:* I think I would enjoy that sort of thing. Um-hmmm . . . It sounds interesting.	
Paraphrase, open question	Client, problem/ concern		53. *Allen:* Sounds like you have also given a good deal of thought to . . . ah . . . extending that to training in general. How aware are you of the business field as a place to train and teach employees?	Mary's background and interest in a second alternative are explored.

(Continued)

▲ **TABLE 13-2** The Allen and Mary Five-Stage Decisional Interview (Continued)

Skill Classifications				
Listening & Influencing	Focus	C	Counselor and Client Conversation	Process Comments
	Client, problem/ concern, environmental context		54. *Mary:* I don't know that much about it. You know, I worked one summer in my dad's office, so I do have an exposure to business. That's about it. They all have been saying that a lot of teachers are moving into the business field. Teaching is not too lucrative, and with all the things happening here in California and all the cutbacks, business is a better long-term possibility for teachers these days. It just seems like an intriguing possibility for me to investigate or look into. The latest business cutbacks are scary, too.	Mary talks in considerably greater depth and with more enthusiasm when she talks about business. The important descriptive words she has used with teaching include *boring, security,* and *interpersonal interactions,* while *interest* and *excitement* were used for training and teaching psychologically oriented subjects as opposed to physical education. Now she mentions cutbacks. Business has been described with more enthusiasm and as more lucrative. We may anticipate that she will eventually associate the potential excitement of business with the negative construct of risk and the lack of summer vacations and time to be with her children.

▲ **TABLE 13-2** (Continued)

Skill Classifications				
Listening & Influencing	Focus	C	Counselor and Client Conversation	Process Comments
Paraphrase, reflection of feeling	Client, problem/ concern	C	55. *Allen:* Mm-hmm, . . . so you've thought about it . . . looking into business, but you've not done too much about it yet. Neither teaching nor business is really promising now and that's a little scary.	This paraphrase is somewhat subtractive. Mary did indicate that she had summer experience with her father. How much and how did she like it? Allen missed that. The paraphrase involves a confrontation between what Mary says and her lack of doing anything extensive in terms of a search. The reflection of feeling acknowledges emotion.
	Client		56. *Mary:* That's right. I've thought about it, but . . . ah . . . I've done very little about it. That's all . . .	Mary feels a little apologetic. She talks a bit more rapidly, breaks eye contact, and her body leans back a little. Mary's response is at Level 2 on the CCS. She is only partially able to work with the issues of the confrontation.
Interpretation	Problem/ concern		57. *Allen:* And, finally, you mentioned that you have considered the counseling field as an alternative. Ah . . . what about that?	Allen omitted further exploration of business. If Allen had focused on positive aspects of Mary's experience and learned more about her summer experience, the confrontation

(Continued)

▲ **TABLE 13-2** The Allen and Mary Five-Stage Decisional Interview (Continued)

Skill Classifications				
Listening & Influencing	Focus	C	Counselor and Client Conversation	Process Comments
				(of thinking without action) probably would have been received more easily. As this was a demonstration interview, Allen sought to move through the stages perhaps a little too fast. Also, the counseling field is an alternative, but it seems to come more from Allen than from Mary. An advantage of transcripts such as this is that one can see errors. Many of our errors arise from our own constructs and needs. This intended paraphrase is classified as an interpretation, as it comes more from Allen's frame of reference than from Mary's.
	Problem/ concern, others		58. *Mary:* Well, I've always been interested, like I said, in talking with people. People like to talk with me about all kinds of things. And *that*	Mary starts with some enthusiasm on this topic, but as she talks her speech rate slows and she demonstrates less energy.

▲ **TABLE 13-2** (Continued)

Skill Classifications				
Listening & Influencing	Focus	C	Counselor and Client Conversation	Process Comments
			would be interesting . . . ah . . . I think, too.	
Encourage			59. *Allen:* Um-hmmm.	
	Problem/ concern		60. *Mary:* You know, to explore that. (pause)	Said even more slowly.
Encourage			61. *Allen:* Um-hmmm. (pause)	Allen senses her change of enthusiasm, is a bit puzzled, and sits silently, encouraging her to *talk more.* When you have made an error and the client doesn't respond as you expect, return to attending skills.
	Problem/ concern		62. *Mary:* But . . . I'd have to take some *courses* . . . if I really wanted to get into it.	One reason for Mary's hesitation appears.
Interpreta- tion/reframe	Client, problem/ concern		63. *Allen:* So putting those three things together, it seems that you want people-oriented occupations. They are particularly interesting to you.	This is a mild interpretation, as it labels common elements in the three jobs. It could be classified also as a paraphrase. Not all skill distinctions are clear.
	Client		64. *Mary:* Definitely . . . and that's where I am most happy.	Mary has returned to a Level 3 on the CCS.

(Continued)

▲ **TABLE 13-2** The Allen and Mary Five-Stage Decisional Interview (Continued)

Skill Classifications				
Listening & Influencing	*Focus*	*C*	*Counselor and Client Conversation*	*Process Comments*
Feedback	Client, problem/ concern	C	65. *Allen:* And, Mary, as I talk I see you . . . ah . . . coming across with a lot of enthusiasm and interest as we talk about these alternatives. I do feel you are a little less enthusiastic about returning to school. (*Mary:* Right!) I might contrast your enthusiasm about the possibilities of business and training with your feelings about education. There you talk a little more slowly and almost seem bored as you talk about it. You seem lively when you talk about business possibilities.	Allen gives Mary specific and concrete feedback about how she comes across in the interview. There is a confrontation as he contrasts her behavior when discussing two topics. Confrontation—the presentation of discrepancies or incongruity—may appear with virtually all skills of the interview. It may be used to summarize past conversation and stimulate further discussion, leading toward a resolution of the incongruity.
	Client, problem/ concern		66. *Mary:* Well, they sound kind of exciting to me, Allen. But I just don't know how to go about getting into those fields or what my next steps might be. They sound very exciting to me, and I think I	Mary talks rapidly, her face flushes slightly, and she gestures with enthusiasm. She meets the confrontation and seems to be willing to risk more. This, however, may still be considered a

▲ **TABLE 13-2** (Continued)

Skill Classifications				
Listening & Influencing	*Focus*	*C*	*Counselor and Client Conversation*	*Process Comments*
			may have some talents in those areas I haven't even discovered yet.	Level 3 on the CCS, although there may be movement ahead.
Feedback, information, logical consequences	Client, problem/ concern	C	67. *Allen:* Um-hmmm. Well, Mary, I can say one thing. Your enthusiasm and ability to be open will be helpful to you in your search. Ah . . . at the same time, business and schools represent different types of lifestyles. I think I should give you a warning that if you go into the business area you're going to lose those summer vacations.	This statement combines mild feedback with logical consequences. A warning about the consequences of client action or inaction is spelled out. Mary is also confronted with some consequences of choice.
	Client, problem/ concern, others		68. *Mary:* Yeah, I know that . . . and you know, that special friend in my life—he's in education—I don't think he would like it if I was, you know, working all summer long. But business does pay a lot more, and it might have some interesting possibilities. (*Allen:* Um-hmm.) . . . It's a difficult situation.	Confrontations often result in clients presenting new important concepts and facts that have not been discussed previously. A new problem has emerged that may need definition and exploration. Mary is still responding at Level 3 on the CCS, but Allen is obtaining a more complete picture of the problem and of the client.

(Continued)

▲ **TABLE 13-2** The Allen and Mary Five-Stage Decisional Interview (Continued)

Skill Classifications				
Listening & Influencing	Focus	C	Counselor and Client Conversation	Process Comments
Encourage/ restatement	Problem		69. *Allen:* A difficult situation?	Again, the encourager is used to find deeper meanings and more information.
	Client, problem, others		70. *Mary:* Um-hmm. I guess I'm saying that . . . I'm . . . ah . . . you know, my friend . . . I don't think he would approve or like the idea of me having two weeks' vacation. (*Allen:* Uh-huh.) He wants me to stay in some field where I have the same vacation time I have now so we can spend that time together.	Mary has more speech hesitations and difficulties in completing a sentence here than she has anywhere in the interview. This suggests that her relationship is important to her, and her friend's attitude may be important in the final career decision. Much career counseling involves personal issues as well as career choice. Both require resolution for true client satisfaction.
Interpretation/ reframe, open question	Client, others, cultural/ environmental context	C	71. *Allen:* I hear you saying that your friend has a lot to say about your future. How does that strike you as an independent woman who has been on your own successfully for quite a while?	Here we see the introduction of gender relations as a cultural/environmental/ contextual issue. Allen's reframing of the situation offers Mary a chance to explore her relationship with Bo from a different contextual perspective.

▲ **TABLE 13-2** (Continued)

Skill Classifications				
Listening & Influencing	Focus	C	Counselor and Client Conversation	Process Comments
	Others		72. *Mary:* It really is . . . well, Bo's a special person . . .	Mary's eyes brighten.
Interpretation	Client, others		73. *Allen:* And, I sense you have some reactions to his . . .	Allen interrupts, perhaps unnecessarily. It might have been wise to allow Mary to talk about her positive feelings toward Bo.
	Client, problem/ concern		74. *Mary:* Yeah, I'd like to be able to explore some of my own potential without having those restraints put on me right from the beginning.	Mary talks slowly and deliberately, with some sadness in her voice. Feelings are often expressed through intonation. Here we see the beginning of a critical gender issue. Women often feel constraints in career or personal choices, and men in this culture often place implicit or explicit restraints on critical decisions. Feminist counseling theorists argue that a male helper may be less effective with these types of problems. What are your thoughts on this issue?
Interpretation/reframe, check-out	Client, problem/ concern, others, cultural/environmental context	C	75. *Allen:* Um-hmm . . . In a sense he's almost placing similar constraints on you that you	This interpretation relates the construct of boredom and the implicit constraint of being held down

(Continued)

▲ **TABLE 13-2** The Allen and Mary Five-Stage Decisional Interview (Continued)

Skill Classifications				
Listening & Influencing	Focus	C	Counselor and Client Conversation	Process Comments
			feel in the job in physical education. There are certain things you have to do. Is that right?	with the constraints of Bo. The interpretation clearly comes from Allen's frame of reference. With interpretations or helping leads from your frame of reference, the check-out of client reactions is even more important. The drawing of parallels is abstract, formal-operational in nature.
	Client, problem/ concern, others		76. *Mary:* Yes, probably so. He's putting some limits on me . . . setting limits on the fields I can explore and the job possibilities I can possibly have. Setting some limits so that my schedule matches his schedule.	Mary answers quickly. It seems the interpretation was relatively accurate and helpful. One measure of the function and value of a skill is what the client does with it. Mary changes the word *constraints* to the more powerful word *limits.* Mary remains at Level 3 on the CCS, as she is still expanding on aspects of the problem.
Open question, oriented to feeling	Client		77. *Allen:* In response to that you feel . . . ? (deliberate pause, waiting for Mary to supply the feeling)	Research shows that *some* use of questions facilitates emotional expression.

▲ **TABLE 13-2** (Continued)

Skill Classifications				
Listening & Influencing	*Focus*	*C*	*Counselor and Client Conversation*	*Process Comments*
	Client, problem/ concern		78. *Mary:* Ah . . . I feel I'm not at a point where I want to *limit things*. I want to see what's open, and I would like to keep things open and see what all the alternatives are. I don't want to shut off any possibility that might be really exciting for me. (*Allen:* Um-hmm.) A total lifetime of careers.	Mary determinedly emphasizes that she does not want limits.
Reflection of feeling, paraphrase	Client, problem/ concern	C	79. *Allen:* So you'd like to have a life of exciting opportu- nity, and you sense some limiting . . .	A brief, but impor- tant, confrontation of Bo versus career.
	Client, problem/ concern, others, cultural/ environmen- tal context		80. *Mary:* He reminds me of my relationship with my first husband. You know, I think the reason that all fell apart was my going back to work. You know, assuming a more nontraditional role as a woman and exploring my potential as a woman rather than staying home with the children . . . ah . . . you know, sort of a similar thing happened there.	Again, the con- frontation brings out important new data about Mary's present and past. Is she repeating old relationship pat- terns in this new relationship? The counselor should consider issues of cultural sexism as an environmental aspect of Mary's planning. This does not appear in this interview, but a broader focus on issues in the next session seems

(Continued)

▲ **TABLE 13-2** The Allen and Mary Five-Stage Decisional Interview (Continued)

Skill Classifications				
Listening & Influencing	Focus	C	Counselor and Client Conversation	Process Comments
				imperative. Other focus issues of possible importance include Mary's parental models, others in her life, a women's support group, the present economic climate, the attitudes of the counselor, and "we"—the immediate relationship of Mary and Allen. Thus far he has assumed a typical Western "I" form of counseling where the emphasis is on the client. Due to the development of new, more integrated data, this could be development of a more inclusive construct (Level 5 response on the CCS).
Summary	Client, problem/ concern, others, cultural/ environmental context	C	81. *Allen:* There really are a variety of issues that . . . you're looking at. One of these is the whole business of a job. Another is your relationship with Bo and your desire to find your own space as an independent woman.	The interview time is waning, and Allen must plan a smooth ending and plan for the next session. He catches the incongruity that Mary faces between work and relationship. Allen fails to pick up fully on the C/E/C focus. Many of Mary's

▲ **TABLE 13-2** (Continued)

Skill Classifications				
Listening & Influencing	Focus	C	Counselor and Client Conversation	Process Comments
				issues relate to women's issues in a sometimes sexist world.
			82. *Mary:* (slowly) Um-hmmm . . .	Mary looks down, relaxes, and seems to go into herself.
Reflection of feeling	Client		83. *Allen:* You look a little sad as I say that.	This reflection of feeling comes from nonverbal observations and picks up on her facial reactions.
	Problem/ concern		84. *Mary:* It would be nice if the two would mesh together, but it seems difficult to have both things fit together nicely.	Mary is describing her ideal resolution. Here the interview could recycle back to Stages 2 and 3, with more careful delineation of the problem between job and personal relationships and defining the ideal resolution more fully. *A problem exists only if there is a difference between what is actually happening and what you desire to have happen.* This sentence illustrates the importance of problem definition and goal setting. Mary's response to the confrontation is 4 on the CCS. We have an important new

(Continued)

▲ **TABLE 13-2** The Allen and Mary Five-Stage Decisional Interview (Continued)

Skill Classifications				
Listening & Influencing	Focus	C	Counselor and Client Conversation	Process Comments
				insight, but insight is not action. She also needs to act on this awareness.
Information, directive	Problem		85. *Allen:* Well, that's something we can explore a little bit further. It seems this is an important part of the puzzle. Let's work on that next week. Would that be okay? I see our time is about up now. But it might be useful if we can think of some actions we can take between now and the next time we get together.	Many clients bring up central issues just as the interview is about to end. Allen makes the decision, difficult though it is, to stop for now and plan for more discussion later. Note that Mary is still talking about her relationship mainly from an abstract, formal-operational orientation. Clients often bring up central issues late in the session.
STAGE/DIMENSION 5: Conclude—generalize and act on new stories				
Summary, open question	Client, problem/ concern		86. *Allen:* We have come up so far with three things that seem to be logical: business, counseling, and training. I think it would be useful, though, if you were to take a set of career tests. (*Mary:* Uh-huh.) That will give us some additional things to check out to see if	Allen continues his statement and moves to Stage 5. He summarizes the career alternatives generated thus far and raises the possibility of taking a test. Note that he provides a check-out to give Mary an opportunity to make her own decision about testing.

▲ **TABLE 13-2** (Continued)

Skill Classifications				
Listening & Influencing	Focus	C	Counselor and Client Conversation	Process Comments
			there are any additional alternatives for us to consider. How do you feel about taking tests?	
	Client, problem/ concern		87. *Mary:* I think that's a good idea. I'm at the stage where I want to check all alternatives. I don't want *anything* to be limited. I want to think about a lot of alternatives at this stage. And I think it would be good to take some tests.	Mary approves of testing and views this as a chance to open alternatives. She verbally emphasizes the word *anything,* which may be coupled with her desire to avoid limits to her potential. Some women would argue that a female counselor is needed at this stage. A male counselor may not be sufficiently aware of women's needs to grow. Allen could unconsciously respond to Mary in the same ways she views Bo as responding to her.
Information	Client, problem/ concern, interviewer		88. *Allen:* Then another thing we can do . . . ah . . . is helpful. I have a friend at a local firm who originally used to be a coach. She's moved into personnel and training at Jones. (*Mary:* Ummm.)	Allen suggests a concrete and specific alternative for action. Mary is predominantly abstract formal-operational; she has tended to talk about issues and avoid action. This avoidance of action is also indicative of

(Continued)

▲ **TABLE 13-2** The Allen and Mary Five-Stage Decisional Interview (Continued)

Skill Classifications				
Listening & Influencing	Focus	C	Counselor and Client Conversation	Process Comments
			I can arrange an appointment for you to see her. Would you like to go down and look at the possibilities there?	Level 3 on the confrontation impact scale. Until Mary takes some form of concrete action or resolves the issue in her mind, she will remain at Level 2 or 3 on the CCS. If some action is taken on the issue during the coming week, then she will have moved at least partially to Level 4 on the CCS.
	Client, problem/ concern		89. *Mary:* Oh, I would like to do that. I'd get kind of a feel for what it's like being in a business world. I think talking with someone would be a good way to check it out.	Stated with enthusiasm. The proof of the helpfulness of the suggestion will be determined by whether she does indeed have an interview with the friend at Jones and finds it helpful in her thinking.
Feedback, open question	Client, problem		90. *Allen:* You're a person with a lot of assets. I don't have to tell you all the things that might be helpful. What other ideas do you think you might want to try during the week?	Allen recognizes he may be taking charge too much and pulls back a little. Although he is pushing Mary for action, he is now using her ideas. Too much direction and advice can make a client resistant to your efforts.

▲ **TABLE 13-2** (Continued)

Skill Classifications				
Listening & Influencing	*Focus*	*C*	*Counselor and Client Conversation*	*Process Comments*
	Client, problem		91. *Mary:* What about checking into the university and ah . . . advanced degree programs? I have a bachelor's degree, but . . . maybe I should check into school and look into what it means to do more coursework.	Mary, on her own, decides to look into the university alternative. This is particularly important, as earlier indications were that she was not all that interested. Note that real generalization is usually concrete *action*.
Summary	Client, problem, cultural/ environmental context		92. *Allen:* Okay, that's something else you could look into as well. (*Mary:* Uh-huh.) So let's arrange for you then to follow up on that. I'd like to see you doing that. (*Mary:* Um-hmmmm.) And . . . ah . . . we can get together and talk again next week. You did express some concern about your relationship with your friend, Bo, ah . . . would you like to talk about that as well next week? And, as I look back on this session, one theme we haven't discussed yet is how being a woman with family responsibilities relates to	Allen is preparing to terminate the interview. Fortunately he does consider the women's issue. Probably this should have been done sooner in the session. Is this an issue with which he can help, or would you recommend referral?

(Continued)

▲ **TABLE 13-2** The Allen and Mary Five-Stage Decisional Interview (Continued)

Skill Classifications				
Listening & Influencing	Focus	C	Counselor and Client Conversation	Process Comments
			all this. Maybe this is something to be explored next week as well?	
	Client, cultural/ environmental context		93. *Mary:* I think so, they sort of all . . . one decision influences another. You know. It all sort of needs to be discussed. And thanks for bringing up the women's issue and my children. That's important to me.	An important insight at the end. Mary realizes her career issue is more complex than she originally believed. If you were Allen's supervisor, would *you* recommend a primary emphasis on career counseling or on personal counseling in the next session? Or perhaps some combination of them both? What else would you advise him to do?
Self-disclosure	Client, interviewer		94. *Allen:* Okay. I look forward to seeing you next week, then.	
			95. *Mary:* Thank you.	

MODULE 13.4
TRANSCRIPT ANALYSIS AND TREATMENT PLANNING

KEY CONCEPT QUESTIONS

▲ **What is the pattern of skills used by the interviewer in the decisional counseling transcript?**

▲ **What are some key issues and client implications in treatment planning, note taking, and referral?**

Through the way you listen and the topics you select to reinforce by attending, you influence what happens in the session. Effective listening will increase the control clients have and allow them to become partners or "co-constructors" of what happens in the session. Examine your behavior in the interview and become aware of your impact on your client. If you plan a career session, you most likely will have a career session. If you decide to "let the client talk and see what happens," the interview may lack direction, but "what happens will happen." Of course, the interview may not completely follow your plan, but it is your personal decision that heavily determines what happens. This is a critical reason to develop interview plans, examine your notes, and reexamine your own style. We recommend a detailed analysis of your interviewing style and behavior continuously through your career. We also suggest appropriate sharing of your thoughts and analysis with your clients. Seek colleagues and supervisors to review your work, as this will provide a constant way to grow and improve.

Skills and Their Impact on the Client

What do you see as strengths of this interview? What do you think should have been done differently? How would you have approached a client such as Mary? What advice would you give Allen for the future?

Let us turn to a microskill analysis of the interview. Table 13-3 presents a skill summary of Allen's interview with Mary and you will see that each stage of the interview involved different patterns of microskill usage.

Stage 1 (Initiate the session). The interview began with Allen using both listening and influencing skills. We see open questions, a combined paraphrase and reflection of feeling, information giving, and self-disclosure. He focused immediately on Mary's wellness strengths in swimming, obtained permission to record the session, and offered the opportunity for Mary to ask questions of him. Observation skills helped Allen decide when it was time to move on with the session.

Stage 2 (Gather data). Only listening skills were used to draw out Mary's story and concerns. The primary focus was on changing careers from physical education to either counseling or business.

Stage 3 (Mutual goal setting). Again, only listening skills were used as Mary spoke about her goals in more detail. The issue of security in teaching versus risk in business was an important issue as revealed in the reflection of meaning with a confrontation (*Allen 43*).

Stage 4 (Explore and create). In this "working" phase of the interview, Allen used both influencing skills and confrontation of incongruity and discrepancies extensively. The cultural/contextual/issue of gender is explored though interpretation/reframing, listening skills (*Allen 71*), and an important summary (*81*).

Stage 5 (Conclude). The interview closes with specific plans for generalization and homework for Mary. This stage begins with a summary of the interview and ends with a summary of plans for the future.

In terms of a total balance of skill usage, Allen used a ratio of approximately two attending skills for every influencing skill. When you look at competence levels, Allen

▲ **TABLE 13-3** Skill Summary of Allen and Mary Interview Over Five Stages

	Skill Classifications																				
	Listening/Attending							Focus							Influencing						C
	Open question	Closed question	Enc./restatement	Paraphrase	Reflection feeling	Reflection meaning	Summary	Client	Main theme/problem	Significant others	Family	Mutuality	Interviewer	C/E/C	Interpretation/reframe	Logical consequences	Self-disclosure	Feedback	Info./adv./etc.	Directive	Confrontation
STAGE/DIMENSION 1: **Initiating the session** 6 attending skills 3 influencing skills	2	2		2	1			6	2				3				2		4		
STAGE/DIMENSION 2: **Gathering data** 4 attending skills 0 influencing skills 2 confrontation skills	1			1			1	5	2		1										2
STAGE/DIMENSION 3: **Mutual goal setting** 14 attending skills 0 influencing skills 2 confrontation skills	3	3	2	2	1	1	2	8	6	2											2
STAGE/DIMENSION 4: **Exploring and creating alternatives** 16 attending skills 15 influencing skills 7 confrontation skills	4	1	3	4	3		1	15	14	4				3	6	1		3	3	2	7
STAGE/DIMENSION 5: **Concluding** 5 attending skills 3 influencing skills	2						3	5	4				2	1			1	1	1		
Total: 45 attending skills 21 influencing skills 11 confrontation skills	12	6	5	9	5	1	7	39	28	6	1	0	5	4	6	1	3	4	8	2	11

is able to identify and classify the several skills and stages of the interview. He is able to identify the impact of his skills on the client. Allen also demonstrates his ability to use the basic listening sequence to structure an interview in five stages and to employ intentional interviewing skills. Note that Allen focused primarily on the client in the earlier phases of the interview and only in the later portions increased emphasis on the career issues. This demonstrates that he can balance focus between the person and client concerns and problems. An ineffective interviewer might have focused early on the problem and missed Mary as a unique person.

In terms of focus dimensions, Allen's focus remained primarily on the client, although the majority of his focus dimensions were dual, combining focus on Mary with focus on the issues and concerns Mary brought to the session. Focus analysis points out that Allen did not focus extensively on others and the family (Bo and Mary's children, for example). The relationship with Bo appeared with greater clarity later in the interview. Allen brought in the cultural/environmental/contextual focus (*71, 75,* and *81*), enabling a beginning discussion of gender issues that clearly need further work.

Mary appeared to move a little deeper into personal insights concerning her present and future life following each of the 11 confrontations in Stage 4. Mary responded primarily at Level 3 on the Client Change Scale (CCS) each time. Note that Mary was led into the important area of her personal life and relationship with Bo (*Allen 71*). At *79*, Allen comments on Mary's desire to have a life of "exciting opportunity," but she senses that Bo is putting limits on her. Mary moves easily here to discuss her own personal wishes in more depth. Allen included a check-out at the end of a slightly inaccurate confrontation (*Allen 75*), and Mary was able to introduce her important construct, substituting the word *limits* for Allen's *constraints*.

As the session ended, Mary appeared ready and willing to take action. On the Client Change Scale, she has moved to a "4," or a new way of thinking about her issues. The CCS is a systematic way for you to monitor the progress of your clients toward their goals both inside and outside the session. The real proof of the success of the interview, however, will have to wait until the next meeting so that we can determine whether the generalization plan was indeed acted on. Thoughts, feelings, and behaviors need to change for true generalization. *The work that clients do after the interview is as important as or more important than what they do in the session.*

You can also evaluate the effectiveness of an interview in terms of the number of choices available to Mary. "If you don't have at least three possibilities, you don't have a choice." Mary appears to have achieved that objective in the interview. In addition, the issue of her relationship with Bo has been unearthed, and this topic may open her to further counseling possibilities. The question must be raised whether Allen, as a man, is the most appropriate interviewer for Mary to see. Answers to that question will vary with your personal worldview. Again, what are your evaluations? What would you do differently?

Note Taking

When preparing for the next session, an interviewer can sometimes forget what happened in the last meeting. Good notes facilitate planning for your next contact. Additionally, legal and professional accountability for our interviews requires accurate note taking. Although Allen's notes are not shown here, interview notes can be structured using the five stages. In Stage 1, *rapport* is evaluated as good and the early decision to work on career issues would be noted. This is followed by separate paragraphs on *gathering data* (Stage 2) and *mutual goal setting* (Stage 3). What happens in generating ideas and alternatives is discussed in *explore and create* (Stage 4). Here Allen should comment on his limited response to personal issues such as the relationship with Bo. His rationale might have been "One can't talk about everything. I think Bo is important, but I felt it was more critical to focus first on career decisions as that was her presenting issue. We need to work on that in the next interview as she chooses." Last but not least, include notes on *generalization plans* (Stage 5) and possible referral, if needed.

Structured notes give data to the supervisor so that a quick understanding of the interview is gained. How might you use the process of microsupervision to help Allen work more effectively? What did he do right? What needs change or improvement?

BOX 13-2 National and International Perspectives on Counseling

 What's Happening With Your Client While You Are Counseling?
ROBERT MANTHEI, CHRISTCHURCH UNIVERSITY, NEW ZEALAND

There is more going on in interviewing beyond what we see happening during the session. Clients are good observers of what you are doing and they may not always tell you what they think and feel. Research shows that clients expect counseling to be shorter than do most counselors and therapists. Clients see counselors as more directive than counselors see themselves. And what the counselor sees as a good session may be seen otherwise by clients and vice versa. Counselors and clients may vary in their perceptions of interviewing effectiveness.

I conducted a study of client and counselor experience of counseling. Among the major findings are the following:

Clients often have sought help before. Most people don't come for counseling immediately. Talking with friends and family and trying to work it out on their own were usually tried first. Reading self-help books, prayer, and alcohol and drugs are among other things tried. Some deny that they have problems until these become more serious.

Implications for practice. Ask clients what they have tried before they came to you and find out what aspects of prior efforts seemed to have helped. You may want to build on past successes. This is an axiom of brief solution-oriented counseling (see the next chapter).

First impressions are important. That first interview sets the stage for the future and the familiar words "relationship and rapport" are central. I found that clients generally had favorable impressions of the first sessions and viewed what happened even more positively than counselors. Sometimes sharing experience helps. One client who did not feel positive about the

first session commented, "Maybe if the counselor had gone through a similar experience of divorce and children, it would have helped."

Implications for practice. Obviously, be ready for that first session. Cover the critical issues of confidentiality and legal issues in a comfortable way. Structuring and letting the client know what to expect seems important. Some personal sharing, used carefully, can help. And empathic listening always remains central.

Counseling helps, but so do events outside of the interview. Resolution of their issues was attributed to counseling by 69% of clients, while 31% believed events outside the session made the difference. Among things that helped were talking and socializing more with family and friends, taking up new activities, learning relaxation, and involvement with church.

Implications for practice. The interview is important, but generalization of behavior and thought to daily life is central. Homework and specific ideas for using what is learned in the session are important.

Things that clients liked. Relationship variables such as warmth, understanding, and trust were important. Clients liked being listened to and being involved in making decisions about the course of counseling. Reframes and interpretations helped them see their situations in a new way; also valued were new skills such as imagery, relaxation training, and thought-stopping to eliminate negative self-talk.

All the above speak to respecting the client's ability to participate in the change process. I think it is vital that we tell clients what we are doing, but also ask them to share their perceptions of the session(s) with us. We can learn from and learn with more client participation.

In supervision or microsupervision, focus on things that are done well with concrete specifics, rather than evaluation. On this positive foundation, the supervisee is better prepared for constructive feedback and eventual change and growth.

Referral

The word *referral* appears in the interview process notes. No interviewer has all the answers, and in the case of Mary, Allen thought referral to a women's group might be helpful as many of her issues are common to women looking for career change. In addition, his notes indicate the need for a referral to the university financial aid office. An important part of individual counseling is helping your clients find community resources that may facilitate their growth and development. The community genogram helps interviewers and clients think more broadly and consider appropriate referral sources.

A key referral issue is whether or not this is a case where interviewer expertise and experience are sufficient to help the client. Just because the counselor thinks that he or she is working effectively may not be enough; this may be a case where supervision and case conferences can be helpful. Opening up your work to others' opinion is an important part of professional practice. Clients, of course, should be made aware that you as counselor or therapist are being supervised.

Sometimes the client/interviewer relationship simply doesn't work as well as we all would like. When you sense the relationship isn't doing well, avoid blaming either the client or yourself. Focus on client goals and seek to hear the story completely and accurately. Ask the client for feedback on how you might be more helpful. Seek consultation and supervision and most often these "difficult patches" can be resolved to the benefit of all. When an appropriate referral needs to be arranged, we do not want to leave our clients "hanging" with no sense of direction or fearful that their problems are too difficult. Maintain contact with the client as the referral process evolves, sometimes even continuing for a session or two until arrangements are complete.

Most often, referral will be to specialized professionals who can help your own work with the client. You continue with the client while others provide supportive services. Examples would be family therapy, a psychological evaluation, a school tutoring program, the career office, or to community agencies such as welfare, childcare, or youth activities. Working closely with other professionals often facilitates the change process. Your advocacy involvement with the community and social justice action can be a vital part of effective helping.

Treatment Planning for Further Interviews

Treatment plans with specific goals are becoming more standard and often are required by agencies and insurance companies. The more structured counseling theories, such as cognitive-behavioral, strongly urge interview and treatment plans with specific goals developed for each issue. Their interview and treatment plans are often more specific than those presented here. Less structured counseling theories (Gestalt, psychodynamic, person-centered) tend not to have treatment plans, preferring to work in the moment with the client. In short-term counseling and interviewing, the interview plan serves as the treatment plan. As you move toward longer-term

BOX 13-3 Second Interview Plan and Objectives

This is Allen's interview plan for the second session with Mary; the plan is developed from information gained in the first interview and organizes the central issues of the case, allowing for new input from Mary as the session progresses.

Stage/Dimension Key Questions	Counselor Assessment and Plan
Initiate the session—develop rapport and structuring *What structure do you have for this interview? Do you plan to use a specific theory? What special issues do you anticipate with regard to rapport development?*	Mary and I have reasonable rapport. As I look at the first session, I note I did not focus enough on Mary's context nor did I attend to other things that might be going on in her life. It may be helpful to plan some time for general exploration *after* I follow up on the testing and her interviews with people during the week. Mary indicated an interest in talking about Bo. Two issues need to be considered at this session in addition to general exploration of her present state. I'll introduce the tests and follow that with discussion of Bo. For Bo, I think a person-centered method emphasizing listening skills may be helpful.
Gather data—draw out stories, concerns, problems, or issues *What are anticipated problems? Strengths? How do you plan to define the issues with the client? Will you emphasize behavior, thoughts, feelings, meanings?*	1. Check how Mary sees her career concerns defined now. Use basic listening sequence. 2. Later, and as appropriate, open up the issue of Bo with a question, then follow through with reflective listening skills. Be alert to a woman's perspective. 3. Mary has many assets. She is bright, verbal, and successful in her job. She has good insight and is willing to take reasonable risks and explore new alternatives. These assets should be noted in our future interviews. 4. Explore women's issues with her.

counseling (5 to 10 sessions), a more detailed treatment plan with specific goals is often required. The several problems and issues raised by the client may be outlined in much the same fashion as in the interview plan. The interview and treatment plan forms suggested here represent a midpoint that you may find helpful in thinking through your own opinion on this important issue. Share your treatment plan with your client.

Specific, identifiable goals for client treatment and how you plan to reach stated goals are especially important for agencies and insurance companies. The University of Massachusetts Behavioral Medicine Clinic (2004) has a brief one-page form that is completed after each session.

Patient (client) strengths/skills

Problem list (not diagnosis)

What is the goal and outcome behavior?

Interventions (what treatment strategies and theories are to be used?)

Progress toward goal

Estimated time goal may be reached

BOX 13-3   (Continued)

Stage/Dimension Key Questions	Counselor Assessment and Plan
Set goals mutually—establish outcomes *What is the ideal outcome? How will you elicit the client's idealized self or world?*	We have already discussed her career goals, but they may need to be reconsidered in light of the tests, further discussion of Bo, and so on. It is possible that late in this interview or in a following session we may need to define a new outcome in which careers and her relationships are both satisfied.
Explore and create alternatives—confront client incongruities and conflict, restory *What theories would you probably use here? What specific incongruities have you noted or do you anticipate in the client? How will you generate alternatives?*	1. Check on results of tests and report them to Mary. 2. Explore her reactions and consider alternative occupations. 3. Use person-centered, Rogerian counseling and explore her issues with Bo. 4. Relate careers to the relationship with Bo. Give special attention to confronting the differences between her needs as a "person" and Bo's needs for her. Note and consider the issue of women in a changing world. Does Mary need referral to a woman or a women's group for additional guidance? Would assertiveness training be useful?
Conclude—generalize and act on new stories *What specific plans do you have for transfer of training? What will enable you, the interviewer, to personally feel that the interview was worthwhile?*	At the moment it seems clear that further exploration of careers outside the interview is needed. We will have to explore the relationship with Bo and determine her objectives more precisely.

▲ **MODULE 13.4**

SUMMARY

- ▲ Self-analysis of one's own interviewing style and its impact on the client, micro-supervision, or consultation with teachers and expert colleagues, both short and long term, is recommended as a continuing part of professional practice.
- ▲ The five-stage structure of the interview is clinically useful for short and long-term interviewing planning. Specifying goals and outcomes is particularly important.
- ▲ Interview notes and treatment plan notes should be made available to the client if he or she wishes to see them.
- ▲ When referral is necessary, provide sufficient support during the transfer process.

INTEGRATING MICROSKILLS WITH THEORY
Person-Centered, Cognitive-Behavioral, and Brief Counseling

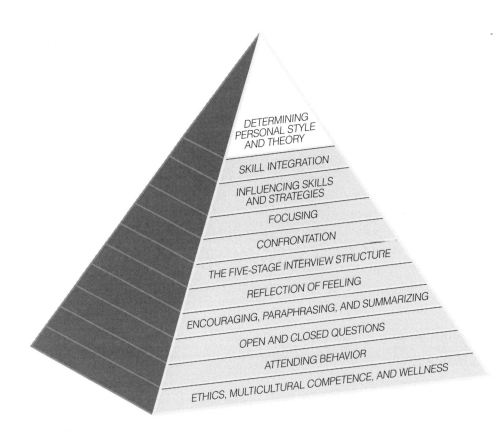

CHAPTER 14

DETERMINING PERSONAL STYLE AND THEORY

SKILL INTEGRATION

INFLUENCING SKILLS AND STRATEGIES

FOCUSING

CONFRONTATION

THE FIVE-STAGE INTERVIEW STRUCTURE

REFLECTION OF FEELING

ENCOURAGING, PARAPHRASING, AND SUMMARIZING

OPEN AND CLOSED QUESTIONS

ATTENDING BEHAVIOR

ETHICS, MULTICULTURAL COMPETENCE, AND WELLNESS

How can integrating the microskills with counseling theory help you and your clients?

CHAPTER GOALS You can use different combinations of microskills with specific approaches to counseling (person-centered, cognitive-behavioral, and brief counseling). This enables you to engage in a variety of interviewing styles, giving you and your clients more alternatives for intentional, effective action.

Awareness, knowledge, and skills developed through the concepts of this chapter will enable you to

▲ Conduct a person-centered interview.
▲ Engage in cognitive-behavioral assertiveness training.
▲ Engage in the basics of brief solution-oriented interviewing and counseling.

MODULE 14.1
MICROSKILLS AND THEORETICAL APPROACHES TO THE INTERVIEW

KEY CONCEPT QUESTION

▲ **How do microskills and the five-stage structure relate to theoretical approaches to counseling?**

We face a time in the helping field when we are asked for clear and measurable results from our work. We are learning to be culturally aware and come up with new ways to help clients make sense of their world. At the same time, there is a great need to maintain the traditions of the past with a focus on human dignity. These are weighty demands on us and on the helping profession.

Decisional theory has several advantages because it allows varying theoretical approaches to become part of the session (Chapter 13). You can help clients engage in deeper counseling about personal issues by adding the skill of reflection of meaning and using ideas from the person-centered approach. Cognitive-behavioral assertiveness training will help your clients take decisions into action. Brief counseling supports quick problem resolution.

This chapter shows how microskills and the five-stage structure of the interview can be used to understand various theories and how theory may be used in practical ways. Theory specifics are *not* presented in this chapter, except in the most general manner. You are not expected to master all of the ways to organize and structure the interview discussed here; if you master one or more of the methods in this chapter, you will be well prepared for integrating theory with practice. This will lead to intentional interviewing and counseling practice and enable you to master many theories and strategies in the helping fields. View Table 14-1 to see how four theories use the five-stage sequence.

▲ **MODULE 14.1**
SUMMARY

▲ Microskills and the five-stage structure of the interview can be used to understand various theories and how theory may be used in practical ways.

MODULE 14.2
PERSON-CENTERED COUNSELING AND EXAMPLE INTERVIEW

KEY CONCEPT QUESTION

▲ **What are some basics and specifics of practice of person-centered theory?**

Carl Rogers, the founder of person-centered theory, revolutionized the helping fields as he clearly identified the importance of listening as the foundation for human change. A major assumption of person-centered theory is that the client is competent and self-actualizing. Interviewer skills are used to help the client uncover internal

▲ **TABLE 14-1** Four Major Approaches to Counseling and the Five-Stage Interview Structure:
An Outline for Practice

Decisional Counseling: Counselor Actions	Person-Centered Counseling: Counselor Actions	Assertiveness Training: Counselor Actions	Brief Counseling: Counselor Actions
Stage/Dimension 1. Initiate the session—develop rapport and structuring ("Hello; this is what might happen in this session.") All systems give special attention to developing rapport and building a supportive alliance in a natural and personal style.			
▲ Outlines purpose of session and what client can expect. ▲ May state what to expect in each stage of the interview.	▲ Tends not to discuss structure and moves immediately to direction established by client. ▲ May subtly point out importance of allowing client to direct the session.	▲ Emphasizes importance of client participation in the session and may state the importance of the client's defining specific goals for the session. ▲ Points out that specific observable behaviors are the session focus.	▲ Clearly lets the client know what to expect—"What's your goal today?" "What has gotten better about the problem even before you got here?" ▲ Searches early for wellness strengths and positive assets.
Stage/Dimension 2. Gather data—Draw out stories, concerns, problems, or issues ("What's your concern? What are your strengths or resources?") The basic listening sequence (BLS) is central in all four approaches.			
▲ Uses BLS to draw out facts, feelings, and organization of client's problem or decisional issue. ▲ Draws out individual and multicultural strengths.	▲ Uses listening skills to draw out client concerns with a focus on the individual client and feelings. ▲ Maintains constant emphasis on positive regard and client strengths.	▲ Uses BLS to draw out concrete behaviors in specific situations. ▲ Focuses broadly on both individual and contextual issues. ▲ Typically uses role-plays to discover behavioral specifics.	▲ Draws out client story briefly focusing on wellness and positive assets. ▲ Normalizes concerns and searches for contextual support systems. ▲ Seeks concrete examples of past successes.
Stage/Dimension 3. Set goals mutually—establish outcomes ("What do you want to happen?") Each system helps the client find her or his own goals.			
▲ Uses BLS to draw out client's ideal decisional and career goals. ▲ Makes client goals concrete and accountable.	▲ Reveals client goal through listening, but even Carl Rogers has been known to ask "What would you like to see happen?" ▲ Helps client define distinction between the real self and the ideal self.	▲ Continues search for concrete goals for behavior change and may seek to define goals more precisely here.	▲ Emphasizes goal setting; clearly defined objectives may solve the problem ▲ Uses more questions to facilitate the process—"What are exceptions to the problem?"

▲ **TABLE 14-1** (Continued)

Decisional Counseling: Counselor Actions	Person-Centered Counseling: Counselor Actions	Assertiveness Training: Counselor Actions	Brief Counseling: Counselor Actions
Stage/Dimension 4. Explore and create alternatives—confront client incongruities and conflict, restory ("What are we going to do about it?") The distinctions between the four systems are reflected as each system confronts discrepancies and incongruity.			
▲ Considers the basic confrontation between the present decisional problem and the goal. ▲ Balances influencing and listening skills. Helps client see impact of decision via reframing and logical consequences. ▲ May use career testing, information giving, and other strategies to facilitate decisional process.	▲ Confronts the ideal self with the real self with hope of integration. ▲ Continues to use listening skills, although reflection of meaning may become central. May engage in brief self-disclosure. ▲ Maintains little focus on problem solving while helping client get a better sense of self.	▲ Considers basic confrontation between the present behavior and the goal behavior. ▲ Repeats role-play until client is able to demonstrate the goal behavior fully. ▲ May emphasize environmental factors related to behavioral change.	▲ Often combines Stages 4 and 5; emphasis is on finding specific ways to change what occurs in the real world. ▲ Uses wellness strengths as levers to change and generalization of new thoughts, feelings, and behaviors. ▲ Expects to involve client fully in the process of brainstorming and exploring alternatives.
Stage/Dimension 5. Conclude—generalize and act on new stories ("Will you do it?") Many beginning *and* experienced human service professionals fail to plan for change beyond the interview. For change to occur generalization plans need to be made.			
▲ Prescribes homework or action to follow up on the session. ▲ Uses techniques drawn from other theories to facilitate generalization.	▲ Historically has given little attention to generalization in the belief that significant changes in attitudes, thoughts, feelings, and meanings will eventually result in major changes.	▲ Gives the most attention to generalization of any theory. Expects client to leave with a clear behavioral change plan. ▲ Provides specific follow-up to ensure that change is maintained.	▲ Uses strategies from other theories if the client has difficulty transferring learning from the session to daily life.

strength and resilience. A person-centered counselor is most often interested in focusing on the meaning and feelings of the client; the actual facts of the problem are considered less important. The focus is much more on the person and less on the problem.

Person-centered theory in its purest form is most effective with verbal, abstract, and self-directed clients who are best able to think through their own direction. The goal is self-actualization, helping clients realize themselves more fully. Decisions may be made, but it is how the client feels about himself or herself that is most important. Questions are considered intrusive and usually are avoided in this orientation.

To illustrate, review the case study from Chapter 13, specifically the vocational problem which Mary talks about in *Mary 12*. Allen, the decisional counselor, used the basic listening sequence to draw out client facts and feelings and then summarized them (*Allen 19*). The problem focus was on career and decisional issues. If Mary were to see a person-centered counselor, very different things would happen. The person-centered counselor might wait for Mary to initiate the conversational topic. After a moment's pause, Mary begins:

MARY: Well . . . ah . . . I guess there's a lot of things that I'd like to talk about. You know, I went through a difficult divorce and it was hard on the kids and myself and . . . ah . . . we've done pretty well. We've pulled together. The kids are doing better in school and I'm doing better. I've . . . ah . . . got a new friend. (Breaks eye contact) But, you know, I've been teaching for 13 years and I'm really kind of bored with it. It's the same old thing over and over every day; you know . . . parts of it are okay, but lots of it I'm bored with.

ALLEN: Mary, sounds as if *you* feel rather good about *yourself,* yet there are parts of *you* that feel bored and incomplete.

This reflection of feeling includes a strong dimension of recognition and confrontation of mixed feelings. Person-centered counselors personalize the interview by giving attention to the word *you* and emphasizing it through verbal underlining (Chapter 3).

MARY: Yes, sometimes I feel confused. I know I've done well, but where do I go next? Something seems to be missing. Here I am, 36, alone and feeling stalemated. What does it all mean?

ALLEN: Mary, you say something is missing; you feel alone and stalemated when you look at *yourself* from a deeper level. There's something *missing* for you . . . (pause) . . . there's something missing that's *meaningful.*

This is a reflection of meaning. The counselor believes that if Mary finds her true self, she will self-actualize and solve many issues spontaneously. The counselor is also searching for Mary's underlying values and meanings. Here you see the client-directed abstract style in which clients are expected to be able to solve their own dilemmas.

MARY: Yes. . . . (pause) . . . (starts quietly crying) . . . I feel so alone. Nothing ever seems to work out. It's been so hard over the years . . . I feel so alone! What should I do?

ALLEN: You've felt alone at the deepest level. You've had the strength and wisdom to work through many difficulties, but somehow, somewhere, something meaningful is missing for *you.* . . .

This is a complex statement, typical of those who adopt the person-centered style. Note the reflection of feeling at the beginning, followed by feedback that points out positive assets of the client; this is characteristic of the person-centered concept of positive regard. The final portion of the statement refers to meaning: the underlying, deeply felt issues that impel us to action, often without our awareness. If you wish to extend your skills in person-centered theory and include multicultural issues in this approach, specifics of taking the theory into practice may be found in Ivey, D'Andrea, Ivey, and Simek-Morgan (2007). Carl Rogers's *On Becoming a Person* (1961) provides the basics of his theory, and Bozarth (1999) provides an update of person-centered theory and practice.

Specifics for structuring a person-centered interview may be four
From a skills perspective, the following guidelines are suggested:

1. Eliminate or minimize questions.
2. Do not use interpretation/reframes, advice, or directives.
3. Focus almost exclusively on the client; use the words *you* and *your* and the client's name.
4. Search for and reflect underlying meaning, and consider reflection of meaning along with paraphrasing, reflection of feeling, and summarization as the basic skills.
5. Constantly use the positive asset search to help clients frame their experience in forward-moving ways that lead to self-actualization.
6. Use selected influencing skills of confrontation, feedback, and self-disclosure, but sparingly.

Bringing Multicultural Issues Into the Person-Centered Approach

The focus on the individual client is predominant, but you can use a double focus. Focusing on both person and the cultural/environmental context can enrich client experience. Gender is a multicultural issue that might contribute to the person-centered discussion. Note below how dual focus on cultural/environmental/contextual issues and the client broadens the discussion and helps Mary see herself more completely.

ALLEN: *Mary, you* feel good about what *you* as a *woman* have done in a difficult situation. *Your* strengths as a *woman* are many.

MARY: Exactly. I have many women friends who have supported me. I know I am not alone in this struggle. My mother's example and strength have also been important.

When listening, you face two profound and important ethical and practical questions. The first question is critical. *How do you listen?* The second question is ultimately not answerable, but you will grapple with this value issue throughout your helping career—*How should you listen?* The way you listen obviously influences the way clients respond. Person-centered counseling was once called "non-directive counseling," but it became clear that "non-direction" is impossible and thus came the effort to focus on the person, while attempting to minimally influence the process. If you decide to focus exclusively on the person, however, you can miss multicultural and other relevant concerns.

It is essential that you constantly examine your own behavior in the session. Choosing to listen exclusively to "I" statements or focusing on culture, gender, and context in the person-centered mode affects the way clients talk about their issues. Examine how selective attention affected the progress of the example interview (*Allen 13*) and review the discussion of this topic in Chapter 3. We are always involved in the process and progress of the interview.

MODULE 14.2

SUMMARY

▲ Person-centered theory is considered most appropriate for verbal, abstract, self-directed clients who are best able to think through their own direction and seek to understand and realize themselves more fully.

▲ The focus is generally on the client, although multicultural issues may be introduced. Supporting strengths in the client through positive regard is important.

▲ Questions are considered intrusive and to be avoided. The listening skills and reflection of meaning are central. The interview can follow the five-stage structure, but more often will be unstructured. Influencing skills may be used, but relatively rarely.

MODULE 14.3
COGNITIVE-BEHAVIORAL ASSERTIVENESS TRAINING
AND EXAMPLE INTERVIEW

KEY CONCEPT QUESTION

▲ What are some basics and specifics of the practice of cognitive-behavioral assertiveness training?

Cognitive-behavioral approaches work on the assumption that changing behavior will result in more immediate change and that changes in attitudes toward self will follow. Assertiveness training is an important cognitive-behavioral strategy developed in the late 1960s (Alberti & Emmons, 2001) and has come to be one of the more widely accepted techniques regardless of one's theoretical orientation. For example, many feminist-oriented helpers use this method to help women become more direct and achieve their goals. In working with acting out or overly aggressive males, assertiveness training can help them learn more effective, socially appropriate ways to reach their goals. Appropriate assertiveness will help career counseling clients communicate better at work or present themselves more effectively in job interviews.

Stage 1: Initiate the Session—Develop Rapport and Structuring

Cognitive-behavioral counseling, once assumed to be an imposition on the client, has become one of the most sophisticated methods of helping and works actively to ensure that the interview is "person-centered" in the best sense of the term. The initial part of the interview will not differ much from other types of counseling. Rapport will be established with the client, because a caring, relaxed atmosphere is essential for change. The cognitive-behavioral counselor, oriented to *behavioral* change, would search for directly observable behavior that might be identified and changed. In contrast to the abstract person-centered approach, the behavioral counselor tends to assume a concrete, coaching approach and is concerned with action and *doing*, helping clients operate concretely in their environment.

ALLEN: You say you are *bored*, even though you sound very busy and active. What is going on, what are *you doing* when you are bored? What's happening around you? (Notice the search for concrete behavioral specifics as contrasted with abstract internal reflection.)

MARY: Well, so many things are happening, between the job and the kids, that I never get time to stop and think. Something is happening all the time. I just keep going. There is always someone demanding something from me. . . . It's very frustrating not being able to *ever* have a minute, yet overall, I'm still bored.

ALLEN: I see; never a minute for yourself and it goes on endlessly. What are some of your objectives here today? What do you want to have happen?

The counselor is aware that the session could go in many possible directions. As is typical of cognitive-behavioral counselors, there is an emphasis on having Mary *participate* in that direction and goal selection. The person-centered counselor does not direct the client, but the behaviorally oriented counselor usually has specific objectives in mind, although the client decides the ultimate goals.

MARY: Well, I heard that you were good at helping people become more assertive, expressing themselves more . . . maybe by being more assertive I can find myself.

ALLEN: That sounds like a reasonable objective, Mary. If I hear you correctly, you feel pretty overwhelmed by life and are tired of living without time for yourself. You're hoping assertiveness training can be part of that process. Is that right?

Note an emphasis on *doing* and on *observable behavior.* The decisional counselor, the person-centered counselor, and the behavioral counselor all use basic listening skills to draw out the client stories, but they listen for different things, thus leading the session in widely differing directions. Consider the potential value in each of these very different theories of helping. Mary could profit from a clearer career choice; she could also benefit from becoming more self-directed and aware of herself; and she certainly could become more assertive in expressing her point of view. The following comment would most likely precede the introduction of gathering data (Stage 2).

ALLEN: Mary, we are going to try assertiveness training. As you know, this enables us to speak up more effectively and obtain our goals, without overruling or overrunning other people. We'll discuss your situation and then role-play some ideas that may help you work through some of the issues. Is that okay?

Mary would be involved in the decisional process as much as possible. Telling clients what is to happen (structuring) helps them understand what is going on and enables them to work with the therapist in a more mutual fashion.

Stage 2: Gather Data—Draw Out Stories, Concerns, Problems, or Issues

Mary has stated her general problem as never having a minute for herself and the desire to speak more clearly for her needs. The interview now has set some general objectives, but the counselor wants more behavioral, observable specifics. The interview continues.

MARY: Yes, that's right, everyone seems to run over me. I can't say no.

ALLEN: Could you give me a specific, recent example of a time when you didn't say no? What happened? What did you do? (Search for concreteness)

MARY: Well, I was talking to the principal today. He wants me to take on advising still another club. I'm coach of two sports now and advising the Tri-Hi-Y's. Every activity I do makes me stay after school and I get home late. And when I get home late the kids want even more from me . . . and then Bo seems to want more too! I can't say no to any of them.

ALLEN: You can't say no to any of them. I can see your frustration and how you are trying. Must be difficult. Let's take your example of the principal.

MARY: The principal . . . he just walks all over me. If I could start with him, maybe I could learn what to do with the others . . . maybe even Bo.

ALLEN: (interrupts) Okay. Rather than talk about it and analyze it to death, I'd like to see what really happens when you have to engage in a decision like that. You know, role-playing. . . . I'm going to be your principal and ask you to take on that activity. You play yourself and react to me just as you did earlier today with him.

> Clear directives and role-playing the actual scenario of the problem are characteristic of assertiveness training. Rather than "hear about" the problem, the counselor observes actual behavior in the "here and now." You do not always need to engage in a full assertiveness-training session. Just having clients briefly role-play their problems and issues will give you a more comprehensive understanding of what is going on in their lives.

ALLEN: Okay? (Mary nods in agreement.) I'm the principal now. Mary . . . thanks for coming in. It's good to see you. You've done a great job with the swim team and the field hockey team this year. We like what we see.

MARY: (smiles) Thanks.

ALLEN: Mary, we've got a problem. The community is asking us to do more about drugs, and a group of parents have assembled a committee and want school participation. You have really good relations with the kids and have done a few workshops on the problems of drugs. I want you to join that committee.

MARY: (smiles, but a little weakly) Uhhh . . . I'd sure like to do it. I'm beginning to see some real problems in some of my classes. But I'm simply overloaded with the teams, and my kids are getting older and need me to drive them places. I don't see how I could. . . . (Hesitates, eyes downcast)

ALLEN: I'm glad you're interested. . . . It's only one night a week. The group wants to work with us in developing a curriculum and I want to be sure our point of view is represented. I'll call and tell them you'll do it.

MARY: (somewhat desperately, but weakly) Michael, I don't see how I can do it. . . . Sure, I'd like to help, but . . .

ALLEN: And you *are* a help. I'll meet with you during the week to give you additional support. I want to keep in touch with this.

MARY: (weakly) Okay.

ALLEN: (leaving role of principal) Is that how it is? You tend to give in rather quickly?

MARY: I'm afraid so. . . . It happens all the time. I'm just so anxious to please others.

ALLEN: I can understand that. Mary, what did you *do* in that role-play that got in your way? What *specifically* were you *doing* that allowed the principal to run over you?

> You want the clients rather than you to identify specific behaviors. They can define *their own* behavioral goals, making behavioral change more likely. But you may need to add to their observations and provide important feedback.

MARY: Well, I certainly give in easily. I noticed I let him do most of the talking. He didn't listen to me. I felt pretty uncomfortable, I know that I often smile when I am insecure and don't know what to do.

ALLEN: Uh, huh . . . and how did that uncomfortableness look? What was your body saying? Where were you looking?

MARY: I guess I look down a lot—it must all be a symptom of wanting to please others.

The interview continues with further discussion of behavior specifics, much of it focusing on what Mary is doing "wrong." There is need for a positive asset search to build wellness strengths. Clients grow from strengths, and Mary has obvious abilities. If your clients know that you respect what they *can* do, they will have greater strength and potential for attacking their problems.

MARY: It makes me very discouraged and tired.

ALLEN: (ignores emotions) But, Mary, let us not forget that you are doing several things right. What are they?

MARY: It all seems pretty bad to me.

ALLEN: First, the principal said you were doing a good job at school . . . you're apparently well respected. He wouldn't have selected you for this job if you weren't effective. And, you couldn't do those things so well if parts of you weren't assertive. Right?

MARY: (brightens up, smiles more hopefully) I hadn't thought of it that way. I guess I can do *some* things. (The counselor then elaborates on Mary's strengths.)

Stage 3: Set Goals Mutually—Establish Outcomes

A concrete example of Mary's problem has been presented with behavioral specifics, which can be seen and even measured. Armed with an awareness of her strengths, she is now able to set up some specific goals for change.

ALLEN: Given what's going on, Mary, what are some specific goals and behaviors you might want to change the next time we try that role-play?

MARY: Well, I'd like to smile less and talk more.

ALLEN: And what about more direct eye contact and a louder, stronger voice?

The interview continues, and Mary and the counselor work out specific goals for behavior change in her interview with the principal. They focus on some dimensions of her attending behavior, as just mentioned—less smiling, for example—and on Mary's assertively saying no.

Stage 4: Explore and Create Alternatives—Confront Client Incongruities and Conflict, Restory

ALLEN: To summarize, Mary, in the past and in this interview with the principal, you gave in, and smiling, looking down, and letting the other person take charge of the topic represents giving in. On the other hand, your goal is to change these behaviors and take more control of your daily life. Does that sum it up?

This is the classic confrontation statement, useful at the beginning of the fourth stage of the interview. The client's problem or past behavior is contrasted with the goal behavior. The discrepancy between the two is the issue to be resolved in this stage. In terms of the Client Change Scale, the goal for Mary will probably be a Level-4 or Level-5 resolution response: the creation of something new—change and development.

MARY: Yeah, that seems to sum it up. What next?

ALLEN: Well, what we do next is another practice role-play, and we continue that until you demonstrate assertiveness with me in these practice role-plays. That may take several sessions or it might be accomplished today. Regardless, what you take back to the school, and to your kids and Bo, is far more important than what happens here. We'll work together until you master these skills and are getting what you want. Okay, let's try another role-play. (The role-play starts.) Mary, I'd like you to take over the new drug program. The parents want your involvement.

MARY: Michael, that sounds great. I wish I could, but I have got so many things going right now, and the kids need me to drive them places. (Her vocal qualities are strong, but her eye contact is still poor.)

ALLEN: I can understand that. It's the ones who are busiest that you always ask. You can do it . . . you've done great workshops on drug education, and it fits with your good work in physical education.

MARY: (more weakly) No, I don't think I can. I don't want to . . . Nuts! There, you can see what I do!

ALLEN: Well, Mary, it was better. You did speak up stronger, and I liked the way you came up with reasons. We'll continue practicing.

Mary and the counselor continue to practice via role-play and discussion. Gradually, Mary gets stronger and demonstrates an assertive no. This represents resolution of the discrepancy between where she was when she started the "problem"—and where she wanted to go—"the goal or outcome." She has generated a new solution (Level 4 on the CCS). There are some "buts" to this rating, however, as you will see in the next stage of this interview.

Stage 5: Conclude—Generalize New Learning and Act on New Stories

Learning in the laboratory of the interview may appear to result in developmental change. However, real change occurs only in life after the interview. Many of your clients will show considerable promise for change in the interview and then continue to behave and think in old patterns after the interview is over. Homework, planned transfer, and prevention of relapse are critical parts of effective change (Witkiewitz & Marlatt, 2004). In the following exchange, the counselor introduces Mary to relapse prevention, a systematic framework to help prevent loss of learning from the counseling session. If you fail to include generalization and transfer of learning from your helping sessions, regardless of your theoretical decisions, much of your helping work will be ineffective.

ALLEN: Well, this is the time, Mary, that is perhaps most important in our interview. You've certainly demonstrated that you can be more assertive and say no. The big question is whether you can generalize this to your principal and start taking charge of your own life.

MARY: Yes, and I want to do it with my kids, with some of my students, and with Bo. Everyone is running all over me.

ALLEN: Generally speaking, it is best to focus on one behavioral change at a time. After you have succeeded with one, you'll find the others will follow. Now, I'd like to go over the Maintaining Change Worksheet with you. This is a way to give you some homework to ensure that you will continue to be more assertive.

The counselor hands Mary the worksheet (Box 14-1). They work through it together; giving special emphasis to things that may come up to prevent Mary from being assertive. Research and clinical experience in counseling both reveal that this may be the most important thing you can do with clients: help them ensure that they actually *do* something different as a result of their experience in the interview. The interview closes with the following:

ALLEN: Well, Mary, we've made good progress today. You've demonstrated that you can be assertive with a little practice. The big test will come tomorrow with Michael. I'm sure you will maintain strong eye contact and vocal tone and will remember your very good reasons for saying no. We'll meet next week to see how it went.

BOX 14-1   Maintaining Change Worksheet: Self-Management Strategies for Skill Retention

I. Choose an Appropriate Behavior, Thought, Feeling, or Skill to Increase or Change

Describe in detail what you intend to increase or change:

_____

_____

Why is it important for you to reach the above goal(s)?

_____

_____

What will you do specifically to make it happen?

_____

_____

II. Relapse Prevention Strategies

A. Strategies to help you anticipate and monitor potential difficulties: regulating stimuli

Strategy	*Assessing Your Situation*
1. Do you understand that a temporary slip may occur but it need not mean total failure?	
2. What are the differences between learning the behavioral skill or thought and using it in a difficult situation?	
3. Support network? Who can help you maintain the skill?	
4. High-risk situations? What kinds of people, places, or things will make retention or change especially difficult?	

B. Strategies to increase rational thinking: regulating thoughts and feelings

5. What might be an unreasonable emotional response to a temporary slip or relapse?	
6. What can you do to think more effectively in tempting situations or after a relapse?	

(Continued)

BOX 14-1 Maintaining Change Worksheet (Continued)

Strategy	Assessing Your Situation
C. Strategies to diagnose and practice related support skills: regulating behaviors	
7. What additional support skills do you need to retain the skill? Assertiveness? Relaxation? Microskills?	
D. Strategies to provide appropriate outcomes for behaviors: regulating consequences	
8. Can you identify some probable outcomes of succeeding with your new behavior?	
9. How can you reward yourself for a job well done? Generate specific rewards and satisfactions.	

III. Predicting the Circumstance of the First Possible Failure (Lapse)

Describe the details of how the first lapse might occur; include people, places, times, and emotional states.

Permission to use this adaptation of the Relapse Prevention Worksheet was given by Robert Marx.

Assertiveness training is useful with many types of clients and is useful with person-centered, brief counseling, and decisional methods. Giving clear directives is particularly important in this technique, and the counselor freely uses feedback on performance. Listening skills remain important; the goal is to give the client as much power and control over the session as possible.

Bringing Multicultural Issues Into Assertiveness Training

Again focusing becomes an important skill. Mary's difficulty with the male supervisor is a common problem among women. This assertiveness training session might be enriched by bringing in the general issue of women's needing to be more assertive in the workplace. Mary then could draw on women models of assertiveness and realize that she is not alone with her issues. When the role-play occurs, the counselor could add, "How would an assertive *woman* act with this man?"

Assertiveness training has other multicultural implications beyond gender. Gay teens, for example, can profit from assertiveness training as they cope with teasing and harassment in the high school. People with disabilities can profit from assertiveness training as they seek to gain their legal rights. Parents who come from an international community in which teachers are viewed as "always right" might benefit from assertiveness training so that they learn how to express themselves more directly in U.S. and Canadian culture.

The final point above is particularly important to observe and consider. Some cultures have a more assertive style than others. For example, what may be standard assertive behavior among African Americans or European Canadians may be seen as overly aggressive by some Asian cultures. People from the United States and Canada in turn may think a traditional immigrant Asian family is too passive. What is often mistakenly interpreted as passive, however, is an effective cultural style in traditional Asian communities. Cultural differences clearly modify the appropriateness of assertiveness training with Latina women. The goals of assertiveness training in this case are sometimes in direct opposition to traditional cultural standards.

All of the above situations can profit from culturally sensitive assertiveness training. As you start this type of work, spend time finding out from your client how he or she views the words *passive, assertive,* and *aggressive.* How does your unique client define these issues in a cultural context? Then you can describe the European American model of assertiveness and how it contrasts with those of other cultures. With women who might be in danger from abuse if they become too assertive, it is important to share the potentially dangerous consequences of assertiveness. In such cases, add culturally sensitive counseling to help clients make decisions.

You will also find that assertiveness training can be useful to those who are seen by others as overly aggressive. For example, an acting-out client diagnosed as antisocial can learn a more useful interpersonal style. Consider the different perspectives on what constitutes assertiveness and how strongly or softly one communicates with others.

⚠ MODULE 14.3
S U M M A R Y

▲ Assertiveness training is a cognitive-behavioral strategy that focuses on behavior change. Theory is very much integrated into practice. Through client-selected goals for change, role-playing, and interviewer encouragement, the client learns that assertiveness is not being passive nor it is being aggressive, but is a culturally appropriate response to many situations.

▲ The five-stage interview provides a solid outline for the practice of assertiveness training. Listening skills remain important, but the use of directives and feedback becomes more central. Questioning is a basic skill. The role-play is essential to help clients take their behavior back home, for generalization of new learning to the "real world" is central. The Client Change Form helps the client plan to avoid relapse or slips in the new behavior.

MODULE 14.4
BRIEF COUNSELING AND EXAMPLE INTERVIEW

KEY CONCEPT QUESTION

▲ **What are some basics, specifics of practice, and important ethical issues of brief counseling theory?**

The following section was written by Allen E. Ivey, Robert Manthei, Sandra Rigazio-DiGilio, and Mary Bradford Ivey.

As you begin brief counseling it is important to recall that building rapport and trust remains essential. Brief counseling often begins with immediate examination of client goals, but many clients still need to tell their story before moving toward solutions.

Since goal setting (Stage 3) is the primary aim of brief counseling, hearing the client's version of what has worked or has not worked is especially important. Careful attention to clients' *stories* and *their goals* is fundamental to avoid imposing our own personal or theoretical agenda.

How long does brief counseling take? Anticipate one to three interviews as typical. The brief approach may be a single interview, or it may extend to as many as 5 or 10 sessions. The key word is *brief*, emphasizing solutions rather than problems. A major assumption of brief counseling is that clients have their own solutions readily available if we help them examine themselves and their goals.

Whereas person-centered methods use very few questions, brief counseling makes questions the central skill. In the early stages of your practice with brief counseling, consider using the specific questions presented here and sharing them with your client. As you gain experience and confidence with this method, you may wish to continue sharing—counseling and interviewing can be more powerful and real in an egalitarian co-constructed framework.

Stage 1: Initiate the Session

Basic Questions. Start solution-based thinking at the very beginning of the session. The positive asset search is central. Even as you listen to the client's story and/or reasons for coming to the interview, you can ask the following:

▲ What is your goal here today?
▲ Has anything changed since you decided to come to see me? Are things better in any way?
▲ What has gotten better about your concern/issue/problem? What made that happen?
▲ What's keeping it from getting worse?
▲ Are there any exceptions in this problem? When is the problem not so much of a problem?
▲ What do you do right? What have you been doing to keep this issue from really dragging you down?
▲ How can we keep those things that work going for you?

Your Own Mind-Set. Brief counseling asks that you think differently about helping. Instead of focusing on defining "problems" or a long drawn-out exploration of "what happened and why," you need to focus on "solutions." This means establishing a positive expectation for both yourself and your client. Consequently, your task is to structure the session to achieve success in this important joint venture with your client.

Relationship. Traditional rapport and listening skills remain central, although you will want to use questioning skills as your intervention of choice. Some clients and those who may be culturally different from you may be suspicious of the frequent questions. You may wish to explain that you will be asking many questions and find out whether that is acceptable. Spend more time explaining what you are doing and more time on listening to stories to develop trust.

Structuring the Session. Let the client know what is going to happen. Share what you are going to do in the session and why. For example:

> Many people can accomplish considerable progress in just a few sessions. What we are going to do here today is focus on solutions—the goals you want to achieve. Can you tell me what your goals are *for today?*

The words "for today" are important because they bring the client to the possible *here and now* rather than leading to a lengthy attempt to resolve everything at once. Some issues are too large to be resolved in a few sessions; your client may work on one primary issue now and leave the others for later. Returning to counseling is not failure; rather, it shows willingness to work on the many complexities of daily life. With children or adolescents, the wording may be better phrased as follows:

> Darryl, the teacher asked me to talk with you. Rather than talk about problems, I'd like to know how things might become better for you. Could you tell me one thing that you can do to feel better—happier about the rest of today? (Or "Before we begin, I want to know something that makes you happy. Tell me about what you like to do.")

What Else? Your client will not always respond in depth to your questions. De Shazer (1988, 1993) recommends the frequent use of "What else?" to prompt client thinking and the generation of more complete answers and solutions.

Children and adolescents (as well as adults) may initially respond negatively to your questions and even say "Nothing." Remember the importance of rapport and listening—with many clients, a sense of humor helps! With experience you will develop follow-up questions and help clients explore their issues in new ways.

Next—Stage 2 or Stage 3? If the problem was clearly defined during rapport and structuring and the goal is relatively clear, consider moving directly to mutually setting goals (Stage 3). *Do this especially if the individual is able to identify specific things that have gone better and/or times when the problem is "not a problem."* Examples of clearly defined concerns might be these:

- ▲ I'd like to stop arguing so much with my partner.
- ▲ My son gets up and down during meals and is constantly leaving the table.
- ▲ I'd like to be able to speak up at meetings more effectively.
- ▲ Our lovemaking has become too routine. I want my partner to warm up to me.
- ▲ I want more challenge in my work.

All these require some awareness of times when the problem is not a problem. For example, "When are you able to avoid arguments with your partner? When has lovemaking been real to you?" These *exceptions to the problem* may serve as levers for positive change.

On the other hand, if the concern is vaguely presented ("My relationship is falling apart"), if the client talks about confusing multiple issues, and if the client has difficulty identifying goals, more time needs to be spent in gathering data (Stage 2). Brief methods work best on only one problem at a time; other issues can be dealt with later.

The decision to omit gathering data (Stage 2) is not easy. Many clients need to tell you their story in detail before moving on to stating their goals. When in doubt, it is wise to be more conservative and spend time in exploration. But even here, you can occasionally ask goal-setting questions, building a foundation for more rapid change and client involvement.

Stage 2: Gather Data and Search for Positive Assets

Basic Questions. It is often a good idea to share a list of solution-based questions with your client and explore them together. As you become more familiar with the ideas, remember to continue to work *with* your client, not on her or him.

- ▲ Are there times when you do not have this problem? When does the problem not occur?
- ▲ What are the exceptions to the problem?
- ▲ What's different about the times when this problem does not occur?
- ▲ How do you get more positive results to happen?
- ▲ What are your strengths and resources?
- ▲ Suppose when you go to sleep tonight, a miracle happens and the concerns that brought you in here today are resolved. But since you are asleep, you don't know the miracle has happened until you wake up tomorrow; what will be different tomorrow that will tell you that a miracle has happened? (The miracle question; see de Shazer, 1988, p. 5.)
- ▲ Follow up the miracle question with "How will we know the issue has been resolved?" and "What are the first steps to keep the miracle going?"

These questions are common in brief counseling, but to be fully effective, they require follow-up and exploration. Use the "What else?" question and positive asset search questions ("What is going right?" "What part of the problem is not a problem?"). If you get brief or sketchy client responses to the miracle or other questions, use your natural ability and listening skills to expand and draw out responses.

Being Brief. The summary is particularly helpful in brief counseling to organize the session and serves as a foundation for clearer and more effective goal setting. Many clients will describe their problem using abstractions; be sure to clarify the problem/concern with specifics so that the abstractions are avoided or made concrete. But be sensitive to your client. Specifically, use the basic listening sequence to draw out details and be sure to summarize what has been said. Some people need to tell their stories just as much as or more than they need help changing their thinking, feeling, and behavior. You may tell the client that it may not be necessary to focus on all the details of the problem, and with the client's assistance, generate a brief narrative of the problem, concern, or issue. (See Box 14-2.)

Normalizing the Narrative. It is normal for clients to have concerns, and it is normal to have difficult situations. Your task is to point out to clients that while we all have issues, our concerns are solvable. Your own nonverbal behavior and confidence are part of this process. Normalizing the narrative is not stating that very complex problems are always normal and expected parts of life; rather, normalizing the narrative means focusing on the idea that we all have concerns and it is indeed possible to do something about them. Care must be taken to avoid minimizing serious concerns. An eating disorder, an abusive family history, and racial or sexual harassment are difficult issues.

Cultural/environmental/contextual issues such as gender, race/ethnicity, and spirituality factors may be part of normalizing the narrative. The gay or lesbian client, for example, may begin the session by stating the problem as depression over

BOX 14-2   National and International Perspectives on Counseling

Can't You Be a Little Patient?
WEIJUN ZHANG

I was once hired by an American multinational corporation to counsel its expatriate executives working in China. My first client, a middle-aged Caucasian male, had been in China for the past 3 years, functioning first as a manager of finance and then as the general manager of the joint venture. The reason he sought counseling involved his relationship with his local subordinates. "They are driving me nuts," as he initially put it.

When his eyes first met mine, I could tell right away that he had a big question mark in mind of my ability to counsel him. But after a few minutes of small talk, he seemed to be convinced that this Chinese guy was westernized enough to be his counselor. Before I realized it, he burst into a string of complaints about his sour relationship with the local managers. Apparently he trusted me, for he revealed very specific facts of his situation and made no attempt to hide his hard feelings toward his Chinese colleagues.

Being a fan of the solution-focused approach, and feeling certain of knowing the mind-sets of White male businessmen, I wasted no time in starting to intervene when I heard him say, for the third time, "They are driving me nuts." I replied, "I see that your relationship with the local managers has really deteriorated. I suppose you know that you are not the only Western expatriate who is suffering from this problem. However, let me ask you a question here. Could you recall a period of time, no matter how short it is, when your relationship with your local partner was good, or normal, or not so bitter?"

He looked very surprised upon hearing this solution-oriented question, thought for a few seconds, murmured something like, "There should be, I suppose so . . . ," and then went on criticizing his Chinese co-workers with even more vigor.

I let him continue whining for about 3 minutes before I seized another opportunity to pose another solution question: "Since the operation of this joint venture has been going on for years without interruption, is it reasonable for me to assume that there have been times when you and your local managers have communicated?"

"Yes," he answered indifferently.

"Could you please give me one or two examples of this positive side of your relationship?" Reluctantly, he started to relate an incident in which he and his subordinates had had good cooperation. But when the story was barely half told, he shifted to focus on the negative and went on complaining again!

I am not a person who gives up easily. When I saw a chance to cut in on his grievance, I tried again to switch his focus to the positive side, in hope that we could move to the goal-setting stage faster. My assumption was that since he was a busy executive in a bottom line oriented company, he would surely favor short-term counseling and wanted to see concrete results quickly.

Much to my surprise, he burst into anger at my attempt and began to shout at me: "Why can't you let me finish my stories? Why can't you just listen? I thought I was lucky to have finally met one Chinese who can really understand what is going on here! Why can't you be a little patient?" Seeing I was taken aback by the outburst, he added, "By the way, do you know what PRC really stands for? The People's Republic of China, isn't it. Let me tell you what. It means you have to have PATIENCE and make RELATIONSHIPS in order to earn CASH!"

This left me embarrassed. This Caucasian client of mine, after being in China for 3 years, was now teaching his Chinese counselor, who had been in the States for about twice as much time, the importance of patience and relationships! Apparently, both of us had done a good job in adjusting to the local culture, though in opposite directions.

constant harassment. As you hear this story, you note that the client is focusing on self as if the problem is internal. By focusing on cultural oppression, you help externalize and normalize the story.

The Positive Asset Search and Wellness. As you listen to the client's story, search for strengths, positive assets, community assets, and cultural and/or spiritual strengths. An important part of normalizing client situations is enabling clients to rediscover their wellness strengths and personal power. Sometimes client assets will provide an obvious solution that the client had not thought of. The following questions (also see Chapter 4) are particularly useful to draw out strengths that can be used for solutions:

▲ Considering your ethnic/racial/spiritual history, can you identify some wellness strengths, visual images, and experiences that you have now or have had in the past?
▲ Can you recall a friend or family member who represents some type of hero in the way he or she dealt with adversity? What did he do? Can you develop an image of her?
▲ Tell me concretely about a special family member and what this person means to you. Family can include our extended family, our stepfamilies, and even those who have been special to us over time. For example, some people talk about a special teacher, a neighbor, or an older person who was helpful.

Genuinely complimenting and giving feedback to the client on specific strengths and assets may be useful, but the client must accept wellness strengths as real, or the positive asset search may seem trite or disrespectful. Also some clients and some cultural groups consider direct compliments embarrassing. Indirect ways to compliment a client for her or his strengths include these:

▲ How did you know that?
▲ Where did you learn that?
▲ How did you figure that out?
▲ How did you develop that strength?

Scaling. On a scale of 1 to 10, with 1 meaning the concern is fully resolved and 10 meaning that the concern almost totally overwhelms you, where would you put yourself today? At this moment? In the session? Scaling provides an effective way for you and the client to communicate the current depth of the client concern.

Scaling serves as a temperature gauge so that you know how clients are feeling about their problems at any given moment. Scaling can evaluate whether you and the client are in synchrony, seeing things similarly. Use scaling periodically through the session and consider using it throughout all your interviews, regardless of theory. With children and younger adolescents, actually drawing a scale may be useful. The child can then point to where he or she is on the scale.

With experience and practice, you will want to expand your use of scaling. For example, you could have your client evaluate his or her present level of motivation for change ("How committed are you to solving the problem?"), the confidence of success ("How likely are you to succeed?"), or how he or she will deal with termination ("At what point do you feel that the problem is sufficiently resolved?").

Stage 3: Set Goals Mutually

Basic Questions. Move as rapidly as possible to goal setting. The most important question at this stage is some variation of the following:

> We have heard your concern (summarize again, if necessary to keep interview on track and check accuracy). . . . *Now, what specifically do you want to happen?* Be as precise as possible.

Strengthen the following questions with variations on de Shazer's "What else?" "Can you add anything more?" "Any other thoughts?"

▲ What do you want to happen?
▲ How do you cope with the problem?
▲ What have you done so far that is helpful in achieving that goal?
▲ Let's focus on the *exceptions*. Tell me about the times when the concerns are absent or seem a little less burdensome. What is different about these times? How do you get that more positive result to happen? How does it make your day go differently?
▲ What did he or she do or say when it was better?
▲ How did you get her or him to stop?
▲ How is that different from the way you usually handle it?

These brief questions involve a change of pace and can add humor to the session.

▲ What do you do for fun?
▲ What would help you to feel that life is better? Name one thing that would help.
▲ Let's take a piece of the larger concern and work on that. Okay? We can't solve it all today, but we can make a piece of it a bit better.

Following goal definition, you can obtain very specific ideas about client wishes and desires when combining these with variations of "What else?"

▲ How will your life be different?
▲ Who will be the first to notice?
▲ What will he or she do or say?
▲ How will you respond?

Co-constructing Concrete, Achievable, Clear Goals With the Client. Clients too often want to resolve all concerns simultaneously. Be sure you negotiate specific goals that can actually be reached. Help clients work toward resolving a smaller piece of the larger issue; a small change can lead over time to significant differences in a client's life. Some children and adolescents will have difficulty with goal setting; their life experience has been focused on what people in authority want from them. Patience and setting up concrete, achievable goals are important.

Stages 4 and 5: Explore, Create, and Conclude

Brief counseling combines these last two stages. When you have identified resources, found exceptions to the problem, and identified goals in the first three stages, you have already gone a long way to brainstorm and explore solutions. Constantly focus on the idea that something can be done. Your goal in this stage is to solidify and organize the solutions and move toward concrete action. Work on the clearly defined goals in specific manageable form. Every successful idea for solution needs to have a practical use outside the session.

Basic Questions

▲ What have you been doing right?
▲ What do you have to keep doing so that things continue to improve?
▲ What will tell you that things are going well?
▲ How can we take what we have learned today to daily life?

Thinking About Change and "Taking It Home." We need to change negative conversation to a new conversation about change and possibility. We need to transfer session learning to the real world. General guidelines from de Shazer (1985, 1993) include these:

▲ Note what the clients do that is good, useful, and effective. Find out what efforts they have been making and support their process of change. This is essentially the microskills positive asset search.
▲ Note exceptions to the problem. What is going on when the problem isn't happening? Be concrete and specific in this search.
▲ Promote the two above as they relate to clear, specific client goals.

In effect de Shazer says *work on what we have already done.* If you did a good job with goals, exceptions, and other elements, the solution may already be in hand and may just need to be reemphasized.

Brief counseling represents a contract and commitment to clients. Do not leave them at this point. Stay with them until they accomplish *their goals.* Contract for specific follow-up in the next session or by phone. Assign a task that the client can use to ensure transfer from the interview. Concrete, achievable tasks, set up in small increments, move the client toward significant change. Generalizing, relapse prevention worksheets, work on influencing skills, and other homework may be appropriate assignments for any given client.

As part of brief counseling you could ask the child, adolescent, or adult client to tell the old story from a new frame of reference. Children can be asked to draw pictures of the old story and pictures of the new. The newly developed narrative becomes the cognitive and emotional framework for behavioral change. The skill of interpretation/reframing and focusing can help to describe the problem in new ways. For example, the old perspective may have focused on what other people are doing to make the client's life miserable. The new story focuses on what the client can do or has done to cope successfully with the situation. White and Epston (1992) suggest that counselors write down summaries of the clients' new possibilities and share them in a letter sent to the home or at the next session. Finally, remind your client that he or she is welcome to come back at a future time for more work on this concern or any new issues that may arise.

Bringing Multicultural Issues Into Brief Counseling. A questioning style can be a problem if you have not built sufficient rapport and trust with your client. Establishing a natural and effective rapport is perhaps even more important in this approach

BOX 14-3   Some Practical and Ethical Issues in Using Brief Counseling

Brief counseling, like any form of helping, has limits and is not appropriate for all people. If the client does not respond to brief counseling and you do not have other ideas, seek assistance from a supervisor, consultant, or more experienced colleague. Though this method can be helpful in resolving complicated issues, solution methods may not always be adequate in themselves. More complex matters may require experienced counselors or therapists who use other approaches. Seek referral as soon as possible. This is true for any of the skills, methods, or ideas presented in this text. Evidence that a brief counseling approach is not appropriate for a client includes the following:

1. The client presents with serious symptoms or problems (e.g., substance abuse, relational violence, child abuse, suicidal gestures, alcoholism, eating disorders) and does not respond to brief interventions.

2. The client is not able or willing to try the solutions generated in the session. For example, after several solutions have been successfully rehearsed in session, the client cannot or will not enact these solutions outside the counseling relationship.

3. The solutions are primarily generated by you rather than by the client. In this case the client may be unable or unwilling to construct possible solutions and may be dependent on the ideas of the counselor.

4. The client may not be committed to the process. Solutions are vaguely constructed and not carefully explored for positive and negative consequences.

5. During the final stage of counseling, the client may have difficulty making the solutions real in her or his life. Sometimes clients will refuse to try out ideas that previously looked quite promising.

6. The client's context may not be receptive to certain solutions. The interviewer may need to assess the potential impact of a solution on the client's relationships in a broader context—for example, a woman client's desire to take a much more assertive position in a marriage. If so, is there danger of abuse if the woman speaks up?

7. The client may in fact want a long-term helping relationship. Some clients will respond more favorably to a long-term, safe relationship and may reject you or even terminate if you use only brief approaches. Brief counseling is not for everyone.

than it is in others. Listen to the story until the client is ready; share your questions and interview plan with the client. Emphasis on positives will help make the solution approach culturally relevant.

Brief counseling can easily focus on the individual, with insufficient attention to broader contextual and social issues. However, balancing focus between the individual, the problem/issue, and the cultural/environmental context may make brief work a most valuable addition to a multiculturally aware helping interview. Focusing on the cultural/environmental context can be especially important. For example, you may be interviewing a woman who has experienced harassment in the workplace. If you focus solely on the problem and individual solutions, you may miss the most critical issue. The problem may be located not in the individual but in the system. If there is a family problem, it may be wise to focus on the family and not just on individual solutions.

Example Interview: Brief Counseling

This demonstration is a session conducted by Penny Ann John, a first-year graduate student at the University of Massachusetts, Amherst. We thank Penny for permitting us to share her work with you. As you will note, she worked with a verbal client volunteer with a fairly specific concern and with some obvious solutions. As with all interviews, Penny's work is not perfect, but it is a fine example of how the positive asset search and the focus on exceptions and solutions can make a difference in the life of volunteer and real clients. The interview has been edited for clarity, but it remains the work of Penny.

Particularly note how Penny uses the basic listening sequence and search for positive assets and wellness as a vital part of her example. Balancing the questioning style of brief work with listening skills generally strengthens the interview. As you read this session, think how you might have handled the interview in accord with your own natural style of helping. It will not always be this easy and direct, but sometimes it is. For your first practice in brief counseling, we suggest you find a classmate, friend, or family member. It will take some experience and practice to master these ideas with clients who have more complex issues or who may be resistant to the process.

Stage 1: Initiate the Session—Develop Rapport and Structuring

Penny shared a summary statement on brief counseling with the client and talked about the process initially as she began the session. Carter is a close friend of hers, so she was able to jump right in after explaining the structure of brief counseling. Carter told Penny, earlier, that she wanted to explore the stress she was feeling as the end of the academic term was approaching.

PENNY: Carter, we talked before about what we are going to do today, which is brief counseling, and we are supposed to take an issue or concern for you and work through that and come up with some solutions. You said that you wanted to work on academic stress. Let us take a part of the larger issue—small parts of larger issues are often useful places to start. You've got a list of the questions just as I have here and, if you wish, add any questions I missed that you think are important.

CARTER: OK.

PENNY: So, to start, suppose you tell me what your goal is for today. (Note immediate focus on goal setting.)

CARTER: My goal for today is for us to brainstorm and come up with ideas to manage my stress because I am feeling really stressed out. (Of course, goal definition may not always be this quick and easy. Penny has a client who verbalizes well and who "buys in" to the brief model.)

Stage 2: Gather Data—Draw Out Stories, Concerns, Problems, or Issues

PENNY: OK, sure. What brings this topic to your mind today versus talking about this another time? (Focus on *here and now* and the reason for wanting to discuss it *now*.)

CARTER: Well, I am a graduate student and it is that time of the semester. Everything is coming to what seems like crunch time and that is when I feel the most stress. There are so many things on my plate.

PENNY: Right now it is stressful for you because it is coming toward the end of the semester . . . and you have a lot going on. OK? With all of this going on at the moment, what might be positive about your situation right now? (reflection of feeling—"You feel X because Y"—followed by an open question oriented to strengths and solutions already existing in the client)

CARTER: Well, you know I have got to say, I have talked to a lot of people lately and they have a lot more to do . . . um hum . . . right. And I did not really realize that until I talked to them because I have been plugging right along and doing my papers so I don't have everything to do all at once. And that made me feel a lot better.

PENNY: Great. So you seem pretty organized. You seem like you are getting things done but still have some work to do, but you have been doing things right along. (positive feedback, paraphrase of problem and assets)

CARTER: Yeah, I really have. I am not sure why I feel so stressed because I know I will have the time to do it and I have been doing it so far but I get, I still see the deadline at the end and it is getting closer, so it feels a little stressful.

PENNY: Have there been times in the past when you have felt this type of stress but have dealt with it in a positive way? (brief question seeking exceptions to the problem and past successes)

CARTER: Sure, last semester or even when I was working. There have been times when it seemed like I had a lot to do. I had a very busy job. There are things I like to do when I have time to do them. I like to go dancing. I like to be active. I like to be social and that always . . . it is a real release for me. It is like freedom. You know. (*Penny:* Right.) And then you can forget about it for a while. (*Penny:* Uh huh.) Then it is really good and then I get rejuvenated and I can come back and do what I need to do. OK. It is just finding the time to do that.

PENNY: Oh, that is really terrific. So, in the past when you have been stressed, you have gone out dancing, you have done social things and you have done other things to keep your mind from it and then you get more energized from it also. (positive feedback, paraphrase of strength in dealing with stress)

CARTER: Yeah, it does really work.

PENNY: And then you are able to focus. Oh, great. What is different about the times when you don't feel stressed out? (paraphrase, positive feedback in form of compliment, question searching for positive exceptions to the problem)

CARTER: One of two things. Either I am using the technique to not be stressed out by doing all the social things I need and all of the good things and fun things I enjoy or there is less to do. There is not a crunch time or a deadline time. The summer. I guess when I feel the most organized, when I feel I have things under control, I feel less stressed.

PENNY: OK, so when you feel organized and have things under control, you feel less stressed. (brief summary or paraphrase/reflection of feeling)

Review the interview for focus, and note that virtually every one of Penny's comments focuses both on the client and on possible solutions to the problem. Her enthusiasm communicates hope for Carter. Your interest and belief in change will be heard by your clients.

Stage 3: Set Goals Mutually

CARTER: Right, and when I finish a project and when I see that it is completed and do one thing at a time, I feel less stressed. When I try to do three things and none of them are completed but I have done all this work it is still stressful. I guess when I finish and look at it and say oh, it's done. I did this, whatever task it may be.

PENNY: You feel better when things are organized and you complete your papers. When you do a part of each of your projects but don't finish any complete class project, it doesn't feel so good because you don't feel like you have completed anything. (paraphrase, reflection of feeling)

CARTER: Right, and it might be more work, but it doesn't look that way because I can't check it off the list. You know?

PENNY: Yeah. Say you woke up tomorrow and this stress was miraculously gone, what would it be like? What would it look like? (This is a good time for the miracle question as we have an understanding of Carter's issues and her style. The miracle question often brings out new data, often unexpected, helping us find new solutions. We may find ourselves needing to totally redefine the problem or concern with data provided by the miracle question.)

CARTER: I would have everything done and I would be going on vacation.

PENNY: If you get everything done, then you could be on your vacation with your boyfriend, right? (paraphrase with check-out)

CARTER: Yes, exactly.

Sometimes the miracle question doesn't produce much in the way of useful data at first. In this instance it might have been more productive if Penny had been more specific and had asked, "What would you be doing differently?" Penny could also have followed up for more information on the ideal resolution, particularly as Carter said, "Yes, exactly." Penny was on track and could have asked for more concreteness. Another possibility: "Could you be more specific? What's the first thing you would notice that would be different if the stress were gone?" It takes time and practice to make the miracle question work. Also, this is a point when the client and counselor can look at questions together seeking to elaborate mutually and make the miracle question more concrete, specific, and useful.

PENNY: To recap, your goal has been to brainstorm and identify ways to deal with stress. We've identified some of the strengths in dealing with stress as your organization and your ability to do one thing at a time. And it helps, as you seem to be able to take time off and forget your studies for a while and enjoy yourself. Sounds like organization of your time these next few weeks will be important. (summary)

CARTER: Yes, that's it. I guess my goal is to cool down a bit as I know I can do it. Then my boyfriend and I can be off on vacation for a week.

Stages 4 and 5: Explore, Create, and Conclude

PENNY: Let us talk about some of your strengths, your strengths in the way you can deal with this stress. (directive)

CARTER: I don't know. I am pretty positive about things. I know that I will finish it and I will get everything done. I think that is the strength. It is not a question of if I will do everything; it is just as I am in the moment, things get hectic. I am not a defeatist. I know I will get my work done and I know I will graduate. I know I will and I know what I need to do . . . um hum . . . and I know the things I like to do if I could carve out the time to do them and make sure that I take that time for myself. Then it will be better. So, I think that is strength.

PENNY: Yeah. Some of your strengths are that you are positive, that you know what you need to do, you know how to do it, and you know how to get there. I also heard you say you were organized before. What are some of your strengths in other parts of your life? (summary, open question that may lead to suggestions for dealing with stress)

CARTER: I think those strengths also follow through in other areas of my life. That I am a positive person, that I like to try new things, and am adventurous. I really like life and I think that has always helped me. Right. I think that is a strength and that I can do things.

PENNY: You like to try new things, are positive, and enjoy life. It is interesting. . . . (paraphrase)

CARTER: I just want to do everything very, very well, so sometimes that gets in the way. I want to do it perfectly or as perfectly as I possibly can. Sometimes I feel like I am not doing my best and that bothers me. Even if it is stupid stuff. Even if I know I don't have to do the paper perfectly, I still try to. Right. Sometimes I just need to give myself a break.

PENNY: You have some really great strengths, and with those strengths you were able to obtain your goal today, which was to brainstorm solutions to reduce your stress. Your positive attitude and willingness to do things and being organized and a risk taker will help you work through this stress. On a scale of 1 to 10 where do you see yourself in regard to your stress level at the moment? (Positive feedback with another compliment and summarization followed by scaling. Note that the client in the next statement responds to Penny's incomplete scaling question by defining the end points herself, a sign she understands the concept well.)

CARTER: It is not too bad. Let's say 10 is the most and 1 was the least. I am probably a 5. I don't think it is that bad; talking about it makes it a lot easier. Like I said, it is more when it is in the moment and I have had a crazy day. I was working all day, had my classes, I come home, and I have seven things to do and there are three messages on the answering machine and I think, I can't do everything. I probably could do most of them, and then I have to map it out and prioritize but that is hard because it is so hard to say no. Especially when you want to do fun stuff. I guess it is a 5. Giving myself a break.

PENNY: It seems like you are handling your stress pretty well. (positive feedback)

CARTER: Thanks, yeah, it is not too bad. It is not as bad as it seems in those moments. You know?

PENNY: Um-hum. So there are times when you have a higher stress level and times when you have a lower stress level. When are times when you are a 1? (Encourage, paraphrase, question, search for exceptions. Another useful question would be "So, what do you have to do to reduce your stress from a 5 to a 4?" This later question is an important part of the scaling process, particularly as it focuses on small change rather than total resolution.)

CARTER: When I am not feeling any stress?

PENNY: Yeah. (Encourage.)

CARTER: When I can step away from responsibilities and play with my niece or go home and be with my family or out with my friends and dancing. I am a very active person, so I feel best when I am doing something outdoors or when I am moving or exercising. (Penny's question—focused on total removal of stress—works, but with many clients the smaller change from 5 to 4 would be more manageable.)

PENNY: So, you feel stress-free when you are moving, or exercising, or playing, or are social. On a scale of 1 to 10, what would be your ideal stress level at this time? (Paraphrase; the client's stress patterns are examined by scaling.)

CARTER: An ideal stress level would be a 3, because you can't always be playing. A certain amount of stress is good in order to be productive.

PENNY: What do you want to happen precisely? (Move toward generalization with an open question.)

CARTER: I have 4 weeks left of school. I think I need to map out the next 4 weeks in how I can balance my productive work time and my social outlets. I have six papers left to write and 4 weeks, so that averages to about one and a half papers per week. Now that I put it in that perspective and I see it visually, it doesn't seem so bad after all.

PENNY: No, it doesn't. You have time to do your work and have time for your social outlets. You seem to have a good handle on what you need to do and the amount of time you have to do it. With your strengths, it appears that you will get your work done. You are positive. You know you can get your work done. You are motivated and organized. I like the way you have put it all in perspective. (summary, positive feedback in the form of a compliment)

CARTER: Yes, I feel relieved already.

PENNY: Let's now generate a picture of what the next 4 weeks are going to look like for you. (directive, concretizing the plan)

CARTER: Well, I have four classes and have my assistantship, which is 10 hours per week. I also have these six papers and plenty of time to exercise and I can go out a few times over the next few weekends. My stress level has reduced tremendously already.

PENNY: It sounds like you are doing a lot of things right already and your future plan is very attainable. How about support networks? Do you have people around you for a support system? (positive feedback, open question focusing on support network)

CARTER: Yes, I have my sister and my brother. I also have my housemates and classmates. They are the biggest support because they are going through the same thing with me. I feel like I have a good network around me.

PENNY: You sure do. What positive assets in yourself can you also draw from? (Encourage, return to focus on client and strengths.)

CARTER: My drive and motivation. My positive outlook and energy level.

PENNY: It sounds like you have a lot to draw from. So what are you going to do differently tomorrow? (paraphrase, open question oriented toward generalization)

CARTER: I will exercise first thing in the morning and get started on one of my papers. This week I have a lot of time off, so I can probably get a few papers done and I can also go for a hike or something if the weather improves.

PENNY: Well, this all sounds so clear to me. You know what you need to do. You have your timeline all mapped out and have a good balance of fun and work. Will you let me know in a week or so how it is all working out? (summary, open question)

CARTER: Yes, I will call you next week.

▲ MODULE 14.4
SUMMARY

▲ Brief counseling operates on the theory that clients have their own answers in their past success experiences and wellness strengths. Emphasis is on immediate goal setting and clarity. Questions are a major skill, although many practitioners consider that listening carefully to the client's full story is critical.

▲ Skilled questioning is the major skill of brief counseling. We recommend, at least in the early stages of your practice, that you have, and share with your client, a list of questions for each stage of the interview.

▲ Think about referral or another approach to helping if the client does not respond to brief methods. See Box 14-3 for examples of when brief counseling is inappropriate.

EXAMINE AND DEFINE YOUR PERSONAL STYLE

How Will You Integrate Theory and Practice?

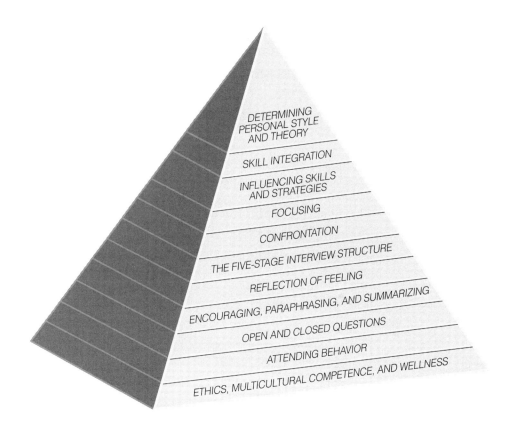

DETERMINING PERSONAL STYLE AND THEORY

SKILL INTEGRATION

INFLUENCING SKILLS AND STRATEGIES

FOCUSING

CONFRONTATION

THE FIVE-STAGE INTERVIEW STRUCTURE

REFLECTION OF FEELING

ENCOURAGING, PARAPHRASING, AND SUMMARIZING

OPEN AND CLOSED QUESTIONS

ATTENDING BEHAVIOR

ETHICS, MULTICULTURAL COMPETENCE, AND WELLNESS

How can determining your own style help you and your clients?

CHAPTER
GOALS

You can be most effective as an interviewer, counselor, or therapist if you generate your own formulation of the helping process. What is your natural style and how does it relate to skills, interviewing structure, and alternative theoretical orientations?

Awareness, knowledge, and skills developed through the concepts of this chapter will enable you to

▲ Recognize the clarity and the complexity of skills, strategies, and approaches to interviewing and counseling.
▲ Facilitate both your own and your clients' development using the rich array of available theories and concepts.
▲ Commit to a lifetime of movement, change, and constant growth as a helping professional.

MODULE 15.1
DEFINE YOUR AUTHENTIC PERSONAL STYLE

KEY CONCEPT QUESTIONS

▲ **What are key aspects of microskills that you want to integrate into your future practice?**

▲ **How do you assess your competence with the skills and ideas presented in this text?**

Determining Personal Style and Theory	*Predicted Result*
As you work with clients, identify your natural style, add to it, and think through your approach to interviewing and counseling. Examine your own preferred skill usage and what you do in the session. Integrate into your own skill set your learning from theory and practice in interviewing, counseling, and psychotherapy.	As a developing interviewer or counselor you will identify and build on your natural style. You will commit to a lifelong process of constantly learning about theory and practice while evaluating and examining your behavior, thoughts, feelings, and deeply held meanings.

Some interviewers and counselors have developed individual styles of helping that require their clients to join them in their orientation to the world. Such individuals have found the one "true and correct" formula for the session; clients who have difficulty with that formula are often termed "resistant" and "not ready" for counseling. Such counselors and therapists can and do produce effective change, but they may be unable to serve very many types of clients. The complexity of humanity and the helping process is missing from their orientation. They do not recognize that some other approach may be more effective than their own fixed style.

Remember that clients have widely different experiences from yours and may wish to head in many directions different from your own. Consequently, it is urgent for you to remain aware that your client may not prefer the skills, strategies, and theories that you favor. Expand your skills and knowledge in areas where you are now less comfortable. You will constantly expand your competence while maintaining your authenticity as a person. You will expand your understanding of cultural differences and diversity. With patience, study, and experience, you will increase your abilities to work with those who are unlike you. The opportunity to learn from clients who are

BOX 15-1   National and International Perspectives on Counseling Skills

Using Microskills Throughout My Professional Career
MARY RUE BRODHEAD, Executive, Canadian Food Inspection Agency

My first encounter with the microskills program was through my master's program in teacher education. I wanted to learn about counseling so that I could better reach teacher trainees. What I learned very rapidly was that teachers often fail to listen to their students—in fact, one research study found that out of nearly 2,000 teacher comments, there was only one reflection of feeling and, of course, most comments focused on providing information. Often when teachers did listen, they weren't able to recognize the verbal and nonverbal cues that were reflecting the reality of their students.

After completing my degree, I entered teacher education and found that microskills lead to a more student-centered teaching. I also found that teachers who matched their students' cognitive/emotional style were the more effective (see Ivey, Ivey, Sweeney, & Myers, 2005). If a student is concrete, the teacher needs to provide specific examples and use concrete questions. If the student is more reflective, then abstract formal operational strategies can be used. Bringing in emotional involvement via microskill strategies enriched teaching.

I next lived on an island off Vancouver where my husband Dale and I worked with the Kwakiutl nation. I trained teachers, but I also counseled and led a group of school dropouts in a special program under the School Board. I actually taught them the same interviewing skills that you are learning in this book. Needless to say, the multicultural orientation helped sensitize me so that I adapted my counseling and teaching to better fit Kwakiutl style.

One of our first activities was a trip in the Chief's fishing boat to gather Christmas trees for the old people, a cherished tradition in the community. This was the first time that most of these young people had participated in the ritual. As they delivered the trees, the recipients, in an expression of gratitude, invited them in for something to eat and began to tell stories. These old people, thrilled to have an audience, would shower attention on the alienated youth who, in response, would listen with attention and respect. And, so an upward cycle of communication began. Eventually we raised money to buy tape recorders and to capture these tales for the future, leading to further strengthening of the students' listening and questioning skills. Attending behavior increased respect and communication on both sides.

After three years in British Columbia, Dal and I returned to Ottawa where I directed an employment equity program. The task centered on providing culturally sensitive counseling and opportunities to members of the Canadian four "equity groups" (visible minorities, Aboriginal peoples, persons with disabilities, and women in nontraditional occupations) to develop the skills needed for career development and success in the Federal Public Service.

As part of my work, I used microskills to train government officials to listen and really hear and understand the variety of perspectives, strengths, and styles of working found within members of our multicultural workforce. Here, I learned the importance of language and I became reasonably fluent in French, an essential skill in bilingual, multicultural Canada. I developed a multicultural counseling course used within fifteen universities in Canada that included many ideas presented here.

My current agency is responsible for animal health, plant protection, and food safety. It is one of those "science departments" involving agriculture, fisheries, scientific research, and many other issues. Given the diversity of my workforce, my first task has been to build a "culture of learning" where vast amounts of information and knowledge can be shared effectively and efficiently. Microskills are key elements in management training and a good communication skills workshop can be vital in team building. And, of course, all my managers need to listen to and motivate those with whom they serve.

Looking back over my career, it is amazing to find that the basic microskills have been useful in my teaching, counseling, multicultural work, and governmental leadership positions. "Training as treatment" and "teaching competence" in microskills can help us all make a difference throughout our careers.

different from us is one of the special privileges of being an interviewer, a counselor, or a therapist.

Developing your own personal approach to interviewing and counseling involves a multiplicity of factors. Reflect on yourself, your values, personal meanings, and your skills. Where are your strengths? What areas need further development? Where would you like to go? To help you in the evolving identification of your own personal style, the microskills hierarchy is reviewed as a matrix for decision making on your part. A brief map showing how these skills and concepts play themselves out in different modes of interviewing and counseling should aid you in the search for your personal style.

How Would You Assess Your Competence With the Microskills?

You have been presented with 33 major concepts and skill categories. Within those major divisions are more than 100 specific methods, theories, and strategies. Ideally, you will commit them all to memory and be able to draw on them immediately in practice to facilitate your clients' development and progress in the interview. Recall the story of the Samurai from Chapter 3. With time and experience, you will develop increased understanding and expertise. As you grow as an interviewer, counselor, or therapist and your skill mastery increases, you will find the ideas expressed here becoming increasingly clear and a natural part of your practice.

Retaining and mastering the concepts of the microskills hierarchy may be facilitated by what is termed *chunking*. We do not learn information just in bits and pieces; we organize it into patterns. The microskills hierarchy is a pattern that can be visualized and experienced. For example, at this moment you can probably immediately recall that attending behavior has certain major concepts "chunked" under it (culturally appropriate visuals, vocal tone, verbal following, and body language—"three V's + B"). You can probably also recall the basic listening sequence, the purpose of open questions and perhaps which questions lead to which likely outcomes (for example, *how* questions lead to process and feelings).

Complete a transcript examining and classifying your own interviewing style (Chapter 13), and the ideas of this book will become especially clear. Reading is a useful introduction to counseling and interviewing, but the results of practice and experience will stick with you far into the future. The skills you practice have the most relevance and are the ones you understand best.

To demonstrate intentional competence, you need to be able to produce *results* due to your efforts in helping. Intentional competence is reflected in what your client does, not in your execution of the skills. And if your effort is not successful, can you flex and intentionally use another skill to reach the same result? If necessary, can you reformulate your approach to the client on the spot? Use the self-assessment in Table 15-1 to determine your mastery of each concept.

1. *Identify and classify the concept.* The microskill language provides a vocabulary and communication tool with which to understand and analyze your interviewing and counseling behavior and that of others. If the concept or skill is present in an interview, can you label it? If you can identify concepts, you have most likely chunked most of the major skill points together in your mind. You may not immediately recall all the types of focus, but when you see an interview in progress you will probably recall which one is being used.

▲ **TABLE 15-1** Self-Assessment Summary

Take some time to review your own competence levels in each of the 33 major areas and indicate your personal competencies on this chart. You may use this as a summary and as a plan for future growth. Can you identify each skill or concept and classify its place in the interview? Can you demonstrate basic competence by using the skill in the session? Most important, can you obtain specific and predictable results in client behavior as a result of your use of the skill or concept?

Skill or Concept	Identification and Classification	Basic Competence	Intentional Competence	Evidence of Achieving Competence Level
1. Attending behavior				
2. Questioning				
3. Observation skills				
4. Encouraging				
5. Paraphrasing				
6. Summarizing				
7. Reflecting feelings				
8. Basic listening sequence				
9. Positive asset search				
10. Empathy				
11. Five stages of the interview				
12. Story–positive asset–restory–action				
13. Confrontation				
14. The Client Change Scale				
14. Focusing				
16. Reflection of meaning				
17. Noting concreteness and abstractions in self and clients				
18. Interpretation/reframe				
19. Awareness of logical consequences				
20. Self-disclosure				
21. Feedback				
22. Information/advice/opinion/ instruction/suggestion				
23. Directives				
24. Analysis of the interview (Chapter 13)				

(Continued)

Skill or Concept	Identification and Classification	Basic Competence	Intentional Competence	Evidence of Achieving Competence Level
Theoretical/Practical Strategies				
25. Ethics				
26. Multicultural awareness				
27. Wellness				
28. Community genogram				
29. Decisional counseling				
30. Person-centered counseling				
31. Cognitive-behavioral assertiveness training				
32. Brief counseling				
33. Defining personal style and theory				

2. *Demonstrate basic competence.* Basic competence means you will be able to understand and practice the concept in an interview. Continued practice and experience becomes the foundation for later intentional mastery.
3. *Demonstrate intentional competence.* Skilled interviewers, counselors, and therapists can use the microskills to produce specific, concrete effects with their clients. Appendix I presents the full Ivey Taxonomy and reviews specific aspects of intentional prediction. If you reflect feelings, do clients actually talk more about their emotions? If you provide an interpretation/reframe, does your client see her or his situation from a new perspective? If you work through some variation of the positive asset search, does your client actually view the situation more hopefully? If you conduct a well-formed, five-stage interview, does your client's self-concept and/or developmental level change? Does your interview produce client changes?

▲ **MODULE 15.1**

SUMMARY

▲ Assessing your positive assets, strengths, and resources is a good place to start as you increase clarity and awareness of your personal style. We suggest that you become competent in more than one theory or method of helping. It is critical that you maintain a personal authenticity in interviewing and counseling practice and continue to study and learn over time.

▲ *Intentional competence* is reflected in what your client does, not in your execution of the skills. If your effort is not successful, can you flex and intentionally use another skill to reach the desired result? Reformulate your approach to the client on the spot?

BOX 15-2   Brain Research: Implications for the Future of Interviewing and Counseling

We are not prisoners of our genes or our environment. Poverty, alienation, drugs, hormonal imbalances, and depression don't dictate failure. Wealth, acceptance, vegetables, and exercise don't guarantee success. . . . Experiences, thoughts, actions, and emotions actually change the structure of our brains. . . . Indeed, once we understand how the brain develops, we can train our brains for health, vibrancy, and longevity. (Ratey, 2001, p. 17)

You likely have noticed stories on television and in the popular media on brain research. This research has now reached a state of precision where it has important implications for you as an interviewer or counselor. Chapter 7 summarized research on empathy and there we learned that the healthy person's brain resonates (empathizes) with the experience of the client. The empathic listening helper facilitates client physical and mental health.

Neuroplasticity and its implications. Neuropsychology can be defined as "the study of relations between brain function and behavior" (Kolb & Whishaw, 2003, p. G16). Perhaps the most important discovery is *neuroplasticity*—the brain develops new neural connections throughout the lifespan and changes in response to new situations or experiences in the environment. "Neuroplasticity can result in the wholesale remodeling of neural networks . . . a brain can rewire itself" (Schwartz & Begley, 2002, p. 16).

What does this mean for you and the helping process? When you interact with clients, your brain functioning as well as your client's can be measured through a variety of brain imaging techniques, especially functional magnetic imaging (fMRI). An example of neuroplasticity is that both you and your client may learn, change, and develop new neural connections as a result of your interaction. Neuropsychology research on emotion validates past counseling and therapy theory and research from a new perspective.

Systematic learning and the brain. Restak (2003) found that training volunteers in movement sequences produced sequential changes in activity patterns of the brain as the movements became more thoroughly learned and automatic. Systematic step-by-step learning, such as that emphasized in this book, is an efficient learning system used in ballet, music, golf, and many other settings. If there is sufficient practice, changes in the brain may be expected and increased ability in demonstrating these skills will appear in areas ranging from finger movements to dance—and from the golf swing to interviewing skills. Practice of specific skills facilitates a natural automatic style.

Attention as a central process. Attention is not just a psychological concept—it is measurable through brain imaging. When a person attends to a stimulus (e.g., the client's story) many areas of the brain of both interviewer and client become involved (Posner, 2004). Two key factors in attention are arousal and focus. By giving attention to the client, the interviewer's and the client's thought processes have both been activated. Selective attention is a critical aspect of listening—"Focus is brought about by . . . a part of the thalamus, which operates rather like a spotlight, turning to shine on the stimulus" (Carter, 1999, p. 186). Just as attending behavior underlies all the microskills of this book, attention and selective attention provide the physiological foundation for personal growth. When we listen and attend selectively, our brain and the client's brain are reacting and changing.

Brain research supports the wellness approach. The holistic right hemisphere is associated more with positive emotions such as happiness and joy; the left hemisphere and amgydala (deep in the brain) are associated more often with negative feelings. In depression and deep sadness, brain scans reveal that the positive areas are less active (Davidson et al., 2002). Happiness involves physical pleasure, positive meanings, and the absence of negative emotions (Carter, 1999; Davidson et al., 2002). In effect, positive thoughts and action can help override fear, anger, and sadness.

What, specifically does this mean for your practice? When clients focus solely on problems and negative emotions, we can help them through a wellness approach that strengthens and nourishes the individual. In this way we can help clients "build a

(Continued)

BOX 15-2   Brain Research: Implications for the Future of Interviewing
               and Counseling (Continued)

tolerance for negative emotions and gradually acquire a knack for generating positive ones" (Damasio, 2003, p. 275). So the wellness approach is not just "window dressing." This strengthening can be both psychological (reminding clients about positive experiences and personal strengths) and physical (encouraging exercise and sports, nutrition, and adequate sleep). A base of strengths facilitates problem solving and working through the many complex issues we all face.

Looking to the future. Throughout your career, you will want to explore how brain research relates to interviewing practice and everyday life. Brain research is not in opposition to the cognitive, emotional, and behavioral emphasis of interviewing and counseling. Rather,

it will help us pinpoint types of interventions that are most helpful to the client. In fact, one of the clearest findings is that the brain needs environmental stimulation to grow and develop. You can offer a healthy atmosphere for client growth and development.

Human development depends on cultural/environmental/contextual influences. If clients grow up and live in stressful, impoverished situations, both mental and physical development will be impaired. Our interviewing practice needs also to address social issues in our society. We need to balance individual interviewing and counseling with a commitment to social justice, action in the community, and efforts to prevent problems and issues before they occur.

MODULE 15.2

THEORIES OF INTERVIEWING AND COUNSELING: Alternatives for Your Action

KEY CONCEPT QUESTIONS

▲ **What skill patterns are demonstrated in different theories of interviewing and counseling?**

▲ **What types of meaning or topic focus are stressed by varying theories?**

▲ **How do your personal preferences for skills and meaning issues relate to these and other theories?**

Alternative Theories of Interviewing and Counseling

Equipped with the foundation skills of listening, observing, influencing, and structuring an interview, you are well prepared to enter the complex world of theory and practice. Soon you will be encountering the 250 or more theories competing for your attention. This final discussion is oriented to assembling what you already know, bringing it together in one place, and looking toward the future.

If you can complete the five-stage interview structured around decisions, you have a good beginning understanding of the basics of interviewing and counseling. Decisional counseling has been around for a long time. Ben Franklin reminded us that much of our life is concerned with making decisions. Some claim that decisional counseling (sometimes known as "problem-solving counseling") is the most widely practiced form of helping in current practice. Samples of decisional daily practice include social work, employment counseling, placement counseling, AIDS counseling, alcohol and drug counseling, school and college counseling, and in the work of community volunteers and peer helpers.

Completing a full interview using only listening skills is a beginning introduction to Carl Rogers's (1961) person-centered theory. You likely discovered that many clients are self-directed, and with a good listener, they can do much to resolve their issues on their own. Mastery of completing a full interview using only listening skills does not make you a person-centered counselor. Study Rogers's work in detail and complete an interview using *no questions* at all, a very different task from the one used in brief counseling or decisional work.

The emphasis in cognitive-behavioral assertiveness training is on observable behavior and making decisions to change actions. In brief approaches, you found your listening skills and the positive asset search enabled you to conduct a very different type of decision-making interview. Questions are a central skill of these two models. If you have mastered basic skills and strategies, you are well prepared to increase your mastery in these distinct interviewing approaches and other theoretical/practical strategies. Note the following key points as you think about these theoretical/practical methods.

1. Different theoretical/practical systems use varying patterns of microskills. These could range from almost all the questions in the brief approach to no questions at all with the person-centered orientation.
2. Theoretical/practical systems tend to focus on different areas of meaning and have different stories they would tell about the interviewing, counseling, and therapeutic process.
   ▲ Decisional counseling focuses on making decisions and resolving issues around practical life issues and problems.
   ▲ Person-centered counseling emphasizes the ways clients understand themselves and make meaning of life.
   ▲ Cognitive-behavioral assertiveness stresses observable behaviors that can be seen directly, counted, and changed.
   ▲ Brief counseling uses client assets and resources to resolve issues.

Table 15-2 illustrates in summary form how the microskills may be used in different approaches to the interview. The table shows that widely varying styles of helping may be understood and practiced via the microskills system. Before you review Table 15-2, indicate your preferred skills in the chart on page 296. Rate each skill on a 3-point scale with 1 representing the skills you most prefer and would like to use most often; 2, those skills that you would commonly use; and 3, those skills you would prefer to use only occasionally. You can also fill in circles as noted in the legend at the bottom of Table 15-2. Compare your preferred skill pattern with those presented there. Where are you headed in terms of theoretical preference? What other theories not presented here might you also consider and perhaps already prefer?

	MICROSKILL LEAD	*Skill Preferences on 3-Point Scale*			*Fill in the Circle as in Table 15-2*
BASIC	Open question	1	2	3	○
LISTENING	Closed question	1	2	3	○
SKILLS	Encourager	1	2	3	○
	Paraphrase	1	2	3	○
	Reflection of feeling	1	2	3	○
	Summarization	1	2	3	○
INFLUENCING	Reflection of meaning	1	2	3	○
SKILLS	Interpretation/reframe	1	2	3	○
	Logical consequences	1	2	3	○
	Self-disclosure	1	2	3	○
	Feedback	1	2	3	○
	Advice/information/and others	1	2	3	○
	Directive	1	2	3	○
	Confrontation	1	2	3	○
SKILL FOCUS	Client	1	2	3	○
	Problem/concern	1	2	3	○
	Significant others (partner, spouse, friends, family)	1	2	3	○
	Mutuality ("we" focus)	1	2	3	○
	Counselor/interviewer	1	2	3	○
	Cultural/environmental context	1	2	3	○
MEANING	Which issues of meaning would you most like to address?				
TALK-TIME	What amount of talk-time do you believe is appropriate? High Medium Low				
THEORY	Which theory (theories) do you prefer?				

Legend: 1 = favored skill, 2 = commonly used skill, 3 = occasionally used skill

▲ **MODULE 15.2**

SUMMARY

▲ Analysis of multiple theories reveals markedly different patterns of skill usage. For example, person-centered theory avoids questions and focuses on listening skills with some emphasis on feedback and self-disclosure. There is no rush to identify specific problems and goals. Brief counseling, on the other hand, uses many questions and is oriented strongly to goals and outcomes.

▲ Different theories focus also on different meaning issues. Cognitive behaviorists tend to focus on observable behavior, although thoughts and feelings can also be important. Decisional counseling and brief counseling emphasize problem solving and decision making while person-centered work is focused on relationship, meaning, and feelings.

▲ **TABLE 15-2** Microskills Patterns of Differing Approaches to the Interview

MICROSKILL LEAD	Decisional counseling	Person centered	Behavioral (assertiveness training)	Solution oriented	Motivational interviewing	Psychodynamic	Gestalt	Rational-emotive behavioral therapy	Feminist therapy	Business problem solving	Medical diagnostic interview	Eclectic/metatheoretical
BASIC LISTENING SKILLS												
Open question	●	○	◐	●	●	◐	●	◐	◐	◐	◐	◐
Closed question	◐	○	●	◐	◐	◐	○	◐	◐	◐	◐	◐
Encourager	●	◐	◐	◐	●	◐	◐	◐	◐	◐	◐	◐
Paraphrase	●	●	◐	◐	●	◐	○	◐	◐	◐	◐	◐
Reflection of feeling	●	●	◐	◐	●	◐	○	◐	◐	◐	○	◐
Summarization	◐	◐	◐	●	●	◐	◐	◐	◐	◐	◐	◐
INFLUENCING SKILLS												
Reflection of meaning	◐	●	○	○	○	◐	○	◐	●	○	○	◐
Interpretation/reframe	◐	○	○	○	●	●	◐	◐	◐	◐	◐	◐
Logical consequences	●	○	◐	◐	●	○	○	●	◐	●	◐	◐
Self-disclosure	◐	◐	○	◐	●	○	◐	○	●	○	○	◐
Feedback	◐	◐	◐	◐	●	○	◐	●	●	◐	○	◐
Advice/information/ and others	◐	○	●	◐	○	○	○	●	◐	●	●	◐
Directive	◐	○	●	○	◐	○	●	●	◐	●	●	◐
CONFRONTATION (Combined Skill)	◐	◐	◐	◐	◐	●	●	●	●	◐	◐	◐
FOCUS												
Client	●	●	●	●	●	●	●	●	○	◐	◐	◐
Concern, main theme	●	○	◐	●	●	◐	○	◐	◐	●	●	◐
Significant others	◐	○	◐	◐	◐	◐	◐	○	◐	○	○	◐
Mutuality	○	◐	○	◐	◐	◐	◐	◐	◐	○	○	◐
Counselor/interviewer	○	◐	○	○	◐	◐	◐	◐	◐	○	○	◐
Cultural/ environmental context	◐	○	◐	◐	○	○	○	○	●	◐	○	◐
ISSUE OF MEANING (Topics, key words likely to be attended to and reinforced)	Decisions	Relationship	Changing behavior	Change	Change	Unconscious motivation	Here-and-now behavior	Irrational ideas/logic	Women's issues	Problem solving	Diagnosis of illness	Varies
AMOUNT OF INTERVIEWER TALK-TIME	Medium	Low	High	Medium	Medium	Low	High	High	Medium	High	High	Varies

LEGEND

● Frequent use of skill
◐ Common use of skill
○ Occasional use of skill

MODULE 15.3
YOUR PERSONAL STYLE AND FUTURE
THEORETICAL/PRACTICAL INTEGRATION

KEY CONCEPT QUESTION

▲ What is your personal authentic style and your story of interviewing and counseling?

There are two major factors to consider as you move toward identifying your own personal style and integrating the many available theories—your own personal authenticity and the needs and style of the client. Unless a skill or theory harmonizes with who you are, it will tend to be false and less effective; however, modifying your natural style and theoretical orientation will be necessary if you are to be helpful to many clients. Remember that you are unique, and so are those whom you would serve. We all come from varying families, differing communities, and distinct views of gender, ethnic/racial, spiritual, and other multicultural issues.

Your interview transcript (recommended in Chapter 13) gives you an excellent beginning for understanding yourself and how clients relate to you. If you are able to engage in the four theoretical/practical methods discussed here, you have at least beginning competency in issues of decisions and finding solutions, meaning-making, and behavioral specifics. Summarize your own story of interviewing and counseling. Box 15-3 asks you to review your goals, your special skills, and your plans for the future. Particularly important is: "Where are you going next?"

We have come to the end of this phase of your interviewing and counseling journey. You have been introduced to the foundation skills and how they are structured in a variety of theoretical/practical interviews. Skills that once seemed awkward and

BOX 15-3   Your Natural Style and Story of Interviewing and Counseling

Consider these issues as you continue the process of identifying your natural style and future theoretical/practical integration of skills and theory.

Goals	What do you want to happen for your clients as a result of their working with you? What would you *desire* for them? How are these goals similar to or different from those of decisional, brief, person-centered, and behavioral assertiveness training? What else?
Skills and strategies	You have identified your competence levels in these areas. What do you see as your special strengths? What are some of your needs for further development in the future? What else?
Cultural intentionality	With what multicultural groups and special populations do you feel capable of working? What knowledge of diversity do you need to gain in the future? How aware are you of your own multicultural background? What else?
Theoretical/practical issues	What theoretical/practical story would you provide now that summarizes how you view the world of interviewing and counseling? Where next would you like to focus your efforts and interests? What else?

unfamiliar are likely more automatic and natural, and you need not think of them too often. The basic listening sequence has become an important part of your interviewing practice and way of thinking.

The next steps are yours. Many of you will be moving on to individual theories of counseling, exploring issues of family counseling, becoming involved in the community, and learning the many aspects of professional practice. Others may find this presentation sufficient for their purposes. We have designed this book as a clear summary of the basics—a naturally skilled person can use the information here for many effective and useful helping sessions. We have selected a few key references to help you with your continued development. Enjoy delving more deeply into our exciting field.

We enjoyed sharing this time with you. Many of the ideas in this book come from interaction with students. We hope you will take a moment to provide us with your feedback and suggestions for the future. Email us at info@emicrotraining.com and say hello. Those pages will be constantly updated with new ideas and information. You have joined a never-ending time of growth and development. Welcome to the field of interviewing and counseling!

Allen and Mary

▲ **MODULE 15.3**
SUMMARY

▲ Write your own story and theory of interviewing and counseling. Honor yourself and your strengths while simultaneously honoring the many differences among your future clients, both individual and multicultural.

Suggested Supplementary Readings

The literature of our field is extensive, and you will want to sample it on your own. We would like to share some books that we find helpful as next steps to follow up ideas presented here. All of these build on the concepts of this book, but we have recommended several books that take different perspectives from our own.

Microskills

www.emicrotraining.com

Visit this website for up-to-date information on interviewing and counseling, microskills, and multicultural counseling and therapy. There are links to professional associations, ethical codes, and many multicultural and professional sites. You will also find interviews with leaders of our field.

Evans, D., Hearn, M., Uhlemann, M., & Ivey, A. (2007). *Essential interviewing* (7th ed.). Belmont, CA: Brooks/Cole.

Microskills in a programmed text format.

Ivey, A., Gluckstern, N., & Ivey, M. (2005). *Basic attending skills* (4th ed.). Framingham, MA: Microtraining Associates.

Perhaps the most suitable book for beginners and those who would teach others microskills. Supporting videotapes are available (www.emicrotraining.com).

Ivey, A., Gluckstern, M., & Ivey, M. (1997). *Basic influencing skills* (3rd ed.). North Amherst, MA: Microtraining Associates.

More data on the influencing skills. Supporting videotapes are available.

Theories of Interviewing and Counseling
With a Multicultural Orientation

Ivey, A., D'Andrea, M., Ivey, M., & Simek-Morgan, L. (2007). *Counseling and psychotherapy: A multicultural perspective* (6th ed.). Boston: Allyn and Bacon.

> The major theories are reviewed, with special attention to issues. Includes many applied exercises to take theory into practice.

Thomas, R. (2000). *Multicultural counseling and human development theories: 25 theoretical perspectives.* Springfield, IL: Charles C Thomas.

> Multiple orientations are presented in a comprehensive fashion.

Suggestions for Follow-Up on Specific Theories

Most of the following books are classics. In many ways they are more comprehensive, thorough, and *important* than more recent writings. We commend them all to you.

Decisional Counseling

D'Zurilla, T. (1999). *Problem-solving therapy* (2nd ed.). New York: Springer.

> An entire counseling model derived from decision making.

Parsons, F. (1967). *Choosing a vocation.* New York: Agathon. (Originally published 1909)

> It is well worth a trip to your library to read Parsons's work. You will find that much of his thinking is still up to date and relevant.

Brief Counseling

Connell, B. (2005). *Solution-focused therapy.* Beverly Hills, CA: Sage.

> The basics of brief counseling in brief form.

Sklare, G. (2004). *Brief counseling that works* (2nd ed.). Beverly Hills, CA: Corwin.

> School-focused and clear. Also available—videotape of a real interview with a child (www.emicrotraining.com).

Person-Centered Counseling and Humanistic Theory

Frankl, V. (1959). *Man's search for meaning.* New York: Pocket Books. (Originally published 1946)

> This is one of the most memorable books you will ever read. It describes Frankl's survival in German concentration camps through finding personal meaning. You will find that referring your future clients to this book is an excellent counseling and therapeutic tool in itself.

Rogers, C. (1961). *On becoming a person.* Boston: Houghton Mifflin.

> The classic book by the originator of person-centered counseling.

Cognitive-Behavioral Counseling

Alberti, R., & Emmons, M. (2001). *Your perfect right: A guide to assertiveness training* (8th ed.). San Luis Obispo, CA: Impact. (Originally published 1970)

> The classic book by the originators.

Davis, M., Eshelman, E., & McKay, M. (2000). *The relaxation and stress reduction workbook* (5th ed.). Oakland, CA: New Harbinger.

One of many books on cognitive and behavioral counseling. This is clear, direct, and easily translatable into microskill approaches to the interview.

Dobson, K. (Ed.). (2002). *Handbook of cognitive-behavioral therapies* (2nd ed.). New York: Guilford.

A comprehensive and specific presentation of key skills, strategies, and theories.

Multicultural Counseling and Therapy

Sue, D. W., Carter, R., Casas, M., Fouad, N., Ivey, A., Jensen, M., LaFromboise, T., Manese, J., Ponterotto, J., & Vazquez-Nuttall, E. (1998). *Multicultural counseling competencies.* Beverly Hills, CA: Sage.

The most comprehensive coverage of the necessary skills and competencies in the multicultural area.

Sue, D. W., Ivey, A., & Pedersen, P. (1999). *A theory of multicultural counseling and therapy.* Pacific Grove, CA: Brooks/Cole.

A general theory of multicultural counseling and therapy with many implications for practice.

Sue, D. W., & Sue, D. (2003). *Counseling the culturally diverse* (4th ed.). New York: Wiley.

The classic of the field. This book helped launch a movement.

Integrative/Eclectic Orientations

Ivey, A., Ivey, M., Myers, J., & Sweeney, T. (2005) *Developmental counseling and therapy: Promoting wellness over the lifespan.* Boston: Lahaska/Houghton-Mifflin.

Ivey, A. (2000/1986). *Developmental therapy.* San Francisco: Jossey-Bass.

Two books that offer skill integration as well as a developmental theory. Useful follow-up from microskill training, particularly due to the focus on skills to match client cognitive/emotional styles.

Lazarus, A. (1989). *Brief but comprehensive psychotherapy: The multimodal way.* New York: Springer.

This is still the basic book for multimodal therapy. You will find the BASIC-ID model useful in conceptualizing broad treatment plans.

APPENDIX I
THE IVEY TAXONOMY
Definitions of the Microskills Hierarchy and Predicted Results From Using Skills

Ethics	*Predicted Result*
Observe and practice ethically and follow professional standards. Particularly important issues for beginning interviewers are *competence, informed consent, confidentiality, power, and social justice.*	Client trust and understanding of the interviewing process will increase. The client will feel empowered in a more egalitarian session. When you work toward social justice, you contribute to problem prevention in addition to healing work in the interview.
Multicultural Issues	*Predicted Result*
Base interviewer behavior on an ethical approach with an awareness of the many issues of diversity. Include the multiple dimensions from the RESPECTFUL model (Chapter 1).	Anticipate that both you and your clients will appreciate, gain respect, and learn from increasing knowledge in ethics and multicultural competence. You, the interviewer, will have a solid foundation for a lifetime of personal and professional growth.
Wellness	*Predicted Result*
Clients discover and rediscover their strengths through wellness assessment. Find strengths and positive assets in the client and in the support system. Identify multiple dimensions of wellness.	Clients who are aware of their strengths and resources can face their difficulties and discuss problem resolution from a positive foundation.
Attending Behavior	*Predicted Result*
Support your client with individually and culturally appropriate visuals, vocal quality, verbal tracking, and body language.	Clients talk more freely and respond openly, particularly around topics to which attention is given. Depending on the individual client and culture, anticipate fewer eye contact breaks, a smoother vocal tone, a more complete story (with fewer topic jumps), and a more comfortable body language.
Client Observation Skills	*Predicted Result*
Observe your own and the client's verbal and nonverbal behavior. Anticipate individual and multicultural differences in nonverbal and verbal behavior. Carefully and selectively feed back observations to the client as topics for discussion.	Observations provide specific data validating or invalidating what is happening in the session and provide guidance for use of various microskills and strategies. The smoothly flowing interview will often demonstrate movement symmetry or complimentarity.

	Movement dissynchrony provides a clear clue that you are not "in tune" with the client.
Open and Closed Questions Open questions often begin with *who, what, when, where,* and *why.* Closed questions may start with *do, is,* or *are. Could, can,* or *would* questions are considered open but have the additional advantage of being somewhat closed, thus giving more power to the clients, who can more easily say that they don't want to respond.	*Predicted Result* Clients will give more detail and talk more in response to open questions. Closed questions provide specific information but may close off client talk. Effective questions encourage more focused client conversations with more pertinent detail and less wandering. *Could, would,* and *can* questions are often the most open of all.
Encouraging Encourage with short responses that help clients keep talking. They may be verbal (repeating key words and short statements) or nonverbal (head nods and smiling).	*Predicted Result* Clients elaborate on the topic, particularly when encouragers and restatements are used in a questioning tone of voice.
Paraphrasing Shorten, clarify the essence of what has just been said, but be sure to use the client's main words when you paraphrase. Paraphrases are often fed back to the client in a questioning tone of voice.	*Predicted Result* Clients will feel heard. They tend to give more detail without repeating the exact same story. If a paraphrase is inaccurate, the client has an opportunity to correct the interviewer.
Summarizing Summarize client comments and integrate thoughts, emotions, and behaviors. Summarizing is similar to paraphrasing but used over a longer time span.	*Predicted Result* Clients will feel heard and often learn how the many parts of important stories are integrated. The summary tends to facilitate a more centered and focused discussion. The summary also provides a more coherent transition from one topic to the next or as a way to begin and end a full session.
Reflection of Feeling The interviewer identifies the key emotions of a client and feed them back to clarify affective experience. With some clients, the brief acknowledgment of feeling may be more appropriate.	*Predicted Result* Clients will be able to experience their emotional states more clearly. They also may correct the interviewer's reflection with a more accurate descriptor.
Basic Listening Sequence Select and practice all elements of the basic listening sequence, open and closed questions, encouraging, paraphrasing, reflection of feeling, and summarization. These are supplemented by attending behavior and client observation skills.	*Predicted Result* Clients discuss their stories, problems, or concerns, including the key facts, thoughts, feelings, and behaviors. Clients feel that their stories have been heard.

The Five Stages/Dimensions of the Well-Formed Interview

1. Initiate the Session Develop rapport and structuring. "Hello, what would you like to talk about today?"	*Predicted Result* The client feels at ease with an understanding of the key ethical issues and the purpose of interview. The client may also know you more completely as a person and professional.
2. Gather Data Draw out client stories, concerns, problems, or issues. "What's your concern?" "What are your strengths and resources?"	*Predicted Result* The client shares thoughts, feelings, behaviors, and their stories in detail as well as strengths and resources.
3. Set Goals Mutually "What do you want to happen?"	*Predicted Result* The client discusses and defines goals, new ways of thinking, desired feeling states, and desired behavior changes. The client may learn how to live more effectively with situations that cannot be changed (rape, death, an accident, an illness).
4. Explore and Create Explore alternatives, confront client incongruities and conflict, restory. "What are we going to do about it?" "Can we generate new ways of thinking, feeling, and behaving?"	*Predicted Result* The client may reexamine individual goals in new ways, solve problems from at least three generated alternatives, and start the move toward new stories and actions.
5. Conclude Plan for generalizing interview learning to "real life" and eventual termination of the interview or series of sessions. ("Will you do it?")	*Predicted Result* The client demonstrates change in behavior, thoughts, and feelings in daily life outside of the interview.
Confrontation Supportively challenge the client: 1. Listen, observe, and note client conflict, mixed messages, and discrepancies in verbal and nonverbal behavior. 2. Point out internal and external discrepancies by feeding them back to the client, usually through the listening skills. 3. Evaluate how the client responds and whether the confrontation leads to client movement or change. If the client does not change, the interviewer flexes intentionally and tries another skill.	*Predicted Result* The client responds to the confrontation of discrepancies and conflict with new ideas, thoughts, feelings, and behaviors and these will be measurable on the 5-point Client Change Scale. If the client does not change, the interviewer flexes intentionally and tries another skill.

Focusing	*Predicted Result*
Use selective attention and focus the interview on the client, problem/concern, significant others (partner/spouse, family, friends), a mutual "we" focus, the interviewer, or the cultural/environmental context (RESPECTFUL multicultural background, community, nation).	Clients focus their conversation or story on the dimensions selected by the interviewer. As the interviewer brings in new foci, the story is elaborated from multiple perspectives.
Reflection of Meaning	*Predicted Result*
Meanings are close to core experiencing. Encourage clients to explore their own meanings and values in more depth from their own perspective. Questions to elicit meaning are often a vital first step. A reflection of meaning looks very much like a paraphrase but focuses beyond what the client says. Often the words *meaning, values, vision,* and *goals* appear in the discussion.	The client discusses stories, issues, and concerns in more depth with a special emphasis on deeper meanings, values, and understandings. Clients may be enabled to discern their life goals and vision for the future.
Interpretation/Reframe	*Predicted Result*
Provide the client with a new perspective, frame of reference, or way of thinking about issues. Interpretations/reframes may come from your observations; they may be based on varying theoretical orientations to the helping field; or they may link critical ideas together.	The client may find another perspective or meaning of a story, issue, or problem. The new perspective could have been generated by a theory used by the interviewer, from linking ideas or information, or by simply looking at the situation afresh.
Self-Disclosure	*Predicted Result*
As the interviewer, share your own related past personal life experience, *here-and-now* observations or feelings toward the client, or opinions about the future. Self-disclosure often starts with an "I" statement. *Here-and-now* feelings toward the client can be powerful and should be used carefully.	The client is encouraged to self-disclose in more depth and may develop a more egalitarian interviewing relationship with the interviewer. The client may feel more comfortable in the relationship and find a new solution relating to the counselor's self-disclosure.
Feedback	*Predicted Result*
Present the client with clear information on how the interviewer believes the client is thinking, feeling, or behaving and how significant others may view them or their performance.	Clients may improve or change their thoughts, feelings, and behaviors based on the interviewer's feedback.
Logical Consequences	*Predicted Results*
Explore specific alternatives and the logical positive and negative concrete consequence of each possibility with the client. "If you do this . . . , then. . . ."	Clients may change thoughts, feelings, and behaviors through better anticipation of the consequences of their actions. Through exploring the positives and negatives of each possibility, the client is more involved in the process of decision making.

Information and Advice	*Predicted Result*
Share specific information with the client—e.g., career information, choice of major, where to go for community assistance and services. Offer advice or opinions on how to resolve issues and provide useful suggestions for personal change.	If given sparingly and effectively, the client will use information and ideas to act in new, more positive ways.
Directives	*Predicted Result*
Direct clients to follow specific actions. Directives are important in broader strategies such as assertiveness or social skills training or specific exercises such imagery, thought stopping, journaling, or relaxation training. They are often important when assigning homework for the client.	Clients will make positive progress when they listen to and follow the directives and engage in new, more positive thinking, feeling, or behaving.
Skill Integration	*Predicted Result*
Integrate the microskills into a well-formed interview and generalize the skills to situations beyond the training session or classroom.	Developing interviewers and counselors will integrate skills as part of their natural style. Each of us will vary in our choices, but increasingly we will know what we are doing, how to flex when what we are doing is ineffective, and what to expect in the interview as a result of our efforts.
Determining Personal Style and Theory	*Predicted Result*
As you work with clients, identify your natural style, add to it, and think through your approach to interviewing and counseling. Examine your own preferred skill usage and what you do in the session. Integrate into your own skill set your learning from theory and practice in interviewing, counseling, and psychotherapy.	As a developing interviewer or counselor you will identify and build on your natural style. You will commit to a lifelong process of constantly learning about theory and practice while evaluating and examining your behavior, thoughts, feelings, and deeply held meanings.

APPENDIX II
THE FAMILY GENOGRAM

The individual develops in a family within a culture. You and your clients will more easily understand the self-in-relation concept if you help them draw a family genogram. We suggest that you consider developing both family and community genograms with many of your clients (see Chapter 9 on focusing). If you keep the genograms displayed during the session, they will remind you and your clients of the cultural/environmental context in which we all live. Moreover, some clients find them comforting as the genograms bring their family history to the interview. In a sense, we are never alone; our family and community histories are always with us.

Much important information can be collected in a family genogram. Many of us have family stories that are passed down through the generations. These can be sources of strength (such as a favorite grandparent or ancestor who endured hardship successfully). These family stories are real sources of pride and can be central in the positive asset search. There is a tendency to look for problems in the family history and, of course, this is appropriate. But use this important strategy positively whenever possible. Be sure to search for positive family stories as well as problems. How can family strengths help your client?

Children often enjoy the family genogram, and a simple adaptation called the "family tree" makes it work for them. The children are encouraged to draw a tree and put their family members on the branches, wherever they wish. This strategy has the advantage of allowing children to present the family as they see it, permitting easy placement of extended family and important support figures as well as immediate family members. Many adolescents and adults may also respond better to this more individualized and less formal approach to the family.

The Drawing a Family Genogram box in this appendix illustrates the major "how's" of developing a family genogram. The classic source for family genogram information is McGoldrick and Gerson (1985). Specific symbols and conventions have been developed that are widely accepted and help professionals communicate information to each other. There is a convention of placing an "X" over departed family members. Once we were demonstrating the family genogram strategy with a client and she commented, "I don't want to cross out my family members—they are still here inside me all the time." We believe that it is important to be flexible and work with the clients' view of family and their choice of symbols. The family genogram is one of the most fascinating exercises that you can undertake. You and your clients can learn much about how family history affects the way individuals behave in the here and now.

We have found family genograms helpful and use them frequently; however, there are situations in which some clients find them less satisfying than the community genogram. There is a Western, linear perspective to the family genogram that does not fit all individuals and cultural backgrounds. It is important to adapt the family genogram to meet individual and cultural differences. You will find *Ethnicity and Family Therapy* a most valuable and enjoyable tool to expand your awareness of

BOX 1 Drawing a Family Genogram

This brief overview will not make you an expert in developing or working with genograms, but it will provide a useful beginning with a helpful assessment and treatment technique. First go through this exercise using your own family; then you may want to interview another individual for practice.

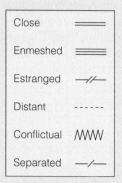

Close	═══
Enmeshed	≡≡≡
Estranged	⟋⫻⟋
Distant	- - - - -
Conflictual	∧∧∧∧
Separated	⟋⫽⟋

FIGURE 1 Basic Relationship Symbols

1. List the names of family members for at least three generations (four is preferred) with ages and dates of birth and death. List occupations, significant illnesses, and cause of death, as appropriate. Note any issues with alcoholism or drugs.

2. List important cultural/environmental/contextual issues. These may include ethnic identity, religion, economic, and social class considerations. In addition, pay special attention to significant life events such as trauma or environmental issues (e.g., divorce, economic depression, major illness).

3. Basic relationship symbols for a genogram are shown on the left, and an example of a genogram is shown below.

4. As you develop the genogram with a client, use the basic listening sequence to draw out information, thoughts, and feelings. You will find that considerable insight into one's personal life issues may be generated in this way.

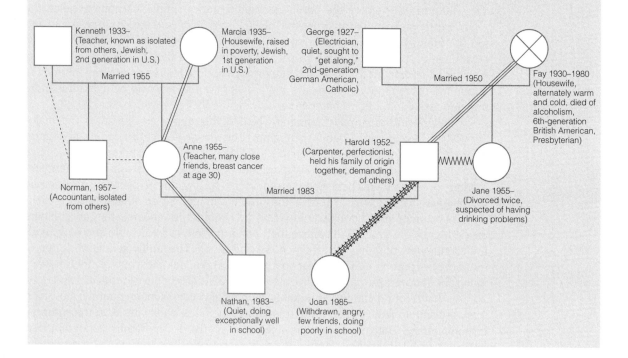

Kenneth 1933–
(Teacher, known as isolated from others, Jewish, 2nd generation in U.S.)

Marcia 1935–
(Housewife, raised in poverty, Jewish, 1st generation in U.S.)

Married 1955

George 1927–
(Electrician, quiet, sought to "get along," 2nd-generation German American, Catholic)

Married 1950

Fay 1930–1980
(Housewife, alternately warm and cold, died of alcoholism, 6th-generation British American, Presbyterian)

Anne 1955–
(Teacher, many close friends, breast cancer at age 30)

Norman, 1957–
(Accountant, isolated from others)

Harold 1952–
(Carpenter, perfectionist, held his family of origin together, demanding of others)

Married 1983

Jane 1955–
(Divorced twice, suspected of having drinking problems)

Nathan, 1983–
(Quiet, doing exceptionally well in school)

Joan 1985–
(Withdrawn, angry, few friends, doing poorly in school)

racial/ethnic issues (McGoldrick, Giordano, & Garcia-Preto, 2005). The family genogram is most effective with a client who has a nuclear family and actually can trace the family over time. We developed the community genogram as some of our clients were uncomfortable with the family genogram. Clients who have been adopted sometimes find the genogram inappropriate. Single-parent families may also feel "different," particularly when important caregivers such as extended family and close community friends are not included. We have talked with gay and lesbian clients who have very differing views of the nature of their family.

Exercise: Developing a Family Genogram

Develop a family genogram with a volunteer client or classmate. After the two of you have created the genogram, ask the client the following questions and note the impact of each question. Change the wording and the sequence to fit the needs and interests of the volunteer.

- ▲ What does this genogram mean to you? (individual focus)
- ▲ As you view your family genogram, what main theme, problem, or set of issues stands out? (main theme, problem focus)
- ▲ Who are some significant others, such as friends, neighbors, teachers, or even enemies who may have affected your own development and your family's? (others focus)
- ▲ How would other members of your family interpret this genogram? (family, others focus)
- ▲ What impact do your ethnicity, race, religion, and other cultural/environmental/ contextual factors have on your own development and your family's? (C/E/C focus)
- ▲ As an interviewer working with you on this genogram, I have learned _____ (state your own observations). How do you react to my observations? (interviewer focus)

Using a Family Genogram to Understand Family Issues

Developing a genogram with your clients and learning some of the main facts of family developmental history will often help you understand the context of individual issues. For example, as you look at the family genogram in Box 1, what might be going on at home that results in Joan's problems at school? Why is Nathan doing so well? How might intergenerational alcoholism problems play themselves out in this family tree? What other patterns do you observe? What are the implications of the ethnic background of this family? The person with a Jewish and Anglo background represents a bicultural history. Change the ethnic background and consider how this would impact counseling. Four-generation genograms can complicate and enrich your observations. (Note: The clients here have defined their ethnic identities as shown. Different clients will use different wording to define their ethnic identities. It is important to use the client's definitions rather than your own.)

REFERENCES

Adams, D. (2005). Cultural competency now law in New Jersey. Amednews.com, April 25, http://www.amaassn.org/amednews/2005/04/25/prl20425.htm.

Alberti, R., & Emmons, M. (2001). *Your perfect right: A guide to assertiveness training* (8th ed.). San Luis Obispo, CA: Impact. (Original work published 1970)

American Counseling Association. (2005). *ACA code of ethics.* Alexandria, VA: Author.

American Psychiatric Association. (2000). *Diagnostic and statistical manual of mental disorders, text revision.* Washington, DC: Author.

American Psychological Association. (2002). *Ethical principles of psychologists and code of conduct.* Washington, DC: Author.

Asbell, B., & Wynn, K. (1991). *Touching.* New York: Random House.

Baker Miller, J., Stiver, I., & Hooks, T. (Eds.). (1998). *The healing connection: Women in relationships in therapy and life.* Boston: Beacon.

Barrett, M., & Berman, J. (2001). Is psychotherapy more effective when therapists disclose information about themselves? *Journal of Consulting and Clinical Psychology, 69,* 597–603.

Blair, R. (2001). Neurocognitive models of aggression, the antisocial personality disorders, and psychopathy. *Journal of Neurology, Neurosurgery, and Psychiatry, 71,* 727–731.

Blanchard K., & Johnson, S. (1981). *The one-minute manager.* San Diego, CA: Blanchard-Johnson.

Bozarth, J. (1999). *Person-centered therapy: A revolutionary paradigm.* Ross-on-Wye, UK: PCCS Books.

Brammer, L., & MacDonald, G. (2002). *The helping relationship* (8th ed.). Boston: Allyn & Bacon.

Camus, A. (1955). *The myth of Sisyphus.* New York: Vintage Books.

Canadian Counselling Association (1999). *Code of ethics.* Ottawa, Ontario: Author.

Carkhuff, R. (2000). *The art of helping in the 21st century.* Amherst, MA: HRD Press.

Carter, R. (1999). *Mapping the mind.* Berkeley: University of California Press.

Damasio, A. (2003). *Looking for Spinoza: Joy, sorrow, and the feeling brain.* New York: Harvest.

D'Andrea, M., & Daniels, J. (2001). RESPECTFUL counseling: An integrative model for counselors. In D. Pope-Davis & H. Coleman (Eds.), *The interface of class, culture and gender in counseling* (pp. 417–466). Thousand Oaks, CA: Sage.

Daniels, T. (2007). A review of research on microcounseling: 1967–present. In A. E. Ivey & M. B. Ivey, *Intentional interviewing and counseling: Your interactive resource* (CD-ROM). Belmont, CA: Thomson Brooks/Cole.

Daniels, T., & Ivey, A. (2006). *Microcounseling: Making skills work in a multicultural world.* Springfield, IL: Thomas.

Davidson, R., Pizzagalli, D., Nitschke, J., & Putnam, K. (2002). Depression: Perspectives from affective neuroscience. *Annual Review of Psychology, 53,* 545–574.

Decety, J., & Jackson, P. (2004). The functional architecture of human empathy. *Behavioral and Cognitive Neuroscience Reviews, 3,* 71–100.

de Shazer, S. (1985). *Keys to solution in brief therapy.* New York: Norton.

de Shazer, S. (1988). *Clues: Investigating solutions to brief therapy.* New York: Norton.

de Shazer, S. (1993). Creative misunderstanding: There is no escape from language. In S. Gilligan & R. Price (Eds.), *Therapeutic conversations.* New York: Norton.

deWaal, E. (1997). *Living with contradiction: An introduction to Benedictine spirituality.* Harrisburg, PA: Morehouse.

Duncan, B. L., Miller, S. D., & Sparks, J. A. (2004). *The heroic client: A revolutionary way to improve effectiveness through client-directed outcome-informed therapy.* New York: Jossey-Bass/Wiley.

D'Zurilla, T. (1999). *Problem-solving therapy.* New York: Springer.

Egan, G. (2002). *The skilled helper* (6th ed.). Belmont, CA: Brooks/Cole.

Ekman, P. (2003). *Emotions revealed.* Woodacre, CA: Owl.

Farnham, S., Gill, J., McLean, R., & Ward, S. (1991). *Listening hearts.* Harrisburg, PA: Morehouse.

Frankl, V. (1959). *Man's search for meaning.* New York: Simon & Schuster.

Frankl, V. (1978). *The unheard cry for meaning.* New York: Touchstone.

Fukuyama, M. (1990, March). *Multicultural and spiritual issues in counseling.* Workshop presentation for the American Counseling Association Convention, Cincinnati.

Gergen, K., & Gergen, M. (2005, February). The power of positive emotions. *The Positive Aging Newsletter,* www.healthandage.com.

Hall, E. (1959). *The silent language.* New York: Doubleday.

Hargie, O., Dickson, D., & Tourish, D. (2004). *Communication skills for effective management.* Basingstoke, UK: Palgrave.

Ishiyama, I. (2006). *Anti-discrimination response training (A.R.T.) program.* Framingham, MA: Microtraining Associates.

Ivey, A. (2000/1986). *Developmental therapy: Theory into practice.* Framingham, MA: Microtraining Associates.

Ivey, A., D'Andrea, M., Ivey, M., & Simek-Morgan, L. (2002). *Theories of counseling and psychotherapy* (5th ed.). Boston: Allyn & Bacon.

Ivey, A., D'Andrea, M., Ivey, M., & Simek-Morgan, L. (2007). *Theories of counseling and psychotherapy: A multicultural perspective* (6th ed.). Boston: Pearson/Allyn & Bacon.

Ivey, A., & Gluckstern, N. (1974). *Basic attending skills.* North Amherst, MA: Microtraining Associates.

Ivey, A., Gluckstern, N., & Ivey M. (2006). *Basic attending skills* (3rd ed.) [Book and accompanying videos]. Framingham, MA: Microtraining Associates.

Ivey, A., & Ivey, M. (2007). *Intentional interviewing and counseling* (6th ed.). Belmont, CA: Thomson Brooks/Cole.

Ivey, A., Ivey, M., Myers, J., & Sweeney, T. (2005). *Developmental counseling and therapy: Promoting wellness over the lifespan.* Boston: Lahaska/Houghton-Mifflin.

Ivey, A., & Matthews, W. (1984). A meta-model for structuring the clinical interview. *Journal of Counseling and Development, 63,* 237–243.

Ivey, A., Pedersen P., & Ivey, M. (2001). *Intentional group counseling: A microskills approach.* Belmont, CA: Brooks/Cole.

Ivey, A. E., & Ivey, M. B. (2007). *Intentional interviewing and counseling: Your interactive resource* (CD-ROM). Belmont, CA: Thomson Brooks/Cole.

Jordan, J., Hartling, L., & Walker, M. (Eds.). (2004). *The complexity of connection: Writings from the Stone Center's Jean Baker Miller Training Institute.* New York: Guilford.

Kim, B., Hill, C., Gelso, C., Goates, M., Asay, P., & Harbin, J. (2003). Counselor self-disclosure: East Asian American client adherence to Asian cultural values, and counseling process. *Journal of Counseling Psychology, 50,* 324–332.

Kolb, B., & Whishaw, I. (2003). *Fundamentals of human neuropsychology* (5th ed.). New York: Worth.

Kübler-Ross, E. (1969). *On death and dying.* New York: Macmillan.

Lane, P., & McWhirter, J. (1992). A peer mediation model: Conflict resolution for elementary and middle school children. *Elementary School Guidance and Counseling, 27,* 15–23.

Mann, L. (2001). Naturalistic decision making. *Journal of Behavioral Decision Making, 14,* 375–377.

McGoldrick, M., Giordano, J., & Garcia-Preto, N. (2005). *Ethnicity and family therapy* (3rd ed.). New York: Norton.

McIntosh, P. (1988). *White privilege and male privilege: A personal account of coming to see correspondences through work in women's studies.* Wellesley, MA: Wellesley College Center for Women.

Meara, N., Pepinsky, H., Shannon, J., & Murray, W. (1981). Semantic communication and expectation for counseling across three theoretical orientations. *Journal of Counseling Psychology, 28,* 110–118.

Meara, N., Shannon, J., & Pepinsky, H. (1979). Comparisons of stylistic complexity of the language of counselor and client across three theoretical orientations. *Journal of Counseling Psychology, 26,* 181–189.

Microsoft Word Mac. (2001). Dictionary, Apple Macintosh System X. Redmond, WA: Microsoft.

Myers, J. E., & Sweeney, T. J. (2004). The indivisible self: An evidence-based model of wellness. *Journal of Individual Psychology, 60,* 234–244.

Myers, J. E., & Sweeney, T. J. (Eds.). (2005). *Counseling for wellness: Theory, research, and practice.* Alexandria, VA: American Counseling Association.

Myers, J. E., Sweeney, T. J., & Witmer, M. (2000). Counseling for wellness: A holistic model for treatment planning. *Journal of Counseling and Development, 78,* 251–266.

National Association of Social Workers. (1999). *Code of ethics.* Washington, DC: Author.

National Organization of Human Service Professionals. (2000). Ethical standards of human service professionals. *Human Service Education, 20,* 61–68.

Obonnaya, O. (1994). Person as community: An African understanding of the person as intrapsychic community. *Journal of Black Psychology, 20,* 75–87.

Office of the Surgeon General. (1999). *Mental health, culture, race, and ethnicity.* Washington, DC: Department of Health and Human Services.

Pack-Brown, S., & Williams, C. (2003). *Ethics in a multicultural context.* Thousand Oaks, CA: Sage.

Parsons, F. (1967). *Choosing a vocation.* New York: Agathon. (Originally published 1909)

Peterson, C., & Seligman, M. (Eds.). (2004). *Character strengths and virtues.* Oxford: Oxford University Press.

Posner M. (Ed.). (2004). Cognitive neuropsychology of attention. New York: Guilford.

Power, S., & Lopez, R. (1985). Perceptual, motor, and verbal skills of monolingual and bilingual Hispanic children: A discrimination analysis. *Perceptual and Motor Skills, 60,* 1001–1109.

Ratey, J. (2001). *A users guide to the brain.* New York: Vintage.

Restak, R. (2003). *The new brain.* New York: Rodale.

Rogers, C. (1957). The necessary and sufficient conditions of therapeutic personality change. *Journal of Consulting Psychology, 21,* 95–103.

Rogers, C. (1961). *On becoming a person.* Boston: Houghton Mifflin.

Roysicar, G., Arredondo, P., Fuertes, J., Ponterotto, J., & Toperek, R. (2003). *Multicultural competencies, 2003.* Washington, DC: Association for Multicultural Counseling and Development.

Schlosser, L. (2003). Christian privilege: Breaking a sacred taboo. *Journal of Multicultural Counseling and Development, 31,* 44–51.

Schwartz, J., & Begley, S. (2002). *The mind and the brain: Neuroplasticity and the power of mental force.* New York: Regan.

Seligman, M. (2004). *Authentic happiness.* New York: Free Press.

Shostrum, E. (1966). *Three approaches to psychotherapy* [Film]. Santa Ana, CA: Psychological Films.

Singer, T., Seymour, B., O'Dougherty, J., Kaube, H., Dolan, R., & Frith, C. (2004). Empathy for pain involves the affective but not sensory components of pain. *Science, 303,* 1157–1161.

Sklare, G. (2004). *Brief counseling that works: A solution-focused approach for school counselors and administrators.* Beverly Hills, CA: Corwin.

Sue, D. W., Carter, R. T., Casas, J., Fouad, N., Ivey, A., Jensen, M., LaFromboise, T., Manese, J., Ponterotto, J., & Vazquez-Nutall, E. (1998). *Multicultural counseling competencies.* Thousand Oaks, CA: Sage.

Sue, D. W., & Sue, D. (2003). *Counseling the culturally diverse.* New York: Wiley.

Sweeney, T. (1998). *Adlerian counseling: A practitioner approach.* Philadelphia: Taylor & Francis.

Sweeney, T. J., & Myers, J. E. (2005). Optimizing human development: A new paradigm for helping. In A. Ivey, M. B. Ivey, J. E. Myers, & T. J. Sweeney (Eds.), *Developmental counseling and therapy* (2nd ed., pp. 39–68). Boston: Lahaska/Houghton Mifflin.

Tyler, L. (1961). *The work of the counselor* (2nd ed.). East Norwalk, CT: Appleton & Lange.

University of Massachusetts Memorial Medical Center, Behavioral Medicine Clinic. (2004). *Treatment plan.* Unpublished document, Griswold Mental Health Clinic, Palmer, MA.

Zhan-Waxler, C., Radke-Yarrow, M., Wagner, E., & Chapman, J. (1992). Development of concern for others. *Developmental Psychology, 28,* 128–136.

NAME INDEX

Subject Index

A

Aboriginal Australians, 48, 70–71
abortion issue, 156–160
abuse, and advocacy, 161
accents, language, 48–49
acceptance and recognition stage, 137, 138
action, taking positive, 9
active listening skills
    and bilingual clients, 86–87
    with children, 77–81
    defining, 75–76
    diversity and, 86–88
    encouraging, 83
    paraphrasing, 84–85
    summarizing, 85
additive empathy, 108
advocacy, 160–161
African Americans, 48, 69
age
    bringing up differences in, 6
    multiculturalism and, 7
    political correctness and, 31
AIDS, counseling persons with, 170
Alisia (client)
    directives, 201–204
    examples of feedback with, 192
    information and advice, 199
    listening skills influencing, 183–186
    logical consequences and, 196–198
Allen (client), 176–177
American Counseling Association (ACA)
    on confidentiality, 24
    on diversity and ethics, 29
    on professional competence, 22
American Psychological
    Association (APA), 23, 27
anger
    associating questions with, 61
    stage, 137, 138
APA (American Psychological Association), 23, 27
arousal, and brain, 293
Asian cultures
    assertiveness seen as aggression, 273
    building trust within, 88
    culturally incorrect attending in, 49–50
    nonverbal behavior issues, 54
    relationship to feelings, 92–93
assertiveness training. *See* cognitive-
    behavioral counseling
attending behavior, 40–55.
    See also observation skills
    body language, 51

    with children, 77
    microskills hierarchy and, 12–13
    multicultural and individual issues in,
        42–44, 47–52
    negative example of, 44–45
    overview of, 40–41
    positive example of, 46–47
    predicted result of, 302
    skills of, 41
    three V's + B and, 41–42
    usefulness of silence, 52
    value of nonattention, 51–52
    verbal tracking, 49–51
    visual/eye contact, 48
    vocal qualities, 48–49
attention, and brain imaging, 293
audio-recording
    discovering natural style of interviewing, 18
    in interview, 125
    sample practice contract, 24
Auschwitz, 162

B

balance sheet, decisional counseling, 212–213
bargaining stage, 137, 138
basic competence, 292
basic empathy, 108
basic listening sequence (BLS), 57–73
    building empathy with, 107–110
    decisional counseling. *See* decisional
        counseling, and five-stage interview structure
    diversity impacting, 110–111
    examples of, 107
    mediation process using, 140
    objectives of, 57
    overview of, 106
    patterns of, 294–297
    predicted result of, 106, 303
    questioning skills in. *See* questioning skills
being-in-relation, 147
Benjamin (client), 60, 73
bilingual clients, 86–87
Black people, 32
blindness, and attending behavior, 43
BLS. *See* basic listening sequence (BLS)
body language
    communicating listening by, 42
    mirroring, 53–54
    multicultural issues, 51
    negative example, 44–45
    paraphrasing and, 84
    positive example, 46–47

TO THE OWNER OF THIS BOOK:

I hope that you have found *Essentials of Intentional Interviewing* useful. So that this book can be improved in a future edition, would you take the time to complete this sheet and return it? Thank you.

School and address:_____

Department:_____

Instructor's name:_____

1. What I like most about this book is:_____

   _____

   _____

2. What I like least about this book is:

   _____

   _____

3. My general reaction to this book is:

   _____

   _____

4. The name of the course in which I used this book is:

   _____

5. Were all of the chapters of the book assigned for you to read?_____

   If not, which ones weren't?_____

6. In the space below, or on a separate sheet of paper, please write specific suggestions for improving this book and anything else you'd care to share about your experience in using this book.

   _____

   _____

   _____

FOLD HERE

BUSINESS REPLY MAIL
FIRST-CLASS MAIL   PERMIT NO. 34   BELMONT CA

POSTAGE WILL BE PAID BY ADDRESSEE

Attn: Marquita Flemming, Counseling

BrooksCole/Thomson Learning
10 Davis Drive
Belmont, CA   94002-9801

FOLD HERE

OPTIONAL:

Your name:_____ Date: _____

May we quote you, either in promotion for *Essentials of Intentional Interviewing* or in future publishing ventures?

Yes: _____   No: _____

Sincerely yours,

Allen E. Ivey and Mary Bradford Ivey